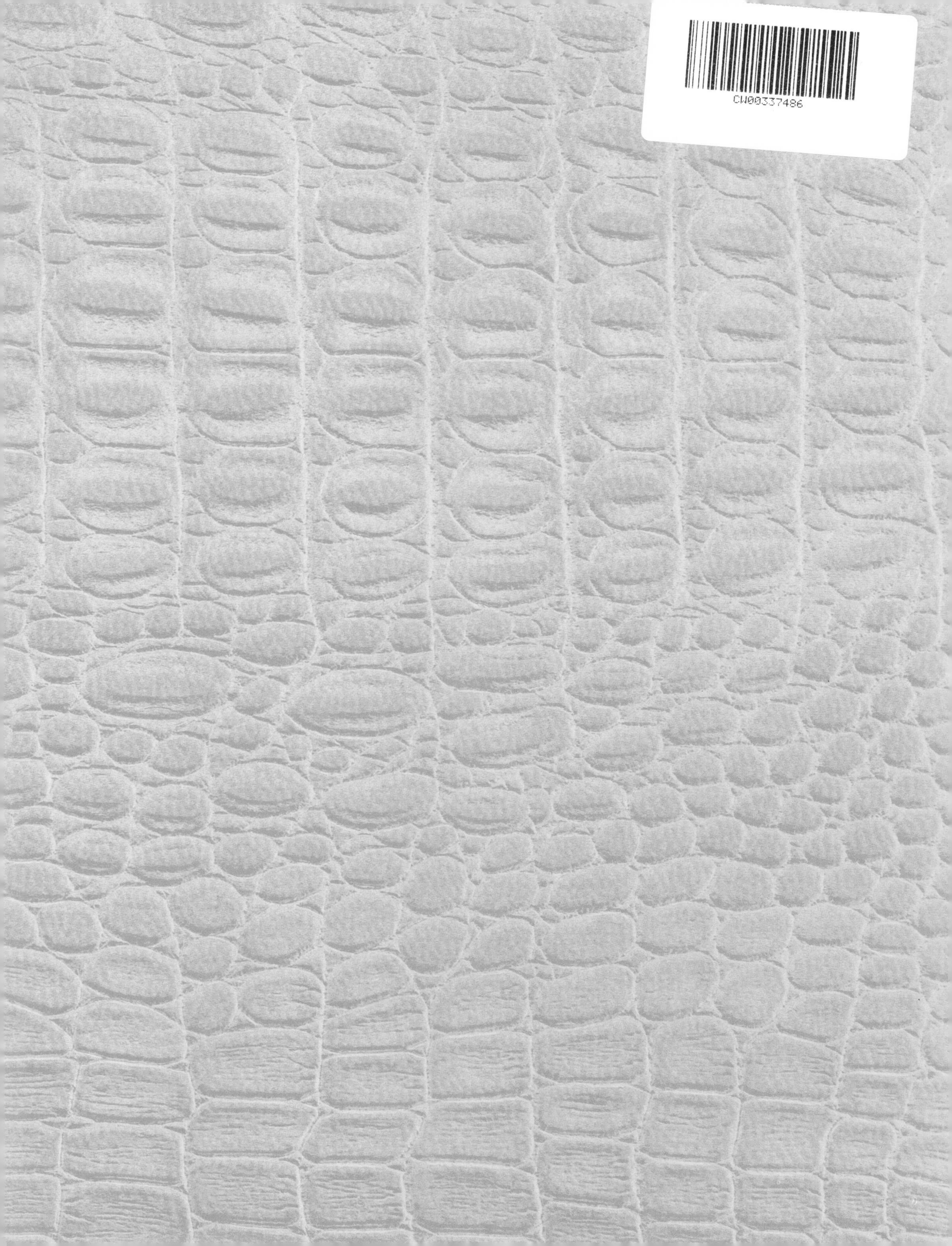
CW00337486

the AMAZING HEALING POWERS *of* NATURE

HOW PLANTS AND ANIMALS ARE HELPING TO IMPROVE OUR HEALTH

More than *1000 extraordinary stories* about modern medicine

the AMAZING HEALING POWERS of NATURE

FOREWORD

When you're sitting under the fluorescent lamps of a hospital waiting room, surrounded by cutting-edge machinery and an arsenal of wonder drugs, twenty-first century modern medicine may seem a world away from dense jungles and ancient herbal remedies. Yet delve a little deeper to look at the contents of the pills and potions that underpin it and an entirely different picture is revealed.

With more than 50 per cent of the world's most commonly prescribed drugs having been derived from plants, animals and microbes, the thick black line that is often perceived to separate synthetic, conventional drugs from traditional, natural medicines is, at best, a little blurry. From the pharmaceutical pillars of morphine and penicillin to some of the most pioneering treatments for cancer and Alzheimer's disease, nature has provided the basis for an astonishing number of the drugs that many of us take every day.

Speaking as a scientist, it doesn't matter to me whether a chemical is found in the cells of a leaf or in a foil-packed capsule: it is its efficacy that counts. And yet, even though modern synthetic medicine has made huge leaps over the past century or so, it is the enormous number of drugs that have been and continue to be discovered in the natural world that I find especially fascinating.

When considered on the level of basic chemistry, it is hardly surprising that nature is such a rich source of complex, biologically active substances with so many curious and unexpected effects. Over billions of years, life has evolved countless strategies in the struggle for survival, with species creating all manner of chemicals to defend themselves from predators, shield themselves from the environment, attract mates or lure prey – creating, in turn, an immense repository of compounds for pharmacists to tap into. There are an estimated 400,000 plant species alone, each packed with hundreds of chemicals – before we even consider the thousands more species yet to be discovered. Once you widen the search further and start looking at animals, bacteria, algae and fungi, this figure expands more than ten-fold, meaning we have only just begun to scratch the surface of the potentially vast living pharmacy out there.

Inspiring, uplifting and rigorously scientific, this book is an authoritative introduction to the extraordinarily diverse sources of nature's healing powers, from exotic desert animals to everyday fruit and vegetables that might be sitting in your fridge. It is surprising, eye opening and filled with useful, 'take home' information. I promise you: after reading this, you will never look at your medicine cabinet the same way again!

James Wong

James Wong, BSc (Hons), MSc, is a botanist, BBC TV science presenter and bestselling author based in London. He trained at the Royal Botanic Gardens, Kew, London, and his research interest in traditional medicinal plants led to him presenting such award-winning programs as the BBC's *Grow Your Own Drugs* – which unveiled a range of easy-to-make homegrown remedies with a firm pharmaceutical basis – and *Our Food* and *The People's Rainforest*.

Left: The axolotl has a remarkable ability to regenerate tissue, including entire limbs.

Following pages: Fungi have provided us with sources of drugs to treat heart disease, bacterial infections and various types of cancers.

CONTENTS

CONTRIBUTORS

The Amazing Healing Powers of Nature draws on the latest medical research and has been compiled by an international team of experienced science writers:

◆ Australian-based consultant and contributor **Karen McGhee** has a background in marine biology and zoology, and as a journalist has focused on natural history, health and the environment. Her writing has been published in books, newspapers and magazines worldwide, and she has worked on television documentaries and museum exhibits.

◆ **Jack Challoner** has written more than 30 books on science and technology, and also acts as a science consultant on books, magazines and television programs. He worked on the London Science Museum's flagship interactive gallery, *LaunchPad*, and has also developed television programs for BBC Scotland.

◆ US-based **Sari Harrar** is a freelance health and science journalist who writes for a wide range of national magazines, books, websites and newspapers. As a recipient of a Council for Advancement of Science Education fellowship, she learned about targeted cancer therapies at Harvard Medical School.

◆ **Becky McCall** studied microbiology and worked in the pharmaceutical and biotechnology industry before becoming a freelance medical and science journalist. She is London based but travels extensively.

◆ Trained in life sciences, **Celia Coyne** has been editing science and natural history books for more than 20 years. She has written numerous articles for publishers in the United Kingdom, Australia and New Zealand and is the author of two books: *Earth's Riches* and *The Power of Plants* (both published by Reader's Digest).

◆ With a background in marine biology, parasitology and land management, **Abbie Thomas** has 20 years experience as a science writer, producer and broadcaster at the Australian Broadcasting Corporation and as a freelancer. She is the co-author of *Digging up Deep Time*, a history of the evolution of life in Australia.

Children in Madagascar display rosy periwinkle flowers. Cultivated locally, they are the source of some of today's most effective cancer-fighting drugs.

Caribbean sea squirt

Honeybee

INTRODUCTION

Did you know that 90 per cent of children diagnosed with leukaemia these days survive – compared to less than 10 per cent in the 1960s – thanks largely to a compound from a popular garden plant, the rosy periwinkle? And that if you suffer from diabetes, there's a good chance the medication you're taking to control your symptoms is based on the venom of a poisonous North American lizard, the Gila monster?

And do you know that many everyday foods – ranging from tomatoes and broccoli to salmon – have been proven by science to contain compounds that protect against cancers, heart disease and dementia? Animals, plants and microbes are nature's pharmacy – and in this book we look at more than 140 species that have yielded or could soon provide significant medical benefits.

Traditions and breakthroughs

Humans have long understood that nature can help safeguard health and even cure disease. Ötzi, a man whose 5000-year-old remains were discovered in the Alps in 1991, was found to be carrying medicinal herbs and antibacterial fungi; and the ancient Egyptians and Greeks employed a wide variety of natural medicines. Observation, trial and error, and the handing down of knowledge over countless generations gave rise to established traditions of natural medicine all over the world.

But the emergence of a more rigorous scientific approach to research in the nineteenth and twentieth centuries took the exploitation of natural sources to a whole new level. Advances in our understanding of biological and chemical processes, as well as the arrival of technologies such as the microscope, allowed scientists, for the first time, to identify many of the active compounds in natural cures. This led to major advances, such as the isolation of morphine in 1803, as well as the making of the first synthetic drugs based on natural compounds, notably aspirin, produced in the 1890s by the German company Bayer from the meadowsweet plant. The stories of many of these landmark discoveries are recounted in the pages of this book.

Turmeric

Aloe vera

Chicken eggs

Breakthroughs like these prompted a proliferation of medical research in the second half of the twentieth century. In laboratories all over the world, plants, animals and microbes were investigated to assess their potential healing powers, resulting in a wave of modern medicines obtained from nature, many of which we have since come to rely on, including antibiotics, painkillers and statins. As a result, more than half of all drugs used today have originally come from plants, animals, fungi and microorganisms and, in the last quarter century, almost three-quarters of all new drugs have been derived from natural sources.

Hidden treasures So does that mean we are close to exhausting the healing potential of nature? Far from it. We share our planet with billions of living things and while we have identified around 2 million other species, it is likely there may be around 9 million more still awaiting identification. Who knows what debilitating human disease might be cured from a compound found in the saliva of a new leech species in a Congo rainforest, or in the venom of a previously unknown group of octopuses living in the cold waters of Antarctica?

The potential healing powers of nature underline the importance of protecting our natural resources, no matter how little used and apparently unproductive they may appear. Increasingly, cures from nature have been coming out of deliberate searches of promising habitats. These are sometimes guided by the practices of indigenous peoples and their traditional therapies and cures, and often driven by adventurous scientists: real-life biomedical incarnations of Indiana Jones, searching ever deeper into the planet's least explored environments in the hope of discovering an answer to cancer, a treatment for heart disease, a balm for pain or a remedy for the common cold.

Some drugs from nature, such as penicillin, have been identified through serendipity, their discovery due largely to chance. Yet others have been uncovered through well-founded hunches

Streptococcus bacteria

African giant pouched rat

Bioprospecting

followed by researchers tuned into nature. The development of the painkiller Prialt, for example, one of the first drugs developed from a marine source, came about when one scientist's fascination for seashells sparked research into the venom of a cone snail.

One thing exhaustive testing has revealed is that many centuries-old natural treatments, folk remedies and 'alternative' therapies have a firm basis in science. Often it's due to an active chemical

A long and costly journey

Developing a new drug from a natural compound has been shown to cost up to $2 billion and seldom takes less than 15 years. Normally, it involves the following stages:

- Testing **IN VITRO** – in other words, in laboratory equipment such as test tubes. The compound may be tested on disease or tissue cells grown in a laboratory. This will take many months, even years.
- Testing **IN VIVO** – on living things. This starts with tests on animals, usually rats and mice, and these, too, can take months or years. If all goes well and no safety issues arise, approval is then sought for testing on humans.
- Human testing, or **CLINICAL TRIALS**. Phase I trials, usually carried out on fewer than 100 healthy volunteers, last one to three years. Phase II normally involves between 100 and 250 patients who are suffering from a relevant condition, and will require at least two years. If the results are encouraging and there are no safety concerns, Phase III trials proceed with larger numbers of patients (1000–3000), usually lasting a further three years.
- Approval to produce a drug might take another six to twelve months. Even then, Phase IV follow-up trials may be required to track side effects. About 20 per cent of compounds that reach clinical trials become drugs.

Grapes fermenting in wine barrels

Echinacea

compound buried deep within a substance, one that really does work wonders. On the other hand, the efficacy of some highly regarded, widely used natural medicines – echinacea and St John's wort, for example – are still in question, with some scientific studies showing real benefits and others none at all. Several articles in the following pages assess the latest evidence for promising traditional therapies.

Advertisement for quinine (derived from cinchona)

What can you do? Would you swallow a worm if it cured you of a debilitating illness? This is a question people suffering from bowel disorders such as coeliac disease and Crohn's disease may soon have to consider as a result of promising research into the therapeutic use of parasitic worms. This and many other unusual – though, fortunately, often more palatable – therapies are among the innumerable nature-based strategies being developed for a wide range of serious illnesses.

With all this research and development going on, we are always on the brink of new revelations. Cures for even the most intractable diseases of modern times could lie just around the corner. We never know what nature might provide, and that means there is always hope.

But, reassuring as it is, hope is for the future. Right now, what can you do? As you will see, that's a question that we ask – and answer – repeatedly throughout this book. For there are almost always practical steps you can take to make the most of the information in these pages, even if a conventional drug or therapy might yet be a long way off.

It could involve making your own home remedies or following our guidance on the safest way to try out an emerging or alternative therapy. Or it could mean asking your doctor for a new medicine or even participating in a clinical trial. Wherever this book takes you, we are confident it will, at the same time, amaze and inspire you. It will provide direction and food for thought, and, most of all, leave you with an enhanced and enduring appreciation of nature's extraordinary powers.

Phantasmal poison frog

PART ONE

PLANTS TO THE RESCUE

Hoodia

Rice

Evidence of the use of medicinal plants dates back to the earliest civilisations. And even today, the role of plants in both the modern pharmaceutical industry and alternative and complementary medicine remains central.

Plants have been used for medicinal purposes for many thousands of years. Records in ancient clay tablets made more than 5000 years ago by the Sumerians of southern Mesopotamia – modern-day Iraq – refer to a person known as an *asu*, who supplied medicines derived from plant extracts, resins and spices. According to accounts left on papyrus, the ancient Egyptians used drug preparations based on castor and linseed oil, pomegranates, aloe, safflower and herbs such as cumin, fennel, and caraway. There's evidence of an ancient Egyptian pregnancy test that required women to urinate on wheat and barley seeds – germination of the seeds indicated that a woman was pregnant. And in fact modern tests show that about 70 per cent of pregnant women would actually produce this reaction, due to high oestrogen levels.

Enduring therapies

The use of plants as a source of drugs and therapies continues to be a feature of traditional medicine in most indigenous cultures, as well as of complementary and alternative medicine in Western nations. Indeed, some medicinal uses of plants that began millennia ago endure unchanged to the modern day. Chewing willow bark to treat fever and inflammation, for example, was described by the famed Greek physician Hippocrates – considered the father of Western medicine – around 400 BC. The bark, which has been used in a similar way for centuries in China and Europe and is still prescribed by modern-day herbalists, contains a compound similar to that found in aspirin.

Even the early development of the modern-day pharmaceutical industry was heavily influenced during the nineteenth and twentieth centuries by natural therapies. The first

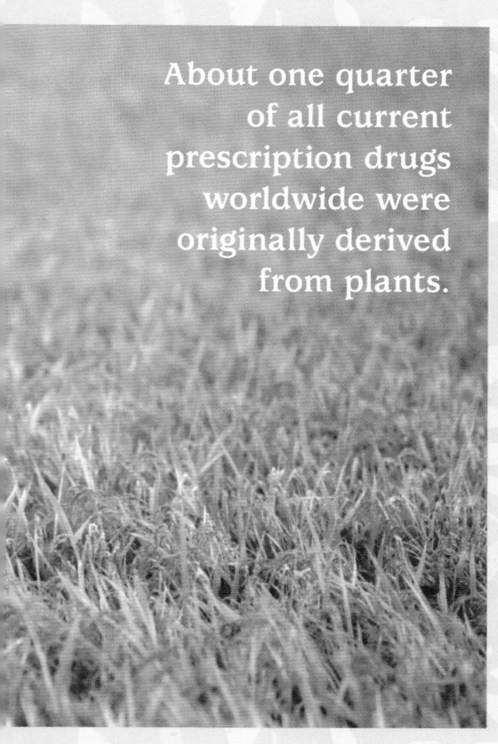

About one quarter of all current prescription drugs worldwide were originally derived from plants.

drug from a plant to be isolated in pure form was morphine in 1805. These days, about one quarter of all prescription drugs worldwide – based on more than 120 active compounds – were originally derived from plants. That number includes many of the world's most significant and widely used pharmaceuticals, such as the anticancer drugs vincristine, vinblastine and paclitaxel, the heart medicines digoxin, reserpine and atropine, the antimalarial drug quinine and the painkiller codeine.

Chilli

The way ahead

Today the use of medicinal plants remains the primary source of healthcare globally. That's mainly as a result of reliance on traditional medicines in the developing world. But interest in plants as a potential source of commercial pharmaceuticals is as strong as ever, worldwide. In an indication of just how keen that interest is, a March 2013 report by the private market research company Global Industry Analysts Inc. forecast that the value of the global market for herbal supplements and medicines was expected to reach more than $US93 billion by 2015. And research continues apace, all over the world. A 2009 review by researchers at the Council of Scientific and Industrial Research, in New Delhi, for example, found that between 1990 and 2004, Chinese scientists alone published almost 2200 research papers about plant-based medicines. The potential for further life-saving breakthroughs is vast.

SWEET WORMWOOD

Artemisia annua

MEDICAL BENEFITS ◆ Treatment for malaria, schistosomiasis (bilharzia) ◆ Possible treatment for cancer

In 1969, using her knowledge of traditional medicine, a Chinese pharmacologist identified an antimalarial compound in sweet wormwood that has since become the source of a widely used, life-saving drug.

Malaria is an ancient disease that still affects hundreds of millions of people worldwide – and kills more than half a million every year. It is the result of infection by a single-celled parasite called *Plasmodium*, which is carried by mosquitoes. *Plasmodium* finds its way into people's blood when carrier mosquitoes puncture the skin. Despite international efforts in the 1950s to eradicate malaria, the disease prevailed, mainly because some strains of *Plasmodium* developed resistance to the anti-malarial medicines of the time, including quinine (see p. 21) and chloroquine.

War against malaria During the Vietnam War, more soldiers were dying from drug-resistant malaria than from the actual fighting. In response, in 1967, the Chinese government of Mao Zedong initiated a secret military program called Project 523 (because it began on 23 May) to find new drugs that would give North Vietnamese soldiers the edge. In 1969, Professor Tu Youyou was appointed leader of a Project 523 team at the Institute of Chinese Materia Medica in Beijing. After scouring ancient texts and interviewing doctors across China, Tu compiled a list of 380 promising treatments for fever and malaria. When she tested them on mice infected with malaria, one stood out: extract of sweet wormwood, known as *qinghao* in China. A tree with fernlike leaves and pretty yellow flowers, sweet wormwood is native to Asia and particularly common above about 1000 m (3300 ft) in China, though it now grows wild in many countries.

The drug of choice After further successful tests, on animals and humans, Tu and her team isolated the active compound in 1972. They named it *qinghaosu* – literally 'the essential

Traditional Wisdom

The earliest mention of sweet wormwood in Chinese medicine is in *Wushi'er Bingfang (Recipes for Fifty-Two Ailments)*, which dates from the second century BC. It suggests sweet wormwood as a treatment for haemorrhoids.

While researching sweet wormwood, Tu Youyou consulted a fourth-century text, *Zhouhou Jiuzufang (A Handbook of Prescriptions for Emergencies)*. She found an antimalarial recipe that involved soaking sweet wormwood leaves in cold water then wringing them out. This fact proved crucial: until then, Tu had had highly variable results, because – as she correctly surmised – the boiling water she had used to make the extract could destroy the active compound. When she prepared the extract cold, the results were consistent – and better than before.

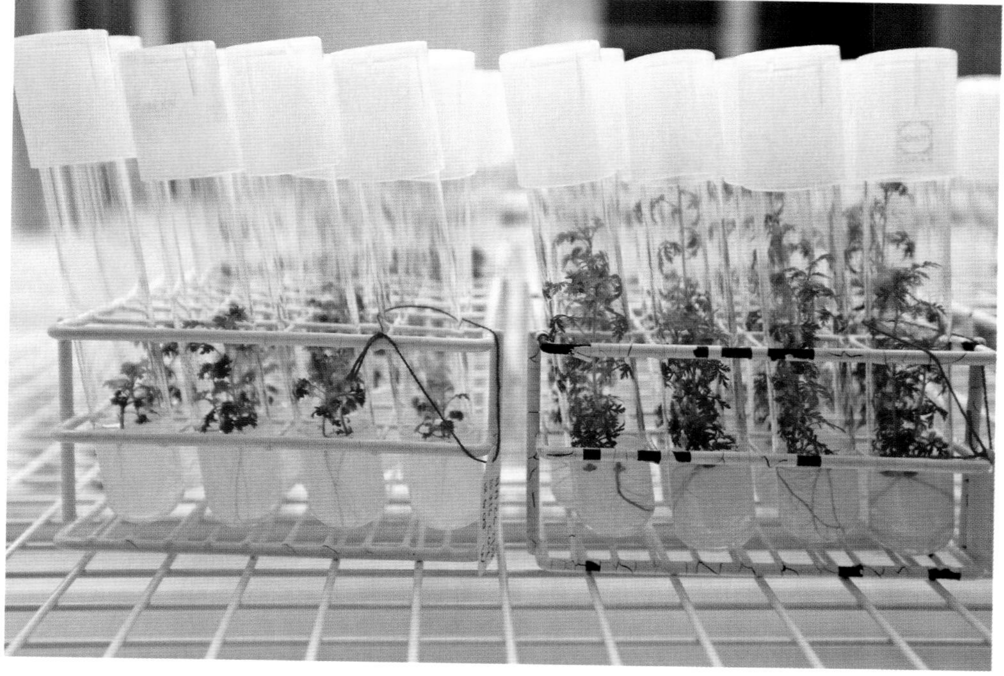

To provide artemisinin, sweet wormwood cultures are often grown in test tubes at research stations.

element of *qinghao*'. Then, in 1981, at a conference sponsored by the United Nations, Tu revealed her team's results to the world at large, to huge acclaim and excitement. Drugs derived from artemisinin, as *qinghaosu* became known in the West, entered large-scale production in the 1990s.

And so, today's most widely used and most effective treatment for malaria is artemisinin combination therapy (ACT), which, used correctly, should help to reduce the number of deaths from malaria for many years to come. Nevertheless, some strains of malaria parasite have developed resistance to artemisinin, and research into other malaria cures is ongoing.

Nearly three-quarters of artemisinin is produced in China and Vietnam.

Other roles In the future, artemisinin may have other important roles in medicine, too. Researchers in China have found that derivatives of the compound – the drugs artemether and artesunate – are effective against blood flukes, parasitic worms that cause the disease schistosomiasis (bilharzia), which is common in tropical developing nations. And in the 1990s, scientists found that artemisinin can kill cancer cells in the laboratory – a finding that is still the subject of research.

OTHER NAMES Sweet sagewort, annual wormwood, sweet Annie, *qinghao* (Chinese)
ORIGIN Native to Asia, but now naturalised across most of the world
PARTS USED Leaves, stems

Hopefully, you are not one of the 200 million or so people who have contracted malaria in the past year. If you are, then chances are you will already have been prescribed an artemisinin-based medicine; the standard antimalarial combination therapy is Coartem, produced jointly by the pharmaceutical companies Novartis and Sanofi-Aventis, in partnership with the World Health Organization. It is worth noting that artemisinin is not used as a preventative medicine; so, if you are travelling to a malaria-affected region, check with your doctor for the most suitable protective medication.

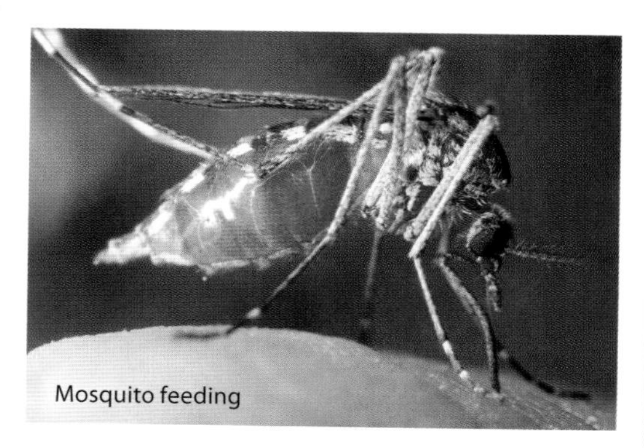

Mosquito feeding

MORETON BAY CHESTNUT

Castanospermum australe

MEDICAL BENEFITS ◆ In trials for treatment of dengue fever, hepatitis C, other viral infections ◆ Possible treatment for HIV, diabetes, obesity, cancer

The chestnut-like beans of this plant contain a compound that holds great promise in the treatment of viral diseases and cancers.

Castanospermine may provide a treatment for dengue fever that will help sufferers such as these children in the Philippines.

The Moreton Bay chestnut is an Australian evergreen tree that grows to around 20 m (60 ft). Its yellow-orange flowers bloom every summer, and seed pods appear after the flowers disappear. The seeds are poisonous if consumed; Aboriginal Australians did eat them, but only after pounding them, soaking them for days to leach out the poisons and then roasting the resulting mush.

Sweet success In 1981, scientists discovered a compound in the beans that they called castanospermine. It was found to inhibit the action of an enzyme that is involved in the formation of compounds called glycoproteins, which play vital roles in the development of cancer cells. Glycoproteins are also involved in the formation of new blood vessels, and since cancerous tumours rely on their own blood supply, this may also play a role in the compound's ability to fight cancers.

In laboratory tests, castanospermine has been shown to prevent the growth of tumours; however, there have been no human trials so far.

Seed pod

In the 1980s, researchers found that castanospermine could reduce the ability of HIV, which causes AIDS, to infect cells in the laboratory. Unfortunately it also had detrimental effects on healthy host cells. But further research has since shown the same effect on other viruses, including hepatitis C and dengue fever, with fewer safety concerns and encouraging results.

Castanospermine also inhibits the action of an enzyme called sucrase, which is crucial in the digestion of the sugar sucrose. As a result, it may one day help to treat obesity and diabetes.

OTHER NAMES Black bean plant, lucky bean plant
ORIGIN Eastern Australia
PART USED Beans (seeds)

What You CAN DO

Sufferers from hepatitis C and dengue fever may soon have a castanospermine treatment available to them. A medicine called Celgosivir is made from castanospermine and has the same effect, inactivating the enzyme involved in forming viral glycoproteins, but does not cause diarrhoea as castanospermine can. Clinical trials are underway; ask your doctor for more information.

CINCHONA

Cinchona spp.

MEDICAL BENEFITS ◆ Treatment for malaria, fever, heart arrhythmias

'More precious than all the gold and silver the Spaniards took from South America' – that's how seventeenth-century Italian writer Sebastiano Bado described the bark of the cinchona tree.

Cinchona is a genus of nearly 40 species of evergreen trees native to northwestern South America. These trees grow best in hot, humid conditions at an altitude of between 1000 and 3000 m (3300–10,000 ft). Their leaves are dark green and waxy, and their small white, pink and red flowers occur in clusters. But it is cinchona bark that made the trees so highly prized.

In the 1630s, Spanish colonialists and Jesuit missionaries in Peru learned of the bark's medicinal properties, probably from indigenous people, who appear to have used it to treat fevers and as a muscle relaxant. With the spread of malaria following Spanish colonisation, indigenous people and colonists alike began using the bark to treat the new disease, too.

The Jesuit cure The name of the plant (pronounced 'sink-oh-nuh') derives from a story about the Countess of Chinchón in Spain. She was said to have been the first to introduce the bark to Europe, after she took it and recovered from malaria. The story has since been shown to be untrue; in fact, no-one is sure who first took the bark to Europe, though it is known that the Jesuits were its most enthusiastic advocates. Indeed, the medicine – dried, powdered bark that was made into a bitter tea – became known in Europe as 'Jesuit's bark'.

Jesuit's bark was strategically important in the overseas colonies of the most powerful nations of the nineteenth century, since malaria struck generals and servants alike, and possessing any kind of cure for this devastating disease was crucial to successful campaigns and to stability. Throughout the seventeenth and eighteenth centuries, Spain had a monopoly on the medicine, and kept prices high. Despite that, it saved countless lives.

Bark of barks In 1820, the French chemists Pierre-Joseph Pelletier and Joseph Caventou discovered the active compound in cinchona bark and named it quinine, after the Peruvian term *quina quina*, meaning 'bark of barks', or 'medicine of medicines'. The two chemists did not patent the extraction process, but instead released it to the world. By the mid-nineteenth century, quinine – rather than powdered bark – was the main treatment for malaria.

OTHER NAMES Jesuit's tree, fever tree, Peruvian bark, quinine tree
ORIGIN South America (it is Ecuador's national tree)
PART USED Bark

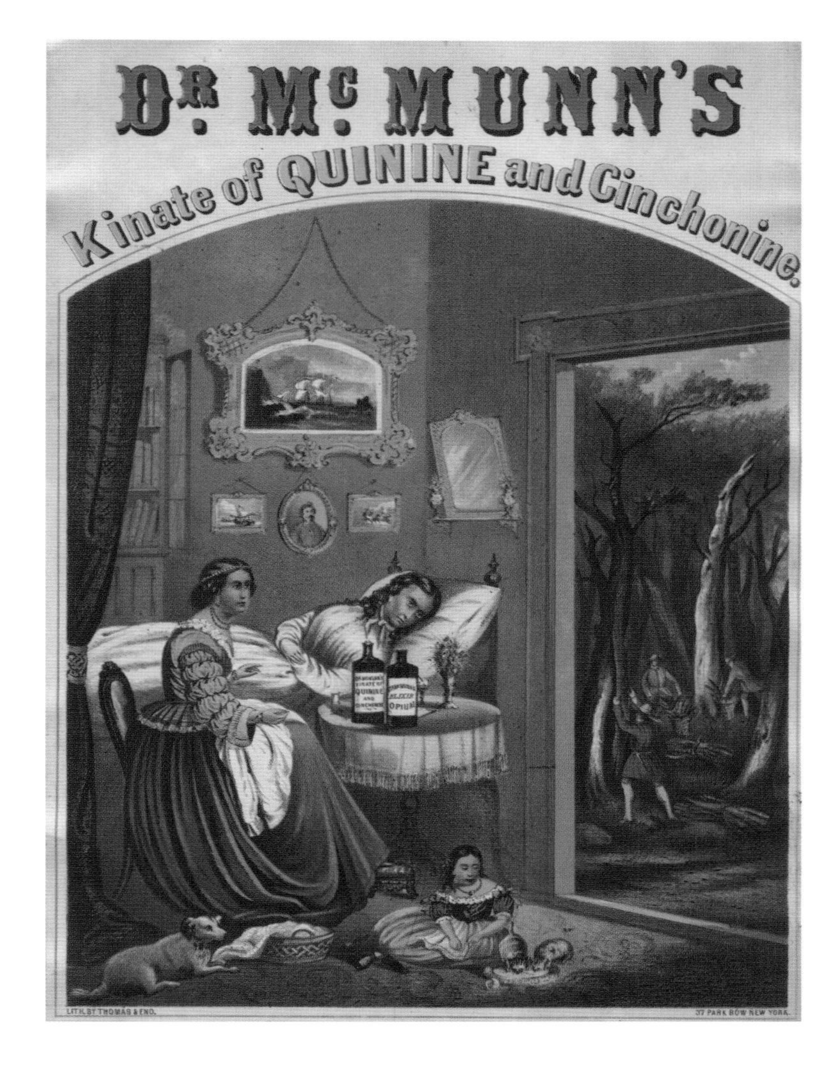

In this US advertisement for quinine, from the 1860s, a patient lies in her bed while, outside, men strip bark from cinchona trees.

This 1924 cigarette card honoured quinine as a major medical achievement of the era.

During the same period, the Spanish monopoly on the cultivation of cinchona was finally broken, as the British and Dutch smuggled seeds out of South America and created successful cinchona plantations in India, Sri Lanka, Indonesia, East Africa and Jamaica.

The use and importance of quinine in the fight against malaria continued until the 1950s, by which time the parasite that causes the disease – the single-celled organism *Plasmodium* – had developed significant resistance to it. Today, other drugs form the first line of prevention against and treatment for malaria (see p. 18), but quinine – still made from cinchona bark – is used in some severe cases of malaria, or where access to other drugs is limited.

As early as the 1750s, the French doctor Jean Sénac noticed that cinchona bark was also effective against irregular heartbeat (arrhythmia), and in 1918 German chemist Walter von Frey discovered that the active compound is quinidine. Today, quinidine is a commonly prescribed anti-arrhythmia medicine.

The start of something

In the middle of the nineteenth century, chemists across Europe tried to synthesise quinine in the laboratory. Eighteen-year-old British chemist William Perkin came close, but instead created, in the coal tar he was using, a vivid purple dye, which he called mauveine. This became the world's first synthetic dye, and was hugely popular; the discovery also marked the beginning of the modern chemical industry. Quinine was finally successfully synthesised in 1944, but cinchona trees remain the only economical source of the compound.

British soldiers stationed in Greece during World War I were given a daily ration of quinine to ward off fevers and disease.

What You CAN DO

You may still be given quinine to treat malaria today, but not normally as a first line of defence. Powdered cinchona bark is available from some pharmacies and health food stores. It is used to aid digestion and to treat a loss of appetite, allegedly stimulating the production of saliva and gastric juices. For many years, people suffering from leg cramps took over-the-counter quinine sulphate, which also acts as a muscle relaxant. But this practice can have serious side effects and health practitioners now advise against high-dose, off-prescription use.

CAMPHOR LAUREL

Cinnamomum camphora

MEDICAL BENEFITS ◆ Treatment for inflammation, muscle pain, coughs, congestion

Noted for its strong odour, camphor has long had a wide range of uses in traditional medicine. Now modern science is beginning to unravel the secrets of this intriguing substance.

A white, waxy solid material when extracted and purified, camphor is present throughout the wood, roots and leaves of the camphor laurel tree. For hundreds of years, it has been traded and used widely as a culinary spice, perfume and medicine.

Old and new In traditional Chinese medicine, camphor is used as an analgesic and to treat a wide range of inflammatory conditions, including rheumatism (joint pain) and bronchitis. In 2005, a research team at the Cheju National University, South Korea, discovered that camphor interrupts the production of prostaglandins and other chemical messengers involved in the inflammatory response and the creation of pain sensations.

Also in 2005, a team at the Harvard Medical School discovered that camphor desensitises a protein called TRPV1, which plays a central role in the body's sensation of heat. Interrupting that process brings a feeling of cooling and helps to reduce the perception of pain. Breathing in camphor vapour produces that sensation of cooling in the nasal passages; laboratory tests in the 1980s showed that it is this cooling effect that is responsible for the perceived decongestant effect of camphor vapour. A 2011 study showed that, additionally, TRPV1 plays a major role in the mechanism behind coughing, and this reinforces camphor's use as a cold remedy. The camphor laurel tree, moreover, produces a compound called cineole, a major constituent of eucalyptus oil (see p. 30); cineole has been shown in clinical trials to have decongestant and anti-inflammatory properties.

OTHER NAMES Camphor tree, camphorwood
ORIGIN Taiwan, Japan, China
PARTS USED Leaves, branches, bark, root

Camphor laurel tree

To treat the symptoms of a cold, including coughing, try using a few drops of camphor essential oil in a hot water vaporiser. Camphor is also a common ingredient in many over-the-counter cold remedies, as well as balms and liniments for treating skin irritation and muscle pain. Note that ingesting even small amounts of camphor can cause stomach pain, seizures, liver failure and even death, so it is for external use only and should not be applied to broken skin; young children and pregnant women are most at risk.

HAZEL

Corylus spp.

MEDICAL BENEFITS ◆ Treatment for high cholesterol ◆ Helps prevent cardiovascular disease ◆ May help prevent and treat cancer

There is more to the humble hazelnut than meets the eye. Not only has it been shown to be highly nutritious, but scientists are also discovering that it has other potent medicinal properties.

Hazelnuts can come from any of the 14 species of hazel tree, the most widely cultivated of which is the common hazel (*Corylus avellana*). The kernels are a good source of protein, unsaturated fats and minerals, as well as vitamins and antioxidants. A 2011 study at the University of Parma, Italy, revealed that hazelnut skins (the papery coating around the kernel) have weight-for-weight 25 times the antioxidant capability of blackberries.

It's in the blood The unsaturated fats in hazelnuts are omega-9 fatty acids, also found in olive oil. Like omega-3 fatty acids (provided in abundance by oily fish) these unsaturated fats have a beneficial effect on cholesterol. When cholesterol builds up in the blood, it is oxidised by free radicals to form a plaque that can impede the flow of the blood and, in turn, cause heart disease. Antioxidants present in hazelnuts limit this process and further reduce plaque formation.

Hazelnut skins have, weight-for-weight, 9 times the antioxidant capability of dark chocolate and 25 times that of blackberries.

In 2004, researchers at the University of Istanbul, Turkey, studied the effects of hazelnuts on rabbits fed a high-cholesterol diet. The team found that not only did the hazelnuts reduce the formation of plaque but also their unsaturated fatty acid content markedly improved the rabbits' blood lipid profile – the ratio of healthy to unhealthy fats in the blood – which also

in CLOSE-UP

Hazelnuts contain other beneficial nutritional elements besides monounsaturated omega-9 fatty acids and antioxidants. For example, fibre typically accounts for between 9 and 10 per cent of the hazelnut's mass – and diets rich in fibre can reduce the risk of colon cancer and curb appetite, according to a large body of research. Hazelnuts are also rich in arginine, an amino acid that plays many important roles in the body, including helping wounds to heal. Furthermore, arginine is a vasodilator, which means that it relaxes and widens blood vessels, and can consequently reduce blood pressure.

Cultivated since classical times, hazelnuts are particularly in demand for confectionery.

helped limit cholesterol build-up. A 2011 study, this time involving humans, at the University of Otago, New Zealand, found similar results, and the researchers concluded that hazelnuts 'can be incorporated into the usual diet as a means of reducing cardiovascular disease risk'.

Cancer fighting A comprehensive 2011 study of hazelnuts at Virginia State University in the United States investigated the effect of hazelnut extract on human colon cancer cells in the laboratory. It found that ground hazelnuts had potent 'antiproliferation' effects – in other words, they could stop cancer cells from multiplying. This is partly due to the antioxidants, which 'scavenge' free radicals that play a part in the proliferation of cancerous cells; but it might also be due in part to the presence of a compound called paclitaxel. It is the active ingredient in one of the most successful anticancer drugs, Taxol. It was discovered in the 1960s in Pacific yew tree (see p. 42), though today most of it is made from a related chemical obtained from the common, or European, yew.

In the late 1990s, with demand threatening to outstrip supply, scientists began looking for paclitaxel in other plants and found it in the kernels, shells and leaves of the hazel tree. The levels of paclitaxel in hazel are low, but the food industry discards such large quantities of the shells that these could be a significant source of the compound. Moreover, it's easier to grow paclitaxel-producing hazel cells in the laboratory than it is to grow yew cells, so cultured hazelnut cells could even become biochemical drug factories. Humble hazelnuts, indeed!

OTHER NAMES None, but the nuts are also called filberts
ORIGIN Temperate Northern Hemisphere forests
PARTS USED Nuts, nut shells

For health benefits, you can simply eat hazelnuts, or use them in cooking, raw or roasted; studies have shown that the beneficial omega-9 fatty acids and antioxidants remain virtually unaltered by roasting. Retain the paperlike 'skin', as that is the part with the highest concentration of antioxidants. Monounsaturated fatty acids make up 50–70 per cent of the kernel; this gives the nuts a fairly high kilojoule value of 33 kilojoules (8 calories) per nut, so eating large amounts could be fattening. Also bear in mind that many people have nut allergies.

Immature hazelnuts

SEARCHING HIGH AND LOW

Given the vast number of plant species that have yet to be investigated for medicinal compounds – perhaps 30 per cent of the 300,000 or so known species – it's no wonder that all major pharmaceutical companies are engaged in 'bioprospecting' – exploring the natural world to find medicine's next big thing.

Although the word 'bioprospecting' was coined as recently as the 1990s, the systematic search for potentially profitable plants and animals began in the eighteenth and nineteenth centuries. Imperial powers across Europe realised that unfamiliar plants growing in their colonies could have enormous value in providing food (coffee, for example), materials (such as cotton) and medicines (such as cinchona bark – see p. 21), and they were keen to discover new plants with wealth potential. From the nineteenth century onwards, chemists began isolating the active compounds in natural medicines with established track records, including morphine from poppies (see p. 98).

A taste for the exotic To maximise the chances of finding new medicinal compounds, it is necessary to search in areas rich in biodiversity, in locations where unfamiliar or undiscovered species are likely to be found. So bioprospectors are often modern-day explorers, venturing to remote jungles, mountaintops and the ocean floor, for example. Rainforests, such as those in the Amazon, are particularly rich in biodiversity, and are a major source of discovery. And, perhaps surprisingly, Antarctica is fast becoming a new frontier in bioprospecting, with more than 250 projects in full swing there, trawling the cold ocean bottoms and collecting lichens and mosses from far-flung islands.

Tools of the trade Just as prospectors searching for gold or other precious metals might use pans, sieves, shovels and metal detectors, so modern bioprospectors searching for potentially valuable chemical compounds use their own characteristic equipment and procedures. Once samples are back in the laboratory, researchers first produce extracts of the organism – for example, a plant's leaves might be blended and mixed with a solvent. The choice of solvent is important, as some biologically active compounds are soluble in water, others in only oils – and while the extraction is easier, quicker and more complete

INSTRUCTIONS INCLUDED

One of the bioprospector's most important modern aids is genomics, the study of the genomes of living organisms. A plant's genome contains all the biological information required to grow and maintain it, usually stored in units called genes. Compounds in a plant are manufactured according to these instructions. So by studying genomes, researchers can work out which compounds are present and how they might function. Furthermore, with genetic engineering reaching new levels of sophistication, genes from plants can be transferred into the genomes of bacteria, which can then be cultured to produce the compound of interest in large quantities – without needing to harvest the organism from which the compound was first isolated.

By mapping the genomes of promising plant species, scientists can work out which genes contain instructions for particular compounds.

Left: Ocean depths, explored by divers and in minisubs, are among the most fertile hunting grounds.

Right: Researchers collect insects in nets atop sitka spruce trees near Vancouver, Canada.

Below: Remote woodlands, such as this Alaskan conifer forest, may yield new and abundant fungi.

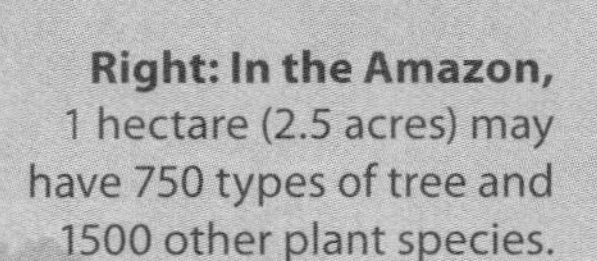

Left: Thermal springs are a rich source of microorganisms.

Right: In the Amazon, 1 hectare (2.5 acres) may have 750 types of tree and 1500 other plant species.

if heat is applied, some compounds denature or decompose at high temperatures, so cold extraction is often preferred.

Next, researchers carry out bioassays to investigate whether the extracts have any medicinal properties. This typically involves administering the extracts to laboratory animals with particular infections, cancers or other conditions – or to cultures of cells in vitro.

A high-tech approach Plant extracts are complex mixtures of chemical compounds. One of the most crucial steps in bioprospecting is to separate the compounds so that the active ones can be identified and synthesised. Separation is usually achieved using high-performance liquid chromatography. With this process, a sample is dissolved into a solvent, which is then pumped under high pressure through a tube containing solid particles. Molecules with low molecular weight pass through the particles more quickly than heavier molecules, so the various compounds are separated out.

Once a compound has been identified and isolated, scientists will work out its molecular structure using mass spectrometers, nuclear magnetic resonance and X-ray and infrared spectroscopes – procedures that are increasingly becoming automated. Chemists will then try to develop ways to synthesise the compound in large quantities – or even to improve upon it – in laboratories or chemical factories.

HAWTHORN

Crataegus spp.

MEDICAL BENEFITS ◆ Traditional treatment for heart ailments ◆ Potential treatment for high cholesterol, high blood pressure, heart failure

Hawthorn has been a popular herbal remedy since ancient times. Two thousand years on, scientists have learned much about its active compounds, though they are still some way from turning it into a conventional medicine.

Extracts from various hawthorn species have been used for medicinal purposes for hundreds of years in Europe, China and North America. And since the nineteenth century, together with garlic, hawthorn has become one of the most popular traditional treatments for heart disease. However, the plant can have significant side effects and cause adverse reactions in people taking other drugs, especially conventional heart medications.

Feeding fish Nevertheless, with more people dying every year from cardiovascular disease than from any other cause, hawthorn's ancient pedigree has prompted much recent research. Some of the most interesting findings have emerged from a study at the University of Cincinnati, in which the 'guinea pigs' were not humans or mice but baby zebrafish.

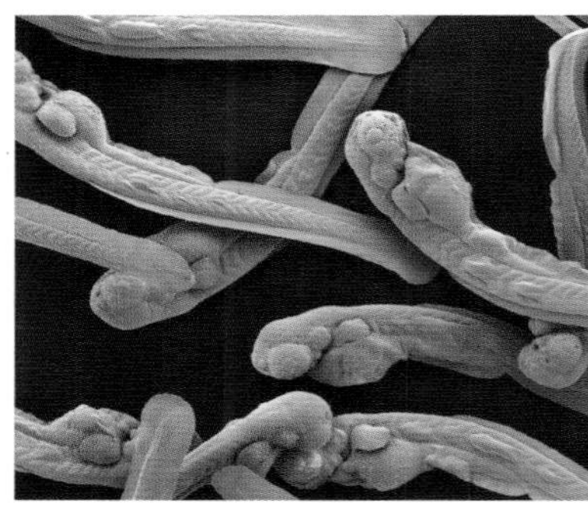

Zebrafish embryos are widely used in medical research as 'model organisms' for testing compounds in vivo, prior to human trials.

The Cincinnati researchers fed zebrafish larvae high-cholesterol diets. Then they divided the fish into three groups: one fed with regular food, one given a high-cholesterol diet and one on a high-cholesterol diet plus an extract of hawthorn leaves and flowers. The results? As noted in the researcher's 2012 report, the high-cholesterol diet significantly reduced cardiac output, as expected; and cholesterol was reduced, and cardiac output increased, in the fortunate fish that had been fed the hawthorn extract.

The heart of the matter A study, carried out at Victoria University in Melbourne, Australia, in 2009, involving mice on a high-cholesterol diet,

Traditional Wisdom

The Greek herbalist Dioscorides included hawthorn in his five-volume work *De Materia Medica*, a standard text across much of the West for 1500 years. Herbal medicine books of the Middle Ages suggest hawthorn as a treatment for diarrhoea and stomach cramps. The plant was first used to treat heart disease around 1600, when a court physician prescribed it for French king Henry IV.

Members of the rose family, hawthorns grow widely in temperate areas of the Northern Hemisphere.

found that hawthorn extract was as good as simvastatin (see p. 269), a standard treatment for high cholesterol. Several studies have been carried out on humans, too. In one trial, people received either a hawthorn extract or a placebo daily for three weeks. Among those who took hawthorn, the blood flow to the heart was improved and symptoms of chest pain (angina) were reduced. In a 2004 German study involving 900 people suffering heart failure (decreased cardiac output), half were treated with 900 mg per day of hawthorn extract over two years; at the end of the trial, all the classic symptoms of heart failure – fatigue, shortness of breath and irregular heartbeat – were significantly improved in those patients.

All of the studies to date involved an extract of hawthorn – a complex mixture of compounds. So, what are the active compounds, which might be having an effect? Most researchers put it down to a class of antioxidants called flavonoids – once dubbed 'vitamin P' – present in many plants, and in abundance in hawthorn.

Hawthorn extract is available from some health food stores, as a tincture or in capsule form, and is included in some herbal remedies, to protect against atherosclerosis and heart failure and to reduce blood pressure. You can also make tea from dried hawthorn leaves, flowers and berries. Possible side effects include nausea, headache and palpitations and there may be adverse interactions with other medicines, notably those for heart disease and high cholesterol. Always follow package instructions carefully and, if in doubt, consult your doctor. Medical experts advise against giving hawthorn extract to children or pregnant women.

Hawthorn berries

A thorny issue But, as well as highlighting the fact that hawthorn extract can reduce cholesterol and increase cardiac output, the zebrafish study found that in fish that did not have high cholesterol, hawthorn actually *reduced* cardiac output. Real-life situations are always complicated, and there is clearly a mixture of many compounds with potent effects. For now, the creation of a hawthorn-based medicine remains tantalisingly out of reach. But further research may change that, and this ancient ally may yet extend its reach to benefit millions more people.

OTHER NAMES Thorn-apple tree, May bush, May tree, May flower, whitethorn
ORIGIN Europe, Asia, North America
PARTS USED Flowers, leaves, fruits (berries)

EUCALYPTUS

Eucalyptus globulus

MEDICAL BENEFITS ◆ Treatment for bad breath and gingivitis ◆ Disinfectant treatment for cuts and burns ◆ Decongestant treatment for coughs and colds ◆ Treatment for muscle and joint pain ◆ Potential treatment for thrush, respiratory infections, leukaemia

Wonderfully aromatic, eucalyptus oil is a main component in cold remedies, anti-inflammatory creams, mouthwashes and soaps, and its abundance of active ingredients is the focus of much modern research.

There are more than 800 species of eucalyptus trees, most of which are endemic to Australia. Their wood is hard and resilient and, when pulped, is used to produce high-quality papers; the trees are also used to make a range of dyes, and the nectars yield fine honey. So useful are eucalyptus trees, indeed, that they have been cultivated in many other parts of the world.

Australia's Aboriginal people have been making the most of the many medicinal applications of eucalypts for thousands of years, especially to help wounds heal and to treat fungal infections. British naturalist Joseph Banks was the first visitor to collect eucalyptus specimens, in the 1770s, and in 1789 a sample of eucalyptus oil was sent to London, after settlers noticed its similarities to peppermint and suggested it might have medicinal qualities. Industrial distillation began in the 1850s, and the use of eucalyptus oil grew quickly – it was even adopted as a disinfectant for catheters in late-nineteenth-century European hospitals.

The Chinese connection

Eucalyptus trees are quintessentially Australian. So how come three-quarters of all eucalyptus oil comes from China? The answer relates to the plant's most potent ingredient, cineole. It is present in other plants, including lavender, rosemary, cardamom and camphor laurel (see p. 23). Although China also grows eucalyptus trees in plantations, it derives most of its 'eucalyptus oil' from camphor laurel trees. Thus, most of the world's so-called eucalyptus oil is not, in fact, from eucalyptus trees at all.

In parts of North America, *Eucalyptus globulus* is considered an invasive species.

Oil supplies Today, eucalyptus oil is normally obtained by steam distillation of the leaves and branch tops of the blue gum (*Eucalyptus globulus*). The oil is a complex mixture of (antibacterial) tannins, (antioxidant) flavonoids and (antibacterial and anticancer) terpenoids. In addition, it contains alpha-pinene, which has proven antibacterial effects. By far the most important and dominant compound, however, is a volatile terpenoid called cineole (or eucalyptol), which supplies the characteristic odour.

With so many active ingredients, it is no surprise there has been much interest in the oil's medicinal properties. A study at the Aligarh Muslim University, India, in 2001, showed that eucalyptus oil has wide-spectrum antibacterial and antifungal properties, including the ability to inhibit the fungus *Candida albicans*, which causes thrush (candidiasis). In a 2006 study at Tehran University of Medical Sciences in Iran, eucalyptus oil inhibited growth in cultures of bacteria taken from 200 patients with respiratory infections, and a 2010 study at the Tarbiat Modares University, Iran, showed that eucalyptus oil can suppress infections of MRSA (methicillin-resistant *Staphylococcus aureus*).

The main attraction Cineole, the most important active component in eucalyptus oil, has been the subject of a good deal of research, too. In 2003, researchers at the Bonn University Hospital, Germany, found that cineole reduced the inflammatory response and production of mucus in patients with severe asthma, and they were able to reduce the patients' reliance on standard steroid-based treatment as a result. Several studies have also highlighted cineole's ability to reduce pressure on the sinuses, its antitussive (cough-suppressing) properties and its analgesic (pain-relieving) properties. And because cineole is volatile, inhaling eucalyptus oil vapour is an effective way of delivering it to the membranes of the respiratory system.

Cineole has even been shown to halt the proliferation of abnormal cells in leukaemia. In 2002, researchers at Mie University, Japan, discovered that cineole causes the cells to self-destruct, by attacking their DNA.

OTHER NAMES Blue gum, Australian fever tree, Tasmanian blue gum
ORIGIN Australia
PARTS USED Leaves, branch tops

Koalas feed almost exclusively on eucalyptus leaves, munching through about 500 g (18 oz) a day, mostly at night.

You can use eucalyptus essential oil in vaporisers as a decongestant – the vapour may also kill bacteria in the respiratory tract. Lozenges, syrups and rubs that contain the oil are also available and can be used to treat coughs and colds. Another way to benefit from eucalyptus's antibacterial properties is by using creams and soaps containing the oil to treat burns and sores. Although you can use fresh eucalyptus leaves to make teas, the oil is toxic if swallowed – and children are particularly at risk. Pregnant and breastfeeding women are also advised not to use eucalyptus.

GINKGO BILOBA

Ginkgo biloba

MEDICAL BENEFITS ◆ Potential treatment for dementia, Raynaud's phenomenon, tinnitus, normal-tension glaucoma

One of the world's most popular herbal medicines, ginkgo biloba is used to treat a range of ailments, notably dementia. Studies aimed at pinning down its active ingredients and precise effects are ongoing.

Some people take ginkgo biloba extract as treatment for tinnitus – a ringing or swooshing in the ears – or to counter Raynaud's phenomenon, a disorder in which circulation is cut off episodically in the fingers and toes, leading to pain, a feeling of cold and discolouration of the skin. Others use it to treat 'normal-tension' glaucoma, a form of glaucoma in which there is no increased pressure in the eye but which still causes vision loss. However, the enormous popularity of ginkgo biloba extract rests principally on widespread claims that it can slow or prevent the onset of dementia – and many elderly people take daily doses in the hope that it will work.

OTHER NAME Maidenhair tree
ORIGIN China
PARTS USED Seeds, leaves

The connection between ginkgo biloba and dementia is based on hundreds of years of use in traditional Chinese medicine, where the seeds are associated with mental alertness and longevity. In the 1960s, German pharmacists introduced a standardised extract to the Western world, made from the tree's leaves. The main biologically active compounds in the extract are flavonoids, which can act as antioxidants, and a group of compounds called terpene trilactones, which have been shown to inhibit blood clotting and relax blood vessels, enhancing blood flow.

Mixed results A large number of studies have been carried out into the effectiveness of ginkgo biloba extract on dementia, with mixed results. An eight-year US study, published in 2008 and involving more than 3000 elderly volunteers,

Against the odds

The ginkgo biloba tree is a survivor. It is the only remaining species of an ancient genus that has existed for more than 250 million years – almost as long as there have been trees. Charles Darwin called it a 'living fossil'. While other species of ginkgo were once widespread, *Ginkgo biloba* is the only one that endured several ice ages, the drifting of continents and the rise of human beings, hanging on in hidden valleys in China and remaining virtually unchanged (as fossils show) for at least 150 million years. Specimens have even survived nuclear weapons: several ginkgo trees within 2 km (1.2 miles) of the blast at Hiroshima in 1945 began budding again soon after the explosion – and thrive to this day.

After the Hiroshima blast, the regrowth of ginkgo trees was among the first signs of new life – and hope.

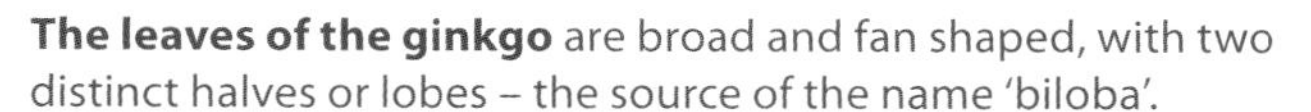

The leaves of the ginkgo are broad and fan shaped, with two distinct halves or lobes – the source of the name 'biloba'.

Ginkgo trees can grow to heights of more than 30 m (100 ft).

found that a twice-daily dose of the extract had no effect on the incidence of dementia or Alzheimer's disease. And another 2008 study, in the United Kingdom, also found that the extract had no positive effect on early-stage dementia patients. However, a major review of evidence, published in 2002, found that there is a real, if small, benefit, and a 24-week study at the University of Cologne, Germany, involving over 400 patients with early-stage dementia, published in 2012, found that ginkgo biloba produced 'significant and clinically relevant improvement in cognition, psychopathology, functional measures and quality of life'.

Studies of the effectiveness of ginkgo biloba extract on patients with tinnitus have also provided conflicting conclusions. A German review of existing well-conducted studies, published in 2011, found plenty of evidence in favour. But a 2012 South Korean study, involving 38 people and lasting two months, compared ginkgo biloba extract with a standard treatment (clonazepam) and found that the extract had no significant effect.

An estimated 2 billion ginkgo biloba tablets have been sold worldwide in the past 20 years.

There has been only one controlled study of the use of ginkgo biloba extract for treating Raynaud's phenomenon, but it did supply a positive result: in the 10-week study, volunteers (blindly) taking the extract had fewer than half the attacks they did normally. Several studies have also indicated that ginkgo biloba extract might help in treating normal-tension glaucoma.

If you want to try ginkgo biloba, you'll find it in most pharmacies and health food stores, normally in the form of tablets or tinctures; you can even buy the dried leaves for making teas. Since the main pharmacological effects of ginkgo biloba extract are to increase blood flow and reduce clotting, health professionals warn against using it if you are taking blood-thinning medications. And if you are taking ginkgo biloba and are due to undergo a surgical procedure, make sure you tell your surgeon. You should also speak to your doctor if you are taking antidepressants, as these may interact adversely with the extract.

TEA TREE

Melaleuca alternifolia

MEDICAL BENEFITS ◆ Treatment of insect bites, skin infections, acne, fungal infections, cold sores, head lice, dandruff ◆ Potential treatment for cancers

Oil from the tea tree is a versatile and popular herbal remedy, with well-known antiseptic and anti-inflammatory properties. In addition, scientists have recently discovered that the oil might help in the fight against cancer.

Australia's indigenous peoples have been crushing the leaves of *Melaleuca alternifolia* to make teas to treat colds and sore throats, as well as poultices to soothe minor infections, for thousands of years. The British explorer Captain James Cook tried the tea, unsuccessfully, as a cure for scurvy among his crew, and coined the name 'tea tree'. The name is rather ironic: healthcare professionals strongly advise against making tea from the tea tree, because it is toxic if taken internally.

Wisdom distilled In the 1920s, the state chemist of New South Wales, Australia, Arthur Penfold, discovered that the distilled oil of the tea tree was 11 times more effective than phenol, the standard antiseptic in use at the time, and thus the tea tree oil industry was born. Today, tea tree oil, steam-distilled from the leaves and branch tops, is routinely used by millions of people worldwide to treat minor injuries and infections.

As a result, researchers have carried out a wide range of experiments with the oil, both in vitro and in humans and other animals (in vivo). They have found that in addition to killing bacteria and reducing inflammation, tea tree oil is effective against candida (the fungus that causes thrush) and tinea (the fungus that causes athlete's foot). It is also effective at treating a number of viral infections: tests have shown that it works, for example, against warts (caused by the human papilloma virus) and cold sores (caused by the herpes virus), for example. And tea tree oil is toxic to insects: research shows that treatment of head lice with tea tree oil gel can be as effective as the popular conventional treatment permethrin.

Terpene time The standard formulation of tea tree oil consists of more than 90 compounds, the most important and biologically active being

in CLOSE-UP

As with most essential oils, tea tree oil breaks down the cell membranes of bacteria and single-celled fungi; some of the constituents of the oil also denature the cells' proteins, helping to destroy the organisms more quickly and more completely. Recent experiments have found that terpinen-4-ol, the principal active ingredient, directly affects DNA, which may explain its antiviral and anticancer properties.

Tea tree was among a wealth of new species discovered by James Cook's expeditions.

Tea tree leaves

Originally found growing only in eastern Australia, tea tree has since been cultivated much more widely. It is often grown on plantations, with the aim of producing oil for medicinal uses.

a class called terpenes. The most abundant and most potent compound is a terpene called terpinen-4-ol, which is also present in nutmeg. On its own, isolated from the oil, terpinen-4-ol is as effective as the whole oil in inhibiting the growth of candida and, being an alcohol, it has antibacterial properties. It also inhibits prostaglandins and other compounds involved in the body's inflammatory response – which explains why tea tree oil is anti-inflammatory. In 1999, a team at the former US National College of Chiropractic in Lombard discovered that terpinen-4-ol even activates white blood cells, the body's main weapons against infection.

In 2004, researchers at the Istituto Superiore di Sanità in Rome carried out an in vitro study in which they found that terpinen-4-ol can inhibit the growth of melanoma (skin cancer) tumours. Since then, several more studies, including some in vivo studies in mice, have shown that terpinen-4-ol has the ability to prevent cancerous tumours from growing or to encourage cancerous cells to self-destruct.

As yet, no anticancer drugs based on terpinen-4-ol have been made. However, it is possible that one day soon the oil that James Cook saw being used more than 200 years ago might help in the fight against one of the most troubling diseases of modern times.

OTHER NAMES Ti tree, narrow-leaved paperbark, narrow-leaved tea-tree, snow-in-summer
ORIGIN Australia
PARTS USED Leaves, branch tops

You can add tea tree oil to shampoo to help treat head lice and dandruff, and a few drops added to a bath will help control the bacteria that produce body odour. In a vaporiser, the oil can help reduce congestion associated with colds and may deactivate the viruses that cause colds. Mixed with a base cream, tea tree oil is an effective antiseptic – but don't use it neat, as it can irritate the skin. It is also toxic if swallowed, so it should only be used externally.

BANISH THE BUGS

Most plants contain antimicrobial compounds that defend against infection, and laboratory tests have confirmed the effectiveness of these compounds in killing bacteria, fungi and viruses. You can harness this bug-killing power by incorporating plant extracts in a range of home remedies.

In most commercially available antimicrobial products – antiseptic creams, handwashes, mouthwashes and surface cleaners, for example – the active ingredients are potent synthetic compounds. Increasingly, however, due to concerns over the toxicity of certain synthetic compounds, the emergence of bacterial resistance to some of them and a desire to live more sustainably, people are turning to natural alternatives. Adding to their appeal, many natural antimicrobial compounds also have antioxidant and anti-inflammatory properties, or can help to promote wound healing.

Essential information The most potent and most widely used antibacterial plant extracts are essential oils. They are 'essential' because they carry the scent, or essence, of the plant, and 'oils' because they do not mix with water. The active compounds in essential oils are phenolics or phenols. Phenolic compounds infiltrate the oily membranes of the single cells that are bacteria, thereby breaking open the cells and killing the bacteria.

In one scientific study of essential oils, from 2006, 19 out of 21 essential oils tested showed antibacterial effects against common bacteria; of these, cinnamon was the most potent. Other studies have shown that thyme, tea tree and oregano are also particularly effective. In addition, oregano, spearmint and cinnamon oils have been found to be effective against both bacterial and fungal infections, as have extracts of St John's wort and marigold.

Homemade healing You can easily incorporate essential oils in homemade creams, lotions, mouthwashes and antibacterial soaps. Take care with the oils, as they are very concentrated and can cause rashes or other skin reactions – they are seldom

BACTERIA BUSTERS

The following essential oils have proven effects against common bacteria:

Cinnamon • Citronella • Clove • Lemon • Lime • Oregano Rosemary • Tea tree • Thyme

used neat. Note, too, that natural compounds do slowly spoil, so you should assume that your preparations will have a shelf life of no more than six months. You can extend this a little by keeping preparations in cool places, in dark or opaque bottles to block sunlight, or by adding a little honey or jojoba oil. If you are making a cream, using a base that is rich in vitamin E will also help the cream last longer.

Thymol, an antibacterial phenolic compound found in thyme and several other plants, is so effective that it is increasingly being added to toothpastes, mouth-washes and hand sanitisers.

HOME REMEDIES

Antiseptic lotion Soak a cotton wool ball in witch hazel water and add a drop of lavender oil. Use to gently wipe a wound, making sure your hands are clean first. Witch hazel water contains rubbing alcohol, itself an effective anti-bacterial compound.

Antibacterial mouthwash Mix half a teaspoon of baking soda into half a cup of water, add two drops of peppermint oil and one drop of tea tree oil. Rinse the mouth thoroughly but do not swallow.

Antifungal footbath
Although lavender oil has only mild antibacterial activity, a 2011 in vitro study showed that it may be more effective than conventional treatments in treating fungal infections such as ringworm, athlete's foot and even candida. A regular footbath with several drops of pure lavender oil could stop or even reverse the growth of fungal infections.

Herbal handwashes
Researchers at the University of Michigan School of Public Health found that plain soap is as effective as specially formulated antibacterial soaps at dissolving bacterial cell membranes (and that you need to scrub for 20 seconds for either to be effective). Adding natural antimicrobials to plain soap will strengthen its antibacterial action, and make it smell good, too. Just grate a bar of plain soap into a pan, warm it with enough water to make it dissolve (but not too sloppy), and add four or five drops of tea tree or other essential oil. Transfer the mixture to a mould, and allow it to cool and harden.

To make a gel-based hand sanitiser, mix one cup of aloe vera gel with one cup of rubbing alcohol (isopropyl alcohol), add seven or eight drops of any of the essential oils listed on the opposite page and mix in a bowl. Both the alcohol and the essential oils kill bacteria, and the oils dissolve in the alcohol.

WILLOW

Salix spp.

MEDICAL BENEFITS ◆ Treatment for headaches, lower back pain, osteoarthritis, fever, inflammation

An inspired piece of self-experimentation by an eighteenth-century clergyman led to the rediscovery of an old herbal remedy, and to the development of one of the bestselling medicines of all time.

In 1758, English clergyman and scientist Edward Stone was sitting under a willow tree near his home in Chipping Norton, England. For some unknown reason, he decided to taste some of the tree's bark, and its bitter taste reminded him of the bark of another tree, cinchona (see p. 21).

At the time, cinchona bark was a popular but expensive treatment for the 'ague' – an old word for intermittent fever, normally associated with malaria. The bitter taste of willow led Stone to administer it to some people suffering from the ague. Over several years of testing, he found that willow bark was an effective painkiller and could reduce his volunteers' fevers.

An old cure revived Stone could find no mention of willow in the literature and so thought he had made a new discovery. Actually, willow bark was a favourite remedy in several ancient civilisations, but had been largely forgotten. Stone reported his experiments to the Royal Society, and word soon spread.

In 1820, French chemists identified quinine as the active compound in cinchona bark – and in 1826, the German chemist Johann Buchner isolated a yellow crystalline substance in willow bark extract. Buchner named the new substance salicin, after the Latin scientific name for the willow family, *Salix*, and it soon became clear that salicin was the main biologically active component of the bark.

OTHER NAMES None, but common species include pussy willow and goat willow
ORIGIN Temperate regions of the Northern Hemisphere
PART USED Bark

Often found along rivers and lakes, willow trees draw up large amounts of water, some of it supplying the very moist bark sap.

Trading in derivatives During the rest of the nineteenth century, chemists prepared a number of derivatives of salicin – in particular, salicylic acid and sodium salicylate. But these new compounds, effective though they were, often caused stomach upset. From the 1850s onwards, several chemists prepared acetylsalicylic acid, and found that it had the same curative properties as the other compounds but without so much irritation. However, the new chemical remained difficult to make – until the 1890s, when chemists at the German company Bayer found a way to produce it reliably.

The Bayer preparation did not use willow, however, but meadowsweet, one of many plants that contain salicylic acid. The (now

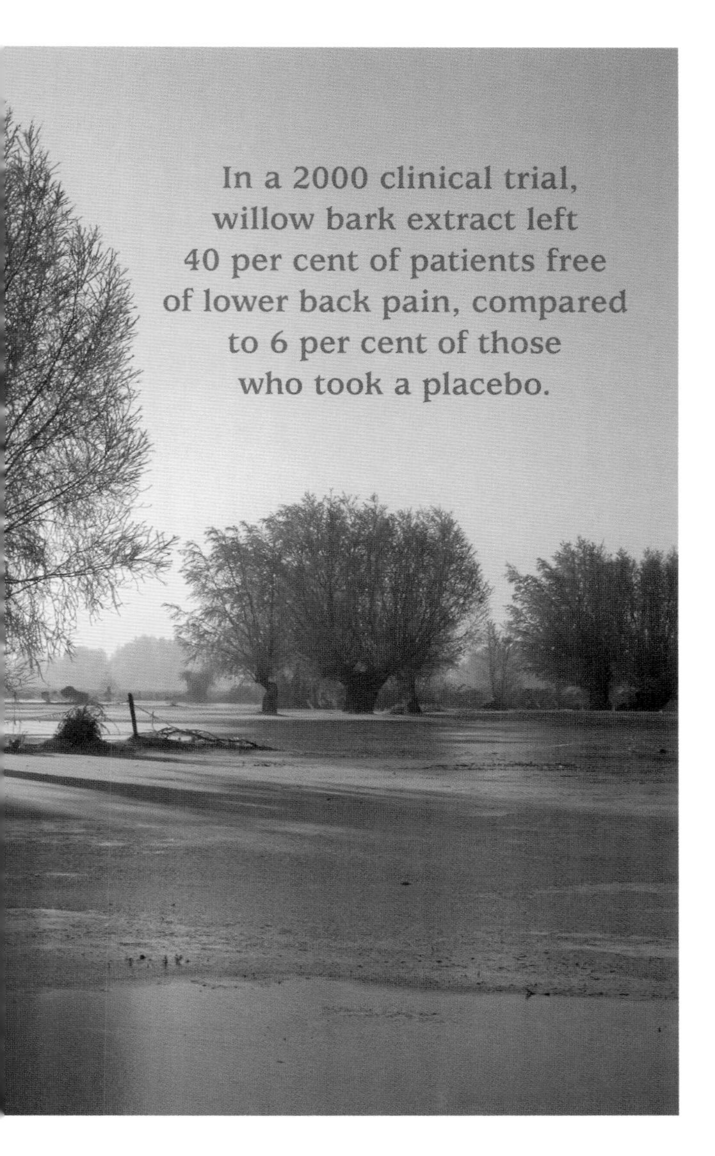

Traditional Wisdom

A 5000-year-old clay tablet from the ancient Mesopotamian city of Ur lists willow bark as one of several commonly used medicinal herbs, and an ancient Egyptian papyrus dating to approximately 1570 BC – but most likely copied from an even earlier document – prescribes willow bark for the relief of pain and inflammation. In ancient Greece, the renowned physician Hippocrates recommended chewing willow bark to relieve pain, inflammation and fever, and many ancient Roman doctors used the bark for similar purposes. Native American peoples have also long taken willow bark medicinally. Yet this ancient wisdom was all but lost, across Europe and Asia, until that day when Edward Stone sat under the willow trees in Chipping Norton.

defunct) Latin name for meadowsweet was *Spiraea ulmaria*, from which the company derived a name for the new medicine: 'aspirin'. It quickly became the number-one-selling medicine in the world.

A natural alternative? Nevertheless, many people continued to use willow bark as a remedy, and it is still popular today as a natural treatment for a range of ailments. What's more, modern scientific research confirms that it is effective against headache, lower back pain and osteoarthritis.

In a 2000 study at the Institute of Technology in Haifa, Israel, sufferers of back pain who received a 240 mg daily dose of willow bark extract experienced significantly greater pain relief than those who received a placebo. And in 2012, an international team of researchers based in Germany and the United Kingdom

Aspirin's popularity soared in the early 1900s. This vehicle was used to market the drug in the Netherlands in the 1920s.

If you want to try willow bark as an alternative to aspirin and other commercial painkillers, you can buy it in strips or a powdered form, both of which can be steeped in water to make a drink, and as a tincture, which can also be added to water to drink. If you are allergic to aspirin, you should avoid willow extract; a few people experience other side effects, including black stools, nausea and fatigue. You should also avoid taking willow extract if you are taking blood-thinning medicines, such as warfarin. The tannin content of willow bark extract is particularly high, and this can leave some people feeling a little nauseous.

Willow bark tea

investigated the mechanism behind willow bark's effect on osteoarthritis (for which it is a popular herbal remedy). Tracking biochemical reactions in detail, the researchers discovered that an extract of the bark encouraged the formation of collagen, which is lost during the normal progression of the disease, and reduced painful inflammation.

Willow bark's ability to reduce inflammation is due to its salicin content. Once inside the body, salicin is metabolised into salicylic acid (as is aspirin). Inflammation involves a cascade of chemical reactions, and one of the most noticeable results is a localised increase in blood pressure, with the pain, swelling and redness that accompanies it. Another effect of inflammation is the raising of the body's temperature: fever. By inhibiting acute inflammation, salicylic acid reduces pain and swelling and reduces body temperature.

Combined effects A tea made from steeped willow bark can therefore be an effective painkiller. However, the amount of salicylic acid present in the body after taking a dose of willow bark – in a tea, for example – is less than one-tenth the amount present after taking a typical aspirin tablet. Therefore salicin alone cannot account for willow bark's anti-inflammatory and analgesic effects. In fact, willow bark extract is a complex mixture of potentially beneficial, biologically active compounds, including antioxidant flavonoids and antibacterial tannins.

Willow bark has some benefits over its close cousin, synthetically produced aspirin. It does not damage the stomach lining, as aspirin is known to do in some cases. And, while aspirin can reduce the tendency for the blood to clot, willow bark does not – and for some people that's a major benefit.

Willow bark is usually harvested in spring or early summer, when the bark is moist and more easily separated from the tree.

CLOVE

Syzygium aromaticum

MEDICAL BENEFITS ◆ Local anaesthetic for toothache ◆ Prevention of stomach ulcers ◆ Antibacterial, anti-inflammatory and antioxidant properties, as well as possible anticancer activity

Clove flowers

Modern investigations are revealing a range of potential medical applications for this widely used spice and popular home remedy for the torment of toothache.

What are commonly referred to as cloves are the dried unopened flower buds of the clove tree; the tree's buds, stems and leaves are also used to make clove oil, an essential oil. Clove oil's effectiveness as a local anaesthetic has been investigated in several studies: in a 2006 study at Kuwait University, for example, clove oil worked as well as the synthetic local anaesthetic benzocaine at numbing the pain of toothache.

Native to Indonesia, cloves are now also cultivated in Sri Lanka and East Africa.

Fully cloved Clove oil has been used for centuries by Ayurvedic healers in India to treat respiratory and digestive ailments. In 2011, researchers at the University of Vale do Itajaí, Brazil, found that clove enhances the production of mucus in the stomach lining, protecting against stomach ulcers. It is also an expectorant, encouraging the production of mucus in the respiratory system, and so eases coughing.

The main component of clove oil, and the compound that carries clove's characteristic aroma, is eugenol. Several research teams have found that eugenol is potently antibacterial and antioxidant, a fact that accounts for clove's use as a food preservative.

It has long been suspected that clove may have anticancer effects, too – and modern science seems to be confirming that. In 2006 researchers at the Chittaranjan National Cancer Institute in India reported that eugenol inhibits the growth of lung cancer tumours in mice, and a 2011 study conducted at the IILM Institute, India, found that in the laboratory clove oil caused cancer cells to self-destruct while leaving normal blood cells unscathed. Research is ongoing.

OTHER NAME Caryophyllum
ORIGIN The Moluccas in Indonesia
PARTS USED Buds, leaves, twigs

Pharmacies sell a range of eugenol-containing products aimed at soothing dental pain. You can also make your own toothache-easing mixture by crushing cloves in a pestle and mortar and adding a little olive oil. These measures are designed to give only temporary relief, however, and it is important to seek professional dental care as soon as possible. Note, too, that clove oil and products containing eugenol can cause irritation in some people and that, in large amounts, clove oil is toxic when taken internally.

PACIFIC YEW

Taxus brevifolia

MEDICAL BENEFITS ◆ Treatment for cancers of the breast, ovaries, lung, head, neck and colon, and Kaposi's sarcoma ◆ Potential treatment for Alzheimer's disease

How do you make enough medicine for tens of thousands of patients, when the only source of the drug is a slow-growing, rare and threatened species of tree?

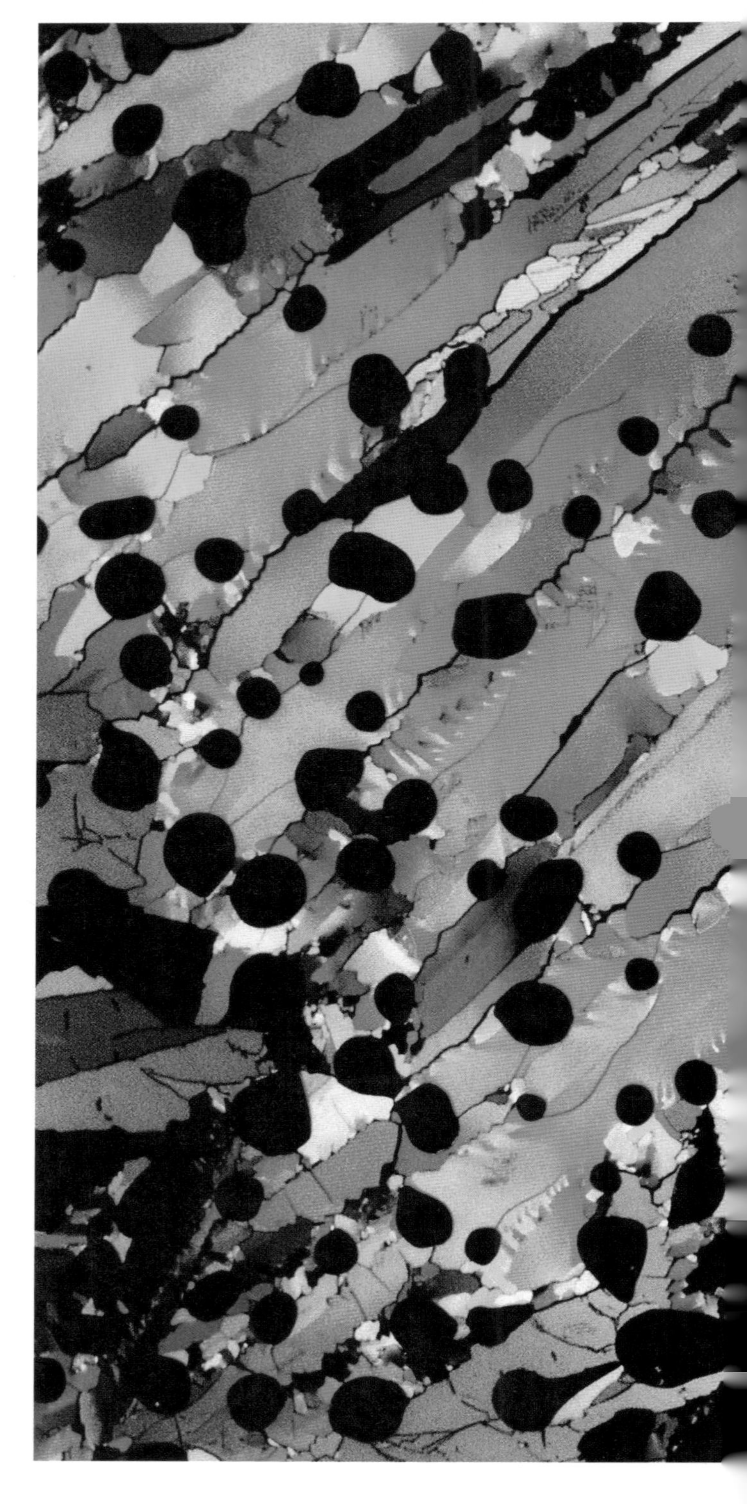

That was the dilemma that faced researchers in the 1980s after clinical trials had shown that a compound extracted from the bark of the Pacific yew tree had the potential to be one of the most effective anticancer drugs ever discovered. Growing in the shade of large established trees in the northwestern United States and southwestern Canada, the Pacific yew takes more than 100 years to reach its maximum height of about 15 m (50 ft). In the eighteenth and nineteenth centuries, settlers prized the tree for its durable hardwood, which was used to make longbows, paddles, fence posts and furniture. However, throughout most of the twentieth century, the timber industry saw the species as little more than a weed. More interested in the larger trees that towered above it, the timber-cutters often hacked down Pacific yew and left it to rot, or simply burned it to make way for new plantings.

A bark with bite All that began to change in the summer of 1962, when samples of Pacific yew were tested as part of a program run jointly by the US Department of Agriculture and the National Cancer Institute (NCI) to find natural compounds that might help fight cancer. After the samples passed an initial test, they were sent to the laboratory of American chemist Monroe Wall. By the end of 1966, Wall and his colleague, Indian-born chemist Mansukh Wani, had isolated the active compound in the samples, and had named it 'taxol'. But despite Wall's best efforts to garner support for further tests, taxol was essentially shelved for several years. This was partly because there were other compounds that seemed to work just as well and partly because of budget constraints within the NCI; but there was also another reason: the yield from each tree was tiny. To extract just 2 g of taxol – only enough for a single course of treatment – 25 kg (55 lb) dry weight of bark was needed. And to harvest that much bark, three mature trees had to be felled.

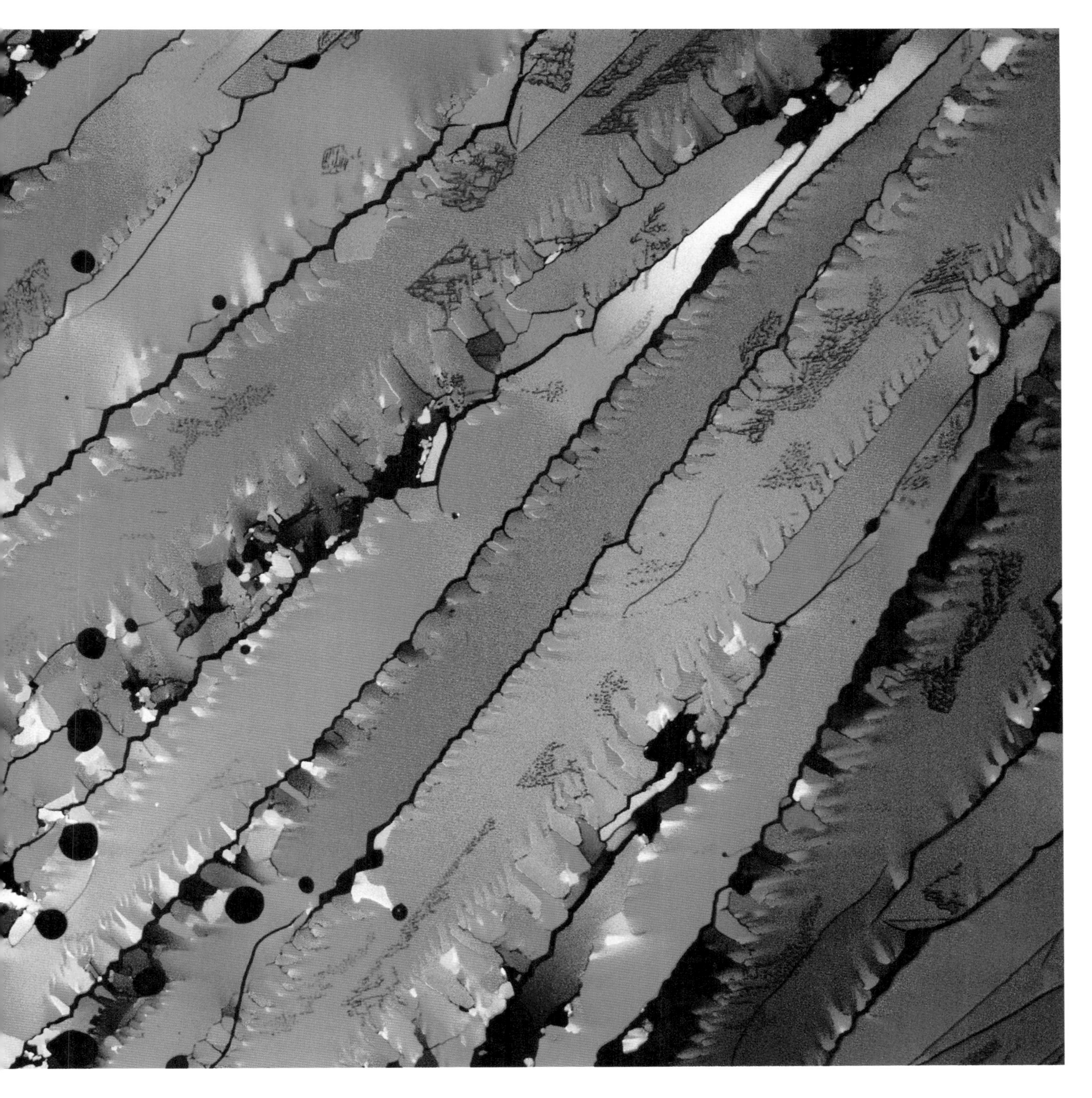

Nonetheless, after taxol was shown to have destroyed melanoma cells in laboratory tests in 1975, the NCI requested the felling of 1500 trees – enough to find out if taxol could be made into a viable chemotherapy drug. In 1978, molecular chemist Susan B Horwitz got hold of some taxol, and managed to work out just how the compound was able to kill cancer cells, and stop tumours from growing. It was

Polarised light micrograph images, such as this one of Taxol, help researchers fathom the structure of a substance and thereby devise ways to synthesise it.

OTHER NAME Western yew
ORIGIN Northwestern United States and southwestern Canada
PARTS USED Bark, leaves, cells

in CLOSE-UP

Like all living tissues, tumours are made of cells, and they grow by repeated cell division. Paclitaxel arrests that cell division by binding to long, thin structures called microtubules. Just before a cell divides, microtubules drag copies of the cell's DNA to two ends of the cell, so that one copy of the complete DNA will end up in each of the two 'daughter' cells. When paclitaxel binds to the microtubules, it stops them from disassembling, preventing cell division and arresting the growth of the tumour.

Legislation designed to protect the northern spotted owl greatly restricted the harvesting of old-growth Pacific yew trees.

a mechanism that no-one had ever seen before (see 'In Close-up', left), and it filled the medical science community with excitement.

Testing times In the 1980s, taxol quickly became big news. Tests involving mice revealed the drug's ability to shrink human breast cancer tumours. When the first human clinical trials involving taxol, on patients with ovarian and skin cancers, finished in 1988, the fledgling drug was shown to have achieved a then-unprecedented 30 per cent response rate in shrinking tumours, notably in patients in whom other drugs had failed.

The problem of supplying the anticipated demand became ever more pertinent. To treat all the patients who had ovarian, breast or skin cancer in the United States alone, more than 300,000 Pacific yew trees would have to be felled each year. Conservationists were up in arms, not least because the Pacific yew is an essential part of the habitat of the endangered northern spotted owl, then already threatened by logging. Meanwhile, cancer sufferers were equally outraged – that they might be denied treatment because of owls.

The NCI continued obtaining tonnes of Pacific yew bark from the field. It also entered into an agreement with a timber company to found a Pacific yew plantation – but that would take years to come to fruition. The whole endeavour became too costly and politically sensitive for the NCI to pursue, and in 1992 it passed on responsibility for developing taxol to the American pharmaceutical company Bristol-Myers Squibb. The company trademarked the compound, with the name Taxol – and changed its generic name to 'paclitaxel'. Taxol was approved for the treatment of ovarian cancer in the United States in 1992, for breast cancer in 1993 – and in about 50 other countries within the next few years.

Making it work But even as Taxol was nearing approval, the problem of producing sufficient quantities of the drug had still not been solved. For ten years, chemists around the world had been attempting to synthesise the drug, with little success. But, fortunately, within a year of Taxol going on sale, scientists at Florida State

University made a breakthrough. They found a way to produce paclitaxel from a similar compound found in the European yew (*Taxus baccata*). That tree is more widespread and faster growing than the Pacific yew, and the compound is present in the needles and twigs, so it can be harvested without felling the trees. Meanwhile a team of chemists in France working on the same process developed a slightly different compound, docetaxel (trade name Taxotere), which acts in the same way as paclitaxel and is also now a widely used chemotherapy drug.

In 1993, before the advent of more economical production methods, Taxol was selling for $5846 per gram.

Most paclitaxel is still made from the needles of the European yew, but some is now produced in tanks containing 'cell lines' taken from Pacific yew trees. The cultured cells produce the compound, which can be extracted without killing the cells. Since the late 1990s, scientists have also been trying to genetically engineer *E. coli* bacteria to produce paclitaxel. If successful, this approach will make the drug much cheaper, and allow scientists to study in greater detail the reactions that produce it. This could also lead to the discovery of other, similar compounds that may have medicinal properties.

The thin brown bark of the Pacific yew tree is often swathed in moss. Native Americans used the wood to make bows and canoe paddles.

New directions

Paclitaxel remains one of the most popular anticancer drugs, and has saved thousands of lives. It is used to treat breast and ovarian cancers and a form of lung cancer, as well as Kaposi's sarcoma, a tumour caused by a herpes virus and often associated with AIDS. Paclitaxel's ability to inhibit the proliferation of cells is also put to good use in cardiac stents – small tubes inserted into constricted blood vessels. The stents are made to expand and thereby increase blood flow. It is commonplace for scar tissue to grow around the stent, but coating the stent with paclitaxel can prevent that tissue from forming. Paclitaxel may also one day be beneficial in the fight against neurodegenerative diseases, such as Alzheimer's disease. Research has shown that, by stabilising the microtubules in neurones (nerve cells) in the brain, paclitaxel seems to slow, and even reverse, the loss of mental function.

If you have or someone you know has breast or ovarian cancer – or even head, neck or colon cancer – chances are paclitaxel has already been considered as part of the treatment. There are several different formulations of the drug, the most common being a clear solvent, in which the compound is dissolved, that is injected intravenously. Research into the anticancer effects of paclitaxel and the related compound docetaxel are continuing, and there are always new clinical trials it may be possible to join. Although Native Americans have used Pacific yew bark in medicinal preparations for hundreds of years – sometimes even chewing it and spitting it onto wounds – the plant is toxic and health professionals strongly discourage ingesting it in any way.

CACAO TREE

Theobroma cacao

MEDICAL BENEFITS ◆ Lowers risk of cardiovascular disease ◆ Suppresses coughing ◆ May ease or reduce the risk of type 2 diabetes

The person with the longest confirmed lifespan, of 122 years, Frenchwoman Jeanne Calment, ate 1 kg (2 lb) of chocolate weekly. So does chocolate have special powers?

The seeds of the cacao tree grow inside large thick-skinned pods. Each pod contains about 50 seeds, often called cocoa beans.

Chocolate is made from the seeds, or beans, of the cacao tree. The main ingredients are cocoa butter, an edible fat extracted from the beans, and cocoa solids, a dark powder made by grinding the beans after the fat has been taken out. Most of chocolate's beneficial substances are found in the solids, which contain more than 300 chemical compounds. Many are polyphenols, potent antioxidants that may help prevent illnesses such as heart disease and cancer.

Risks lowered In 2011, the *British Medical Journal* published a review of the evidence on the potential benefits of chocolate. It concluded that higher levels of consumption lowered the risk of cardiovascular disease by more than one-third. It also cited a Japanese study that found eating chocolate reduced the risk of developing type 2 diabetes; this is consistent with other studies that have shown that the antioxidants present in cocoa can reduce insulin resistance, a major cause of the disease.

A brief history of chocolate

The cacao tree was first cultivated in Central America, where the beans were used to make a drink used in rituals and for medicinal purposes. Spanish explorers came across this drink and named it *chocolate*, probably based on the Mayan words *chokol*, meaning 'hot', and *atl*, 'water'. Hernando Cortés presented chocolate to the Spanish court in the 1520s and later suggested adding sugar and spices. Chocolate spread to other European countries, and to North America, in the 1600s and 1700s, and solid chocolate was first made in Britain in 1830.

In a major US study, people who ate chocolate at least five times a week had half the incidence of heart disease of those who ate none.

Cocoa beans are the most concentrated natural source of the alkaloid compound theobromine, a stimulant similar to caffeine. Though toxic in large amounts, it generally has positive effects on the human body: it relaxes muscles in the digestive tract, which can reduce gastrointestinal problems, and widens blood vessels, which reduces blood pressure. In 2005,

Cacao tree pod

Right: Between 300 and 600 cocoa beans are required to make 1 kg (2.2 lb) of chocolate.

a team of scientists based in the Britain and Hungary also found that theobromine was more effective than the standard treatment, codeine, at suppressing coughing.

Feeling good Every chocoholic knows that chocolate tastes delicious – but there is more to it than that: chocolate makes us *feel* good. At the University of Sussex in England, scientists monitored couples' heart rates and brains after eating dark chocolate and after kissing; the effects of the actions were similar, but stronger and longer lasting after eating chocolate.

The pleasurable and almost addictive properties of cocoa-based products remain something of a mystery, but researchers have found some possible explanations. Theobromine crosses the blood–brain barrier and acts on the central nervous system: it is a stimulant, like caffeine. Chocolate, moreover, contains a compound called salsolinol, which stimulates the production of dopamine, a neurotransmitter associated with pleasure and reward. Present, too, are other pleasure-giving neuroactive chemicals, called tetrahydro-beta-carbolines. And, as a team of scientists in Italy, Switzerland and Israel discovered in 1996, cocoa products also contain a compound called anandamide, a chemical that activates the same brain receptors as cannabis does. There are only tiny amounts of this compound in chocolate – it would take several kilograms of dark chocolate to get the 'high' provided by a cannabis cigarette – but there are two other chemicals that mimic it, which may well add to the effect.

OTHER NAMES Chocolate tree, cocoa tree
ORIGIN Central and South America
PART USED Beans

What You CAN DO

White chocolate contains only cocoa butter; milk and dark chocolate contain both cocoa butter and cocoa solids, with dark chocolate having more of the latter. Given that most of the beneficial compounds are in the solids, dark chocolate is therefore the best choice. And as long as you only eat dark chocolate, you'll get the benefits without increasing levels of body fat: a 2012 study at the University of California found that eating more chocolate can actually help reduce the ratio of fat to weight and height (a measurement known as the body mass index). The authors of the study proposed that chocolate increases the metabolic rate and thus burns off the extra kilojoules. So, regular – but not excessive – chocolate consumption can be part of a healthy diet!

GREEN TEA

Camellia sinensis

MEDICAL BENEFITS ◆ Possible protection against various cancers, AIDS, dental caries, halitosis, dementia, heart disease

Although the scientific evidence doesn't fully support green tea's reputation as a cancer-busting beverage, research does indicate that compounds from the tea *might* help fight cancer and a host of other ailments.

Green tea is made from the dried leaves of the plant *Camellia sinensis*; other types of tea, including black and oolong, are made from the same leaves using other processes (see p. 50). Many studies have shown that green tea can provide some protection against conditions including cardiovascular disease (heart disease and stroke), neurodegenerative disorders such as Alzheimer's disease, obesity, diabetes, liver disease and even dental caries and halitosis.

Tea-riffic The health benefits of green tea rest mainly on the presence of compounds called catechins, which make up about 30 per cent of the dry weight of the leaves and have been shown to have antioxidant, antibacterial and anti-inflammatory properties. In 2006, researchers at Sheffield University, in the United Kingdom, found in laboratory tests that the most abundant and potent green tea catechin, epigallocatechin-3-gallate (EGCG), can inhibit the action of the human immunodeficiency virus (HIV) on immune system cells.

So, what about green tea's purported anticancer properties? Well, epidemiological studies of green tea consumption versus cancer in human populations have been frustratingly inconclusive. For every study that shows

Harvesting of tea is usually done by hand. For the finest teas, only the bud and the next two or three leaves are plucked off the plant.

IN CLOSE-UP

The antioxidant properties of green tea catechins can play an important role in cancer prevention, by mopping up harmful free radicals that can damage DNA. Moreover, researchers have discovered a host of other biochemical mechanisms by which green tea catechins, in the right concentration, can inhibit the development and spread of cancers. They include encouraging apoptosis – cell self-destruction, which normal cells do naturally, but cancer cells do not – as well as reducing levels of insulin-like growth factor and nuclear factor kappa B, compounds linked with an increased risk of several types of cancer. In 2012, US researchers at Case Western University found that EGCG enhances the action of the tumour suppressor protein called p53, which plays a major role in the body's own anticancer defences.

drinking tea is effective in preventing cancer, there is another that indicates that it is not. Moreover, all the major reviews bringing together these epidemiological studies have concluded that the actual benefits of regular green tea consumption remain unproven. Nevertheless, some research suggests that catechins could counter cancer in a range of ways, including impeding the development of cancer cells and enhancing the body's natural defences (see In Close-up).

Furthermore, experiments on cancer cell cultures and in animals are much more encouraging. Just one of many examples is a 2003 study at the University of Alabama, in the United States, in which cream containing EGCG applied to hairless mice over 30 weeks gave 'exceptionally high protection' against developing skin cancer when the mice were irradiated with ultraviolet radiation. This was partly due to the antioxidant catechins destroying damaging free radicals produced in the skin cells by the radiation.

Maintaining concentration The main reason for the discrepancy between epidemiological studies and laboratory studies is that in the lab the concentration of catechins tends to be high, and the extracts are often injected directly into the blood or other tissues. But drink a cup or two of green tea and not all the catechins will make it into the blood – and when they do they are diluted in a large volume of fluid.

One way around that problem is to develop medicines containing EGCG that target cancer cells directly. Recent attempts to do this have brought encouraging results. In a 2012 study at the University of Strathclyde, in the United Kingdom, for example, EGCG was administered to mice with skin cancers in globules containing a protein that attaches to cancer cells. More than half the tumours shrank or disappeared within three weeks, and there was no damage to normal tissues.

OTHER NAME Tea plant
ORIGIN East Asia
PARTS USED Leaves

Studies that show health benefits for green tea suggest that the more you drink the better. And research suggests green tea is safe to drink in large quantities, though consuming more than a few litres may cause diarrhoea and nausea in some people. Capsules containing green tea extract are available from pharmacies and health food stores. A 2004 study confirmed that these have the same physiological effect as the drink, though a 2006 analysis found that the catechin content and antioxidant capabilities of extracts varied markedly. If capsules are not your cup of tea, brew up instead.

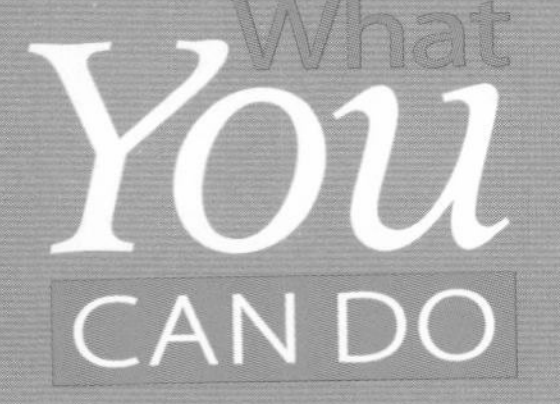

TEA TEST

The second most commonly consumed drink on the planet after water, tea certainly contains compounds with health benefits. But what kind of tea should you drink? And how do you make your own fruit and herbal teas?

Tea drinking originated in China, possibly as long ago as 2700 BC. It may have begun when people began boiling drinking water for hygienic reasons then made the water more pleasant to drink by adding leaves from the tea plant. The drink was introduced to Japan in the thirteenth century by the Zen Buddhist monk Eisai, who wrote, 'Tea has an extra-ordinary power to prolong life'. Many modern scientific studies suggest that he was right.

Green, black or in between? Most of the tea drunk in Asia, and about 20 per cent of tea in the West, is green tea (see p. 48), which is made from the leaves of the plant *Camellia sinensis* with no processing other than drying. Black tea is made from the same plant but subjected to steam so that it dries slowly, allowing an array of chemical reactions to take place. These are responsible for the change in colour – the green pigment chlorophyll breaks down, for example, and red and brown compounds form from the oxidation of compounds called catechins. Catechins have many proven health benefits (see p. 48), so as a result, black tea and other teas, such as oolong, that undergo more extensive processing have a much lower catechin content and therefore fewer benefits.

Nevertheless, black and oolong tea still contain a wide range of beneficial compounds, notably polyphenols, including tannins, and vitamin C. Tannins are responsible for tea's astringent (bitter, cloying) taste, and also for a less desirable effect: they inhibit the absorption of iron in the digestive system. So less iron will be absorbed from a meal if you drink black (and to a lesser extent, oolong) tea just before, during or after the meal than if you drink it between meals – something to bear in mind if you have low iron levels.

Fruit and herbal teas Fruit teas and herbal teas – collectively known as tisanes – are made from dried herbs and fruits, and sometimes extracts of plant roots. They are abundant in antioxidants, which are beneficial in preventing a number of chronic diseases and can slow ageing, and generally free of caffeine. Most also contain beneficial soluble fibre and minerals. Some tisanes, particularly peppermint tea, will, however, inhibit iron absorption, though to a lesser extent than black tea.

Iced mint and blood orange tea

HOME BREW

Take care if making your own teas with garden plants, as some can be poisonous or contain compounds that interfere with medications. Generally, though, edible plants will be safe. Collect the leaves and flowers when they are at their best, normally in the middle of summer, then spread on a rack to dry out for several days. Once they are nearly dry, pack them loosely in a pillowcase and hang it up to dry fully. Homemade tisanes can be stronger than shop-bought ones, so go easy when you begin, and experiment with different varieties and strengths. Strawberry and raspberry leaves are a good option, rosehip is a particularly good source of vitamin C, and mint adds a pleasant taste. You can also include dried orange or lemon peel to add a fruity flavour. (For more tea recipes, see also pp. 112 and 226.)

The differences between the main kinds of tea relate to the length of time they are allowed to wilt and oxidise: the longer, the darker the resulting colour.

The beneficial compounds in tisanes occur in varying concentrations, and often not significantly – especially once they are diluted in the bloodstream. As a result, they cannot generally be relied upon for specific medical purposes. For example, peppermint tea contains the essential oil of the peppermint plant – that's what gives the tea its strong aroma – and the essential oil is known to kill bacteria and even viruses (see p. 134); but in the concentration present in peppermint tea, this effect will be very limited.

Some tisanes have a reputation for specific biological actions: dandelion tea as a diuretic, raspberry leaf tea to help induce labour. The evidence for these effects is sketchy, as very few clinical trials have been carried out to study them. Raspberry leaf has been shown to contract rats' uteruses weakly in the laboratory, but there is no evidence of this happening in humans. However, peppermint tea, one of the most studied tisanes, has been shown to relax muscles in the gastrointestinal tract, and, in turn, ease irritable bowel syndrome.

Tisanes and teas do not 'detoxify' – that job is taken care of by your liver, which will work regardless of how much tea you drink. They taste good, though, are generally safe to drink in large quantities and are an easy way to boost your water intake.

Herbal tea

CURARE

Chondrodendron tomentosum

MEDICAL BENEFITS ◆ Muscle relaxant in anaesthesia ◆ Traditional treatment for enlarged prostate, bruises, urinary tract infections

From deadly arrow poison to medical marvel: the story of curare's centuries-long rise to fame and widespread medical use is as twisting and curious as the plant itself.

Chondrodenron tomentosum is a vine that thrives by wrapping itself around the trunks and branches of trees in the Amazonian rainforest then climbing to reach the top of the dense canopy to catch more sunlight. Indigenous people in the Amazon basin have been using the vine as the main ingredient of a poison for the tips of blowpipe darts and arrows for at least 500 years.

Poison darts The poison is made by crushing curare bark, roots and stems – and often mixing them with snake venom – then boiling the resulting mixture for two days. Subsequent straining and evaporating results in a thick, dark paste. The indigenous people tested the potency of this poison on frogs, pricking them with a poison-coated spike and counting how many jumps they would take before keeling over.

Brazilian Indians are shown making curare arrow poison in this painting by nineteenth-century French artist François-Auguste Biard.

Spanish and Portuguese conquistadors and explorers reported the existence of the poison in the 1510s. A number of the soldiers even experienced it first-hand during battles with South American peoples, dying within minutes as a result – just as happened with the birds and other animals for which the poison was intended. The English explorer Sir Walter Raleigh was the first to use the name 'curare', which is based on the native word *ourari*, which means 'bird killer' or simply 'poison'.

In 1916, curare poison was to be used in a plot to kill Britain's prime minister, David Lloyd George; the plot failed.

Curare is a muscle relaxant: once it reaches the bloodstream, it paralyses the muscles. Involuntary muscles are not affected – the heart continues to beat, for example – but the diaphragm, a voluntary muscle, ceases to function for as long as the poison is present. As a result, the victim's lungs no longer draw in air, resulting in suffocation. Animals killed after being hit with the poison darts are perfectly edible. This is because curare's active compound does not pass from the digestive system to the blood.

Staying alive In 1745, at the end of a scientific expedition to South America, French scientist Charles-Marie de La Condamine took samples of curare to Europe for investigation. English surgeon Benjamin Brodie was one of the first scientists to notice that the heart continues to beat in animals that have been injected with the poison. He wondered if an animal could be kept alive if air was pumped into its lungs through a tube inserted into the trachea – today, this is called intubation. In 1811, he managed to keep a rabbit alive in this way after injecting it with the poison. Together with another English scientist called Charles Waterton, Brodie repeated his rabbit experiment on a much larger animal – a donkey – which they kept alive through two hours of ventilation. (The animal made a full recovery and lived another 25 years.)

In 1844, influential French scientist Claude Bernard carried out a postmortem on a frog just minutes after poisoning it with curare. Seeing the heart still beating, Bernard realised that curare offered an opportunity to study the internal workings of living creatures. Largely as a result of his investigations and influence, curare was used extensively in the 1870s in animal experiments. Many of these experiments were considered cruel – since the animals were kept alive by ventilation, and paralysed but not sedated. As a result, experiments with curare are often associated with the beginnings of the antivivisection movement.

Putting it into operation At the same time as scientists were using curare to experiment with animals, surgeons were benefitting from improved anaesthetics – in particular, ether and chloroform – which could render a patient unconscious during operations. However, some muscles still twitched during operations, making surgery, particularly inside the chest cavity,

---

OTHER NAME Pareira brava
ORIGIN South America
PARTS USED Roots, stems, leaves

If you are going to undergo a general anaesthetic for a surgical procedure, you will almost certainly be given a muscle relaxant – but it won't be curare or even the purified active compound, d-tubocurarine. Extracts of curare are used in South American herbal medicine, in poultices to treat bruises and taken orally to treat certain complaints of the uro-genital system, including enlarged or inflamed prostate; but few, if any, scientific studies have been carried out into the efficacy of these treatments. Some homeopathic practitioners prescribe an extract of *Chondrodendron tomentosum* for problems associated with urination.

extremely difficult. So anaesthetists began using curare as an accompaniment to their sleep-inducing drugs to completely relax the patient's muscles. The first surgeon to try this on a human patient was a German doctor called Arthur Läwen, in 1912. The life-saving operation was successful, but the achievement went unrecognised for thirty years.

After curare's active compound, d-tubocurarine, was identified, isolated and synthesised in 1935, interest in curare was roused once more. The new compound was first used during electroconvulsive therapy, to prevent patients from flailing around. Then, in 1942, in a groundbreaking series of operations at the Homeopathic Hospital in Montreal, Canadian surgeons Harold Griffith and Enid Johnson pioneered its use in surgery. As word spread, some overenthusiastic surgeons used curare instead of anaesthetics, rather than alongside them – with horrifying results. Despite lying completely still during their operations, as if completely unconscious, patients felt every cut of the knife and intense pain and discomfort, but were unable to tell the surgeon or react in any way until after the curare wore off.

Synthetic alternatives Despite these teething problems, historians of medicine consider the introduction of curare into anaesthesia as a watershed moment in surgical practice. Without muscle relaxants many of the great achievements of modern surgery – such as organ transplants and routine brain and open-heart surgery – would probably not have happened. In 1947, Swiss chemist Daniel Bovet (see box at right) worked out how to synthesise d-tubocurarine, and went on to develop many other drugs that work in a similar way. Thanks to Bovet and other researchers that came after him, modern anaesthetists have a wide array of muscle relaxants at their disposal, most of them synthetic compounds having an action similar to curare's – and each one ultimately owing its existence to the indigenous people of South America who first discovered the powers of this twisting, climbing vine.

Synthetic curare

Daniel Bovet won the 1957 Nobel Prize in Physiology or Medicine, for developing synthetic compounds that could 'inhibit the action of certain body substances'. One of those substances was acetylcholine, a neurotransmitter that passes the signal from nerve to muscle. Curare's active compound, d-tubocurarine and Bovet's synthetic muscle relaxants work by blocking the muscle's acetylcholine receptors.

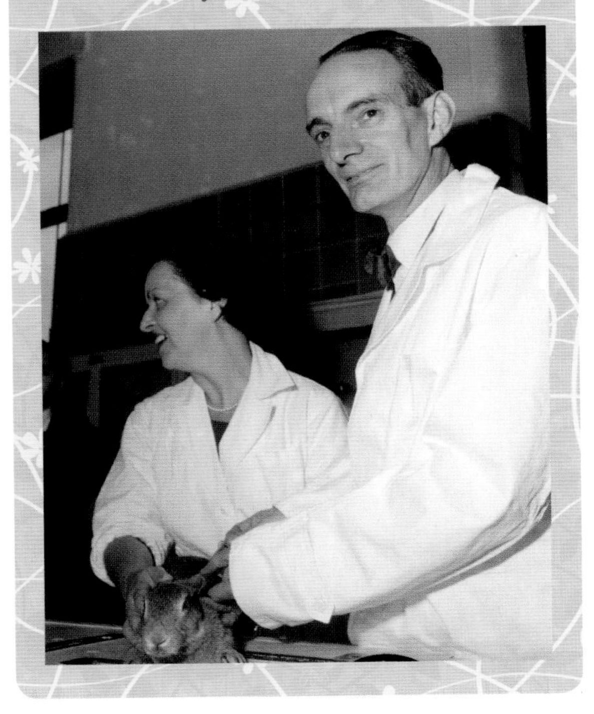

Certain indigenous peoples in the Amazon basin, such as the Huaroni tribe in Ecuador, still make and use curare arrow poison.

WILD YAM

Dioscorea villosa

MEDICAL BENEFITS ◆ Potential treatment for menopausal symptoms, rheumatoid arthritis ◆ Traditional treatment for colic, menstrual cramps, morning sickness, gallstone pain, joint and nerve pain

A cure used by American settlers for the abdominal pain of colic, wild yam enjoyed a comeback in the 1990s as a widely marketed, drug-free menopause remedy. But does it really spell relief from hot flushes, night sweats and insomnia?

In 1941, a young and enterprising Pennsylvania State University chemist named Russell Marker took a bus ride into the mountains of Veracruz in southeastern Mexico. Marker was searching for a natural product that could be used to produce progesterone, a hormone in vogue at the time for menstrual disorders, problem pregnancies and gynaecological cancers. At the time, progesterone was expensive to produce, selling for the sky-high price of $80 per gram. Marker already knew how to convert plant material into progesterone. In fact, his breakthrough 'Marker Degradation' process is still the basis for the production of synthetic hormones today. He returned to his lab with two sacks of large wild yam roots, which yielded appreciable quantities of the compound diosgenin, a steroid saponin that could be converted into progesterone.

When the major American pharmaceutical companies showed no interest, Marker moved his operation to Mexico in order to produce progesterone on a large-scale basis. Ultimately, his work led to the patenting of a yam-derived progesterone variant called norethindrone in 1956. Norethindrone became the active ingredient in one of the world's first birth-control pill formulas, Ortho-Novum, which was approved by the US FDA in 1962, and for decades thereafter was a prime ingredient in a large percentage of all birth control pills.

A creeping vine, wild yam produces small pale green flowers and heart-shaped leaves.

in CLOSE-UP

Can the diosgenin in wild yam creams be converted into progesterone in your body? Experts, including those at the National Library of Medicine in the United States, say no. But in a 2005 study from National Taiwan Normal University, 24 postmenopausal women who ate about 400 g (14 oz) of another yam, *Dioscorea alata*, every day for 30 days saw increases in blood levels of hormones including estradiol and sex-hormone-binding globulin. 'These effects might reduce the risk of breast cancer and cardiovascular diseases in postmenopausal women', the scientists noted.

'Natural' hormone creams made with wild yam for rubbing into the skin may contain *added* progesterone, oestrogen or docosahexaenoic acid (DHA) – the yam does not contain any of these hormones. Do not take wild yam extracts internally longer than advised; a 2008 study at Australia's University of Queensland found that long-term use boosts risk for kidney damage.

Wild yam remained in great demand in the early years of oral contraceptives because it was the world's only source of the diosgenin used to produce progesterone and its derivatives. That all changed in 1970, however, when diosgenin was finally produced synthetically in a lab.

Wild yam scam? In the 1990s, the major US-government-funded Women's Health Initiative study was halted after volunteers taking hormone replacement therapy developed a higher risk for breast cancer and strokes. Inspired by claims from alternative-medicine practitioners, many women then turned to wild yam as a treatment for menopause symptoms.

Progesterone from wild yam is eight times more powerful than progesterone from animals.

But does it work? The research is mixed. In a 2001 study by the Baker Medical Research Institute in Australia, 23 menopausal women who experienced hot flushes, night sweats and insomnia used a yam cream rubbed on the skin or a placebo for six months. While it appeared safe, the researchers concluded the yam cream had 'little effect on menopausal symptoms'. In a 2011 study by researchers from China Medical University and I-Shou University in Taiwan, 50 menopausal women used a wild yam product or a placebo for one year. The yam group saw some improvements after six months, reporting less anxiety, tension and nervousness as well as easing of insomnia and muscle aches.

OTHER NAME Mexican yam
ORIGIN Asia, North and Central America
PART USED Rhizome

While the jury is still out regarding the effect on menopause, interest has grown in other possible uses for wild yam. Preliminary evidence from a 2004 test-tube study at Korea's Kyung-Hee University suggested that the Asian wild yam *Dioscorea tokoro* may hold promise against rheumatoid arthritis. Compounds from this yam appeared to reduce production of inflammatory substances in cells from human joint tissue.

The roots of other *Dioscorea* yams are a staple food in many parts of the world, but *D. villosa* is not edible and can cause illness.

EPHEDRA

Ephedra sinica

MEDICAL BENEFITS ◆ Treatment for symptoms of asthma, hay fever, bronchitis, common cold ◆ Aids weight loss ◆ Enhances physical performance and endurance

Used for centuries in traditional Chinese medicine, the leaves and stems of this plant contain powerful compounds that have health benefits – but also some downsides.

Evidence suggests ephedra was used for medicinal purposes 60,000 years ago in Iraq.

The main biologically active compounds in ephedra are ephedrine and pseudoephedrine, both stimulants. Inside the body, they encourage the release of adrenaline (more correctly known as epinephrine), the 'fight or flight' hormone. Normally released in brief bursts, adrenaline causes blood vessels to constrict, accelerates heart rate and increases blood pressure. It also increases metabolic rate, which causes an increase in available energy and alertness – and a rise in body temperature.

Powerful effects In Chinese traditional medicine, ephedra's main use is treating asthma and other respiratory complaints. The adrenaline released acts on receptors in muscle cells that cause the muscles around the airways to relax – so ephedrine acts as a 'bronchodilator'; the constriction of blood vessels in the nose and throat also helps open up the airways. The plant is used only in small amounts for this purpose, and is combined with other medicinal herbs in specific traditional recipes.

Increasing the metabolic rate has other effects, too. It literally burns kilojoules; combined with ephedra's appetite-reducing effect, this led to the plant becoming a popular weight loss aid in the 1980s and 1990s. It can also boost physical performance and endurance – to the extent that many sports bodies, including the World Anti-Doping Agency, have outlawed ephedra use. Some people take it recreationally, seeking pleasure from a prolonged adrenaline rush.

In recent years, these applications of ephedra have raised safety concerns, as long-term use or overuse can lead to heart attack and stroke, even in otherwise healthy people; those with existing heart problems or a history of seizures and stroke are at particular risk. The higher metabolic rate also causes a rise in body temperature, increasing risk of heat stroke.

OTHER NAME *Ma huang* (Chinese)
ORIGIN Dry regions in Asia, North America, South America, Europe
PARTS USED Stems, leaves

You can buy powdered extract of the plant, or leaves and stems themselves, from herbal medicine outlets. Because ephedra has powerful effects, you should consult with a doctor or a knowledgeable herbalist if you intend to use it. Dietary supplements containing ephedrine and pseudoephedrine – normally made synthetically rather than extracted from ephedra – are banned in many countries, including the United States, the Netherlands, Norway, Italy, Austria, Egypt, Japan and Venezuela. However, ephedrine is permitted as an ingredient in cold remedies.

COTTON

Gossypium spp.

MEDICAL BENEFITS ◆ Possible treatment for cancer ◆ Antifungal and antibacterial properties ◆ Formerly used as a male contraceptive

Cotton, the most widely used natural fibre on the planet, grows inside a capsule called a boll on the cotton plant *Gossypium*. The seeds of this plant contain a curious compound that has some potential medical benefits.

Sliced open, a cotton boll reveals its seeds, swathed in the plant's soft, white fibres.

The compound in question is gossypol, which occurs in little glands throughout the plant (though not in the cotton itself, which is almost pure cellulose). Cottonseed oil, extracted from the seeds, has been used for centuries in cooking. The food industry uses it to this day, but only after it has been refined to remove the gossypol and other slightly toxic components. Recent studies have shown that gossypol has antifungal and antibacterial properties. But those are not its main claims to fame among medical researchers.

Fertile research In the 1920s, Chinese researchers noticed that male infertility was relatively high in areas where people used large quantities of cottonseed oil in their cooking. The researchers identified gossypol as the culprit, and this compound was later found to reduce both sperm cells' motility (ability to move) and their number.

Large-scale trials of gossypol as a male contraceptive, involving thousands of men, were conducted in China in the 1970s and 1980s. The results showed that the compound significantly reduced male fertility, without reducing testosterone or libido. In about one in ten men, however, long-term use led to permanent infertility, and in some cases it reduced the body's potassium levels, resulting in muscle weakness and cramps. Consequently, research on gossypol as a contraceptive ceased around the turn of the millennium.

Switch to self-destruct More recently, attention has turned to gossypol's potential role in anticancer therapy. Clinical trials are underway, involving gossypol and a less toxic derivative compound called apogossypolone, mostly in conjunction with existing chemotherapy medicines. Many research groups have studied the action of these compounds in cancer cells in the laboratory and in living mice, finding that both compounds encourage cancer cells – including breast, prostate, colon, leukaemia, pancreatic and retinoblastoma cancer cells – to self-destruct. Research is ongoing and clinical trials are underway at several research centres.

What You CAN DO

Gossypol is not present in appreciable amounts in food products. If you or someone you know has any form of cancer, you could try to find out about clinical trials to evaluate the potential of gossypol and apogossypolone in chemotherapy. In such studies, these two compounds are often referred to as AT-101 and ApoG2, respectively.

OTHER NAME Cotton plant
ORIGIN Tropical and subtropical regions worldwide
PARTS USED Seeds

WITCH HAZEL

Hamamelis virginiana

MEDICAL BENEFITS ◆ Possible treatment for rheumatoid arthritis, Crohn's disease, bacterial infections ◆ Traditional treatment for minor wounds, skin irritations, inflammation, diarrhoea, haemorrhoids, varicose veins

Witch hazel

Witch hazel extract is a popular herbal medicine. While the efficacy of traditional witch hazel preparations is still under scrutiny, scientists have discovered that one of the plant's active constituents shows promise as a treatment for various illnesses.

Witch hazel has long been used as an astringent and antiseptic. Native Americans brewed witch hazel leaves and bark to make medicinal teas and lotions, and European settlers adopted many of the same practices. In the 1840s, American pharmacists began selling 'witch hazel water', a distilled infusion of leaves and twigs combined with alcohol, which has since become popular worldwide for treating minor wounds and skin irritations.

Today, witch hazel extract is often added to eye drops for inflamed eyes, drunk in teas for treating diarrhoea, and included in suppositories to treat haemorrhoids. It is also a popular treatment for varicose veins, either applied to the skin or drunk in a tea.

Laboratory tests confirm that witch hazel extract does have antioxidant, antiseptic and astringent properties, as a result of its main active constituents, compounds called tannins. However, clinical trials are still inconclusive with regard to the efficacy of traditional treatments; researchers have also noted that witch hazel water contains almost no tannins and that its astringent effects are due to its alcohol content.

A potent antioxidant One tannin in witch hazel, however, known as hamamelitannin, has shown itself to be a particularly potent antioxidant, highly effective in scavenging damaging free radicals that cause ageing and inflammation. And, due to the way it works, it's thought it could be especially useful in the treatments of autoimmune diseases such as rheumatoid arthritis and Crohn's disease.

Hamamelitannin has also been found to inhibit the growth of colon cancers, without having any ill effects on normal colon cells. Furthermore, it has demonstrated an unusual antibacterial effect: rather than killing bacteria, it disrupts communication between them – something microbiologists call 'quorum sensing'. This effect could be a key to controlling the spread of bacteria that have developed resistance to antibiotics.

OTHER NAMES Snapping hazel, winterbloom
ORIGIN Eastern North America
PARTS USED Bark, twigs, leaves

Witch hazel water is widely available but cannot be taken internally due to its alcohol content. You can, however, buy dried leaves and bark (which is especially rich in hamamelitannin) for making teas and consumable tinctures. Although hamamelitannin is used in a few pharmaceutical products – notably those for haemorrhoids – it may be a few years before its newly discovered properties are exploited in commercially available medicines.

JASMINE

Jasminum spp.

MEDICAL BENEFITS ◆ Potential treatment for cancers ◆ May promote healing ◆ Possible protection against stomach ulcers, hepatitis ◆ Traditional treatment for various conditions, including headaches, anxiety, inflammation

Scientists taking a closer look at this sweet-smelling plant in the 1960s made a surprising discovery – one that may soon play a significant role in the fight against cancer.

Jasmine has been used for hundreds of years to treat a dizzying array of ailments, from gallstones to mouth ulcers. Only a few of these traditional applications have been tested or scrutinised by modern medical scientists – albeit with encouraging results.

Under scrutiny Research in 2008 and 2011 unveiled jasmine extract's antiseptic, antioxidant and anti-inflammatory capabilities – all of which should accelerate healing – and in a 2012 study on rats at Banaras Hindu University, India, an ointment made with jasmine extract significantly accelerated the healing of wounds. Another 2012 study – this time at the University of Malaya in Malaysia – found that jasmine extract gave rats protection against stomach ulcers, and a 2009 study on ducklings, conducted at the Academy of Military Medical Sciences in China, found that the level of hepatitis B virus present in the blood could be reduced by administering oleuropein, a compound in jasmine essential oil.

Most notably, two studies at Indian universities, published in 2005 and 2012, found that jasmine extract provided effective cancer

The name 'jasmine' comes from the Persian *Yasameen*, meaning 'gift from god'. There are around 200 species of this flowering shrub.

Traditional Wisdom

Jasmine's long list of suggested uses in folk medicine, across a number of different traditions, includes treatment for headaches, depression, corns, mouth ulcers, cuts and grazes, insect bites, acne, dermatitis, high fever, rheumatism, paralysis, gallstones, diabetes, stomach pain, hepatitis and liver disease. Jasmine also has a reputation as an aphrodisiac, and some practitioners of traditional medicine believe that jasmine can prevent breast cancer.

prevention in rats. And in the past few years, a possible mechanism for this protection has been uncovered – after decades of investigation.

Stressed-out plants Back in 1962, scientists discovered an aromatic compound in jasmine, which they named jasmonic acid. In the 1980s, researchers discovered that jasmonic acid and its related compounds, the jasmonates, are not confined to jasmine, but occur widely in the plant kingdom, and act as stress hormones. These hormones come into play when plants are infected with bacteria or fungi, are under attack by insects or other animals, or find themselves in drought conditions. The hormones initiate complex biochemical responses to infection or damage; for example, jasmonates cause cells in a plant's damaged or infected area to undergo programmed cell death (apoptosis), forming a physical barrier that will stop infection spreading. This response may play a major role in the anticancer activity of jasmine and other plants that has been observed in lab tests and trials.

In the late 1990s, Eliezer Flescher, a medical researcher at Tel Aviv University, Israel, had an idea. He knew that salicylic acid, a stress hormone in willow trees (and the chemical inspiration for aspirin; see p. 38), had been found to have some anticancer properties. So he wondered whether other stress hormones might have anticancer properties, too. When he tested jasmonates on four different types of cancer, in cell cultures, they killed most cancer cells, and without affecting healthy cells. He then tested the most potent jasmonate, methyl jasmonate, on living mice with leukaemia; those that received the compound lived longer than those that did not – and with no side effects.

Since then, Flescher and others have carried out further tests and found that semisynthetic jasmonates derived from methyl jasmonate are more potent than any of the natural forms. Within the next few years, medicines derived from jasmonate stress hormones will be clinically tested – and may soon provide a new class of safe, effective anticancer drugs.

ORIGIN Warm regions of Australasia, Asia, Africa
PARTS USED Flowers, leaves

Jasmonate-based cancer drugs are still some way off. In the meantime, one way to benefit from jasmine's medicinal qualities is to incorporate jasmine essential oil in a homemade antiseptic lotion (see p. 37) – several studies have confirmed the oil's antibacterial and antioxidant effects. Jasmine tea, usually made by mixing dried jasmine flowers with green or oolong tea, can be a refreshing pick-me-up. However, the concentrations of active compounds in such teas are so low that they are unlikely to have any medicinal effects.

Jasmine tea

KUDZU

Pueraria lobata

MEDICAL BENEFITS ◆ May help prevent heart disease and osteoporosis ◆ Can reduce alcohol intake ◆ Traditional treatment for headache, fever, tinnitus, nausea, stiff neck, aching muscles, high blood pressure, heart disease, diabetes, measles, alcohol dependence

The roots and flowers of the kudzu plant are packed with an array of biologically active compounds that can have many beneficial effects – and might be of particular interest to those who like a tipple.

Kudzu is a fast-growing climbing vine. In parts of the world where it is not native, it is often considered a noxious weed. In the East, however, kudzu is a prized herb. Its roots have been used as food for thousands of years, and the stems for making fibres that are often woven into baskets. And it was listed as a medicinal remedy in one of the oldest Chinese guides to herbs, the *Shennong Ben Cao Jing (The Divine Farmer's Book of Medicines)*, written about 2000 years ago, which suggests using kudzu root to combat sickness and fever, and kudzu flowers to rid the body of toxins.

Hangover cure Since then, herbalists have prescribed kudzu for a much wider range of conditions, ranging from neck aches to heart

White and chalky, dried kudzu is sold in many health food stores. Rich in starch, it is also used as an ingredient in Asian cuisine.

What You CAN DO

The bulky, fibrous root is used as a food, and a root extract is available in dissolvable form – including in tea bags – that can be added to soups or other dishes. Kudzu root extract is also available in other forms including tablets, and is often advertised as reducing cravings for alcohol. However, some medical scientists warn that chronic use of the root, especially during or shortly after drinking, may increase the risk of cancers. If you intend to use kudzu to battle an existing cardiovascular condition and you already take medication for it, do not take it without your doctor's supervision, as kudzu can cause side effects and interact adversely with other drugs.

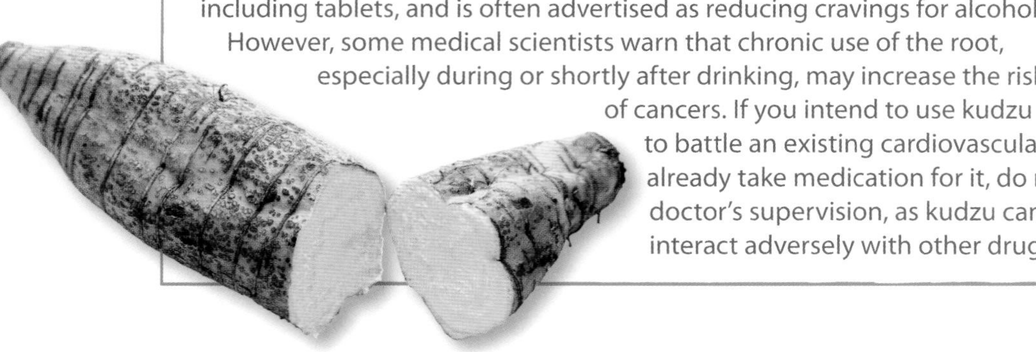

disease and adverse effects of menopause, including osteoporosis. Many studies have been carried out – on cell cultures in laboratory dishes and in living mice – to work out what biologically active compounds kudzu contains and what kinds of mechanisms might be behind its reputation as a medicinal plant. It has been shown, for example, that the flowers can help speed the body's removal of acetaldehyde, a toxic by-product of the breakdown of alcohol in the blood that is responsible for many of the effects of hangovers. Kudzu extract is rich in a class of compounds called isoflavones, which are known to have antioxidant and anti-inflammatory properties – and there is evidence that these compounds may help lower cholesterol and blood pressure, and may protect against osteoporosis and various cancers.

The relatively few clinical studies carried out in humans have yielded mixed results. But one use of kudzu root that *has* proven itself in several human trials is its ability to reduce cravings for alcohol.

In a 2004 US test, volunteers who took kudzu drank half as many beers as those on a placebo.

Don't drink to that For hundreds of years, practitioners of Chinese medicine have prescribed kudzu root for reducing alcohol intake. Starting in the early 1990s, researchers at Indiana University in the United States investigated this effect in rats – and in golden Syrian hamsters, which have a particular liking for alcohol. The results were very encouraging, with the animals' voluntary alcohol intake reducing by more than half in most cases.

Subsequent trials on humans also provided mainly positive results. In 2005, for example, scientists at Harvard Medical School randomly gave male and female heavy drinkers kudzu or a placebo for seven days then had them stay in a mocked-up apartment, with television, sofa and access to as much of their favourite beer as they liked. After taking kudzu, participants tended to drink about half as many beers as after the placebo, and also took more sips and more time to drink each beer.

Researchers have proposed and tested various hypotheses to explain kudzu root's strange ability to curb alcohol consumption. The root actually increases the amount of acetaldehyde in the blood, so it may be that it simply brings on the symptoms of hangover early – although no experiments have spotted any such symptoms. Kudzu also increases heart rate and opens up blood vessels, so it possibly allows alcohol to course more readily around the body.

Invasive species

In several countries, kudzu is considered an invasive species, threatening indigenous plants wherever it takes hold, by climbing over them and denying them shade or nutrients. Yet in most cases, the plant was introduced or cultivated on purpose. For example, after it was displayed as an ornamental vine at the 1876 Philadelphia Centennial Exposition, it was widely planted, spread across the southeastern United States and became popular as cattle feed. And in the 1930s its growth was encouraged in an effort to combat soil erosion in the arid conditions of the 'dust bowl'. As a result, it is now more prolific in Alabama than anywhere else in the world.

OTHER NAMES Japanese arrowroot, *gé gēn* (Chinese), *radix pueraria* (applies to the roots)
ORIGIN East Asia
PARTS USED Roots, flowers

THUNDER GOD VINE

Tripterygium wilfordii

MEDICAL BENEFITS ◆ Treatment for rheumatoid arthritis and other autoimmune diseases ◆ Potential treatment for various cancers, polycystic kidney disease

The thunder god vine is a 'Jekyll and Hyde' plant. Nearly all parts of the plant are highly poisonous – even deadly – but it also contains compounds that have the potential to cure some of the most intractable diseases.

In Chinese traditional medicine, the thunder god vine is known as *Lei gong teng* – Lei Gong being the mythical Chinese 'duke' of thunder. The inner tissue of the vine's root is the only part of the plant that is not poisonous, and it is from there that medicinal extracts are taken. These extracts have been used for several hundred years to treat a range of diseases involving inflammation or overactivity of the immune system – in particular, autoimmune diseases such as rheumatoid arthritis, multiple sclerosis and lupus.

Double life of the thunder god Only a few strictly controlled clinical studies have been carried out on the traditional uses of this extract, and even they reflect the plant's split personality. A 2006 review of clinical trials found that thunder god vine can relieve symptoms of rheumatoid arthritis. But the review's authors fell short of recommending use of the extract, because of side effects including hair loss, headache and skin rash.

A new hope

The compound triptolide, which occurs in thunder god vine, is one of only a few compounds that show any promise in the treatment of polycystic kidney disease (PKD), a serious inherited condition that can lead to renal failure and death. In 2007, researchers at Harvard University discovered that triptolide was effective in mice; the first human clinical trial began in 2008.

Thunder god vine has white flowers and produces small red fruits with three 'wings'.

In 2009, the National Institute of Arthritis and Musculoskeletal and Skin Diseases and the NIH Clinical Center, in the United States, reported the results of a six-month study involving 121 patients with rheumatoid arthritis. Treatment with thunder god vine extract eased joint pain, reduced joint swelling and improved overall wellbeing – but many of the participants withdrew from the study because the extract gave them diarrhoea and indigestion and made them nauseous.

In a 2006 US study, celastrol resulted in more than 70 per cent inhibition of tumour growth in mice with prostate cancer.

Tumour tumult Nevertheless, scientists still hope to isolate the beneficial compounds in the vine so that they might be used without side effects – or so that drugs without side effects

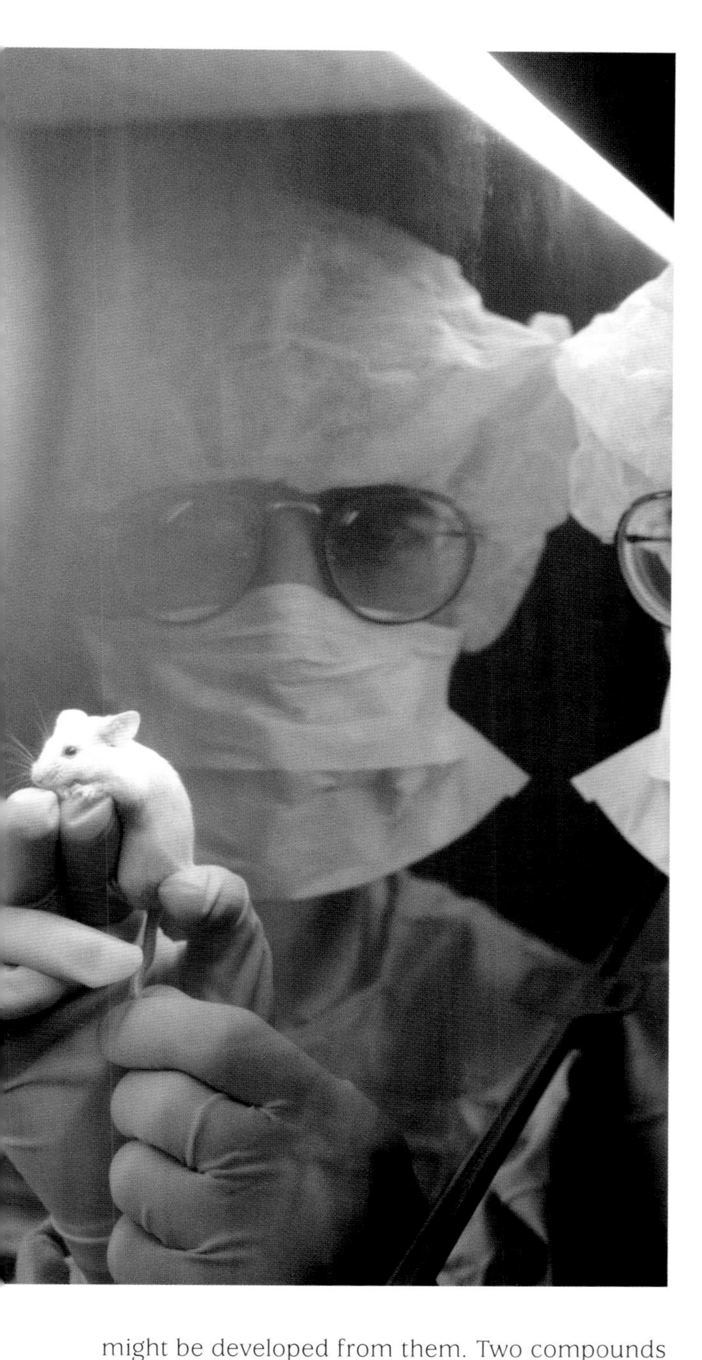

In one 2012 study, mice treated with triptolide showed no signs of tumours after 40 days – nor after discontinuing treatment.

All parts of the thunder god vine are highly poisonous, except the inside part of the root. So if you want to see if you can benefit from the health-giving properties of this plant, take advice from certified herbalists. Also note that even otherwise safe extracts – from the skinned root – can have undesirable side effects. If you or someone you know suffers from cancer or polycystic kidney disease, you can look out for clinical trials involving triptolide or celastrol.

might be developed from them. Two compounds are of particular interest: celastrol and triptolide. Both are powerful antioxidants, have anti-inflammatory properties and affect the body's immune system – and are the reason why the vine has had some success against inflammatory, autoimmune disorders.

Most exciting, however, are the anticancer properties of these compounds. As long ago as 1981, scientists in China found that triptolide significantly prolonged the survival of mice with leukaemia. Celastrol's anticancer capabilities were not discovered till the late 1990s; since then, both compounds have slowed tumour growth in many laboratory studies involving prostate, colon, lung, breast and pancreatic cancers, and in leukaemia – in cell cultures and in mice. Their mode of attack is multipronged, and as with many anticancer compounds, includes causing cancer cells to self-destruct.

A major obstacle to the development of the compounds into medicines is that neither is water-soluble. This makes it difficult to deliver them to cancer cells, because hardly any dissolves in the blood. But in 2011, researchers at the University of Minnesota created a semi-synthetic version of triptolide that does dissolve in water. The scientists carried out tests with the new compound, dubbed 'Minnelide', on mice with pancreatic cancer. In humans, only around 5 per cent of patients diagnosed with pancreatic cancer survive past five years, so any progress against this disease is welcome. The scientists reported their results in 2012: tumours in all the mice treated with Minnelide disappeared completely, and did not return. Human clinical trials will follow – and perhaps Dr Jekyll can shake Mr Hyde once and for all.

OTHER NAME *Lei gong teng* (Chinese)
ORIGIN East Asia
PART USED Root

EUROPEAN MISTLETOE

Viscum album

MEDICAL BENEFITS ◆ Adjunct treatment for chemotherapy ◆ Potential cancer treatment ◆ Traditional treatment for a wide range of conditions including asthma and arthritis

In some European countries, extracts from this parasitic plant are commonplace in mainstream cancer treatment; elsewhere, such treatment is unheard of. So, are some people losing out, or are others wasting their time on a worthless treatment?

The name 'mistletoe' originally applied only to European mistletoe (*Viscum album*), but today it can also be used to refer to a range of closely related species, many of which have been studied by medical researchers. One thing they all have in common is that they are parasitic, surviving by stealing from their host tree.

Ancient cure-all European mistletoe has long been used in folk medicine in various parts of Europe, for many different ailments, notably arthritis, psychological disturbances and asthma. Several ancient civilisations considered it a panacea, and valued it for its supposed curative and fertility-enhancing effects. The plant also featured heavily in mythology, in which it tended to span the divide between life and death – perhaps partly because, as an evergreen shrub, it remains in full leaf during the winter, while its host trees do not.

Mistletoe's connection with cancer dates back to the early twentieth century. It began with Austrian philosopher and educational reformer Rudolf Steiner, founder of the philosophy called anthroposophy, which attempts to combine spiritual and scientific approaches to education, agriculture and medicine. Steiner believed that cancer is the result of weakened defences – a shift in the body's natural balance – and that mistletoe could re-establish that balance and reverse tumour growth.

In the 1920s, Steiner worked with Dutch doctor Ita Wegman, who began injecting cancer patients with a mistletoe extract she called Iscador. To this day, Iscador is the most popular of the mistletoe anticancer treatments available. Yet the alternative nature of Steiner's philosophy has made some sceptical of treating cancer with mistletoe. So does it work?

Chemical cocktail Clinical investigations of mistletoe extract in cancer patients have not shown great promise. Like many major reviews of such studies, a 2008 report concluded that the evidence that mistletoe extract could

Cling on

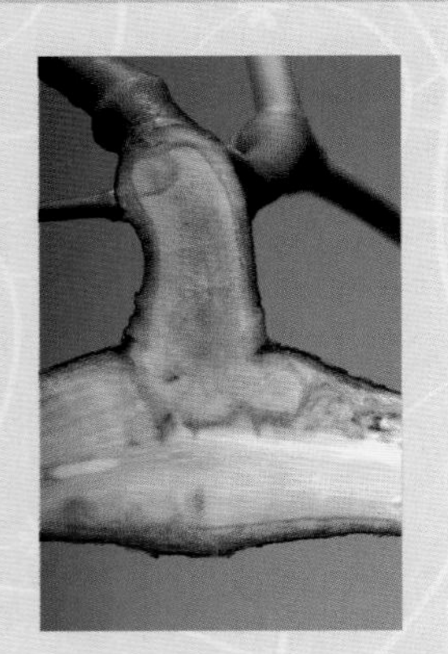

Most species of mistletoe are 'hemiparasitic': they depend upon their host, the tree, but not entirely. Mistletoe seeds normally reach the branches of a tree in birds' excrement, and after they germinate, they secrete compounds that break down the bark; then they extend a probe-like growth called a haustorium through the tree's bark so that it can draw off water and nutrients. But mistletoe produces its own food, via photosynthesis, just like any other plant, so it is not a total parasite.

OTHER NAMES Devil's fuge, golden bough
ORIGIN Temperate regions worldwide
PART USED Whole plant

improve a person's ability to fight cancer was weak – but that there was evidence that it might improve quality of life during chemotherapy by stimulating the immune system. So, most mainstream doctors think of mistletoe as a useful adjunct (accompaniment) to standard chemotherapy rather than a treatment.

About half of all cancer patients in Germany receive some form of mistletoe treatment.

However, the berries and leaves of the mistletoe certainly contain biologically active compounds. Most important are a class called the lectins, which, researchers have found, are very effective in inhibiting tumour growth in the laboratory. As with many potential anticancer compounds, part of the reason for the discrepancy between laboratory studies and clinical studies is that the lectins dissolve into the blood and become diluted. Several teams are therefore trying to get around this problem. Scientists at the University of Canberra in Australia, for example, have developed a way of 'packing' the lectins into a fatty sphere called a liposome that can increase the payload to a tumour.

And new components of mistletoe's medicinal cocktail are still being discovered. Standard treatments are extracted using water, so they only contain water-soluble compounds. But there are many intriguing compounds present in mistletoe that are not water-soluble. In 2012, a team at the University of Freiberg, Germany, prepared a new oily extract that contains several water-insoluble terpenes, and found that they are just as harmful to cancer cells as the lectins.

Being evergreens, mistletoe plants are particularly prominent in autumn and winter on deciduous host trees.

What You CAN DO

Do not consume mistletoe or its berries: most species contain toxic compounds, which can cause visual disturbances, nausea, stomach pain, diarrhoea and, in rare cases, death. Mistletoe injections are currently among the most widely used unconventional cancer treatments in Europe – doctors in the Netherlands, Germany, France and Switzerland prescribe them. Even in countries where the treatment is not approved, such as the United States, scientists often recruit volunteers for clinical trials involving mistletoe extract.

STUDYING WITH THE SHAMANS

Biotech companies developing new medicines draw increasingly on knowledge of plants that has been gained not in modern scientific laboratories but in remote locations and over hundreds of years.

For scientists seeking beneficial compounds in nature (see also p. 26), screening huge numbers of plants is a monumental task. In some parts of the world – notably South America, Africa, Australia and the Pacific Islands – a potential short cut is to consult traditional peoples, who may have accumulated knowledge of local plants and herbal remedies over many generations, knowledge often held and dispensed by traditional healers, or shamans.

Multidisciplinary quest The study of how indigenous peoples use plants medicinally is known as ethnobotany, and it involves growing numbers of researchers venturing to far-flung corners of the globe. Ethnobotanists have to be anthropologists, botanists and pharmacologists, and often conservationists, too, since the rich biodiversity of the regions in which many indigenous people live is also under threat.

One of the pioneers of this multidisciplinary approach was Richard Schultes, whose studies of indigenous peoples and their relationships with plants, in the mid- to late 1900s, gained him the epithet 'the father of ethnobotany'. Schultes was passionate about learning from and preserving traditional knowledge. His work inspired many people in the field, including Mark Plotkin, who formed an organisation called the Amazon Conservation Team, which works closely with indigenous people to protect the rainforest in the Amazonian basin. Plotkin's books *Tales of a Shaman's Apprentice* and *Medicine Quest* have helped to popularise the work of ethnobotanists.

Samoan remedies Another prominent and productive figure in this field is US scientist Paul Cox. In 1984, Cox travelled to a remote village on the island of Savai'i, in Samoa, originally to continue his postgraduate studies of rainforest ecology. He learned the Samoan language and lived among the villagers for several years. Early on, he met with an elderly woman who was tending her sick husband. In a three-hour interview, Cox was astonished by the woman's encyclopaedic knowledge of the local flora and fauna and of traditional Samoan medicine.

Eventually, the woman taught Cox more than 100 herbal remedies, including one that used the wood of the mamala tree (*Homalanthus nutans*) to treat a disease that Cox recognised as viral hepatitis. Cox sent samples of the plant to the US National Cancer Institute, where scientists found that the leaves contained an active compound called prostratin; it has since shown promise in fighting the virus that causes AIDS. Cox was determined that Samoan people would share in the benefits of any drug developed from prostratin, and he worked with local people to protect the rainforest from the threats posed by logging companies, which were offering less than US$2 per hectare ($5 per acre) for the land around the village. In 1997, *Time* magazine made Cox one of its 'Heroes of Medicine'.

Back in the laboratory, an ethnobotanist dries out plant specimens he has collected, in preparation for detailed testing.

Repositories of knowledge With the survival of many indigenous societies under threat from development and habitat destruction, time is of the essence in gathering and compiling their medical knowledge. One recent approach is to create databases of traditional remedies. The Native American Ethnobotany Database, for example, has been compiled over 25 years at the University of Michigan.

More recently, at Macquarie University in Sydney, Australia, researchers from the Indigenous Bioresources Research Group have begun gathering traditional knowledge of medicinal plants from the Yaegl people of New South Wales – and have begun testing the plants in their laboratories. Recording information in this way will make it easier for future medical researchers to discover new cures – and will also help document the relationships that different cultures have with plants.

DOING THE RIGHT THING

When ethnobotanists find a promising lead, the scientific work is not the only challenge they face. There is also the question of intellectual property: who owns the knowledge? Strict international laws are now in place to make sure drug companies share profits with traditional peoples where appropriate; these include the 1992 Convention on Biological Diversity and subsequent offshoots, particularly the 2010 Nagoya Protocol. Notable claims made under such laws include the case brought by the San people of southwestern Africa for a share of the profits from weight-loss products developed by South Africa's Council for Scientific and Industrial Research from hoodia (see p. 87), a succulent long used by the San as an appetite suppressant. An agreement was reached in 2003 and the San now receive 6 per cent of profits.

Left: In Burkina Faso, a Kassena elder explains the medicinal uses of a native tree to a visiting cosmetics researcher.

Below: Australian scientists have mounted numerous surveys to document Aboriginal plant use – before the knowledge is lost.

Above: A medicine woman of the nomadic Dukha people of northern Mongolia displays her portable dispensary of healing plants.

ALOE VERA

Aloe vera, Aloe barbadensis

MEDICAL BENEFITS ◆ Treatment for sunburn, minor burns, cuts, skin irritations

A popular house plant grown on windowsills around the world, aloe vera has an exotic, aristocratic and ancient pedigree as a skin balm, dating back more than 6000 years.

Depicted in stone carvings and papyrus scrolls, aloe vera was a common burial gift to deceased pharaohs and a widely used remedy for everything from boils and acne to hair loss and haemorrhoids. Cleopatra and Queen Nefertiti used it to enhance their legendary beauty, too. While many of these uses have gone by the wayside, those glamorous Egyptian queens understood something important about this plant. And today aloe's reputation for easing skin irritations – ranging from sunburn and rashes to minor cuts and kitchen burns – is stronger than ever.

Healing gel The secret is the gel inside aloe's spiky leaves. Spread on the skin, it hydrates and protects while the body repairs damage – and speeds healing, possibly by improving circulation and encouraging new skin cells to move up into areas that need repairs. In one study from the then Pennsylvania College of Podiatric Medicine, wounds treated with aloe vera decreased in size by 50 per cent over seven days, compared to 25 per cent for a cream without aloe vera. Aloe speeds healing of first- and second-degree burns, too, cutting healing time by nearly nine days, according to a review conducted in Thailand in 2007.

This herbal soother also shows promise for easing the red, scaly skin patches of mild to moderate psoriasis. Aloe has its limits, however. It should not be used on surgical wounds, because it may get in the way of healing. Furthermore, it will not prevent skin burns from radiation therapy.

ORIGIN Mediterranean
PART USED Gel from inner leaf

Cut through the thick, serrated leaf of the aloe and it will immediately ooze clear gel.

Keep an aloe plant on a sunny windowsill, cut off a piece of a leaf and squeeze the gel onto minor skin irritations. Or buy an aloe vera skin cream, lotion or ointment – ideally one bearing the International Aloe Science Council's certification seal. Don't take aloe internally: studies conducted by the US National Toxicology Program found evidence it may be carcinogenic; it can also cause stomach cramping and diarrhoea, interfere with absorption of medications and even cause liver inflammation.

BULLWORT

Ammi majus

MEDICAL BENEFITS
- Treatment for psoriasis

A treatment for psoriasis that uses medication to enhance the sun's effects has its roots in an ancient North African herbal medicine practice based on the sun-sensitising talents of bullwort.

As early as 1500 BC, Egyptian healers would rub the juice of *Ammi majus* on pale patches of skin robbed of pigment then tell their customers to spend some time in the sun. Today, 'photo-medicine' treatments based on this practice have revolutionised the treatment of psoriasis – and still rely on medicines with a chemical structure copied from compounds hidden in the seeds of this lacy-flowered plant.

The active chemicals in bullwort are furocoumarins, compounds known also as psoralens, which absorb light and cause skin to darken. In the 1940s, University of Cairo researchers isolated three compounds from bullwort seeds that they suspected might be the active ingredients in this traditional folk remedy. The eureka moment came in 1948, when Egyptian dermatologist Abdel Monem El Mofty, of the Cairo University Medical School, used one of these chemicals – 8-methoxypsoralen – along with sunlight to successfully treat vitiligo (a condition in which skin loses pigment). By 1964, the first chemically synthesised psoralen was in wide use for vitiligo, and an important new medical skin treatment was born.

Light therapy Today this approach, known as PUVA (psoralens and ultraviolet A light) therapy is rarely used because it can damage skin. But in the 1970s, researchers in the United States and elsewhere tried PUVA to ameliorate the scaly red skin patches of psoriasis. Harvard Medical School experts called it 'exceptionally effective'. The downside? Sensitising skin to ultraviolet rays also boosts skin-cancer risk. As a result, PUVA therapy is reserved for severe cases of psoriasis and is used only when the benefits have been carefully weighed against the risks.

OTHER NAMES Bishop's flower, Queen Anne's lace
ORIGIN Egypt
PART USED Dried seeds

From the Nile Valley bullwort has spread across North Africa, West Asia and Central Europe. It flowers from June to October.

What You CAN DO

If you have severe or hard-to-treat psoriasis, the drug 8-methoxy-psoralen, based on the chemical structure of a compound found in *Ammi majus*, together with UVA light therapy, could be considered as a treatment.

KHELLA

Ammi visnaga

MEDICAL BENEFITS ◆ Source of drugs used to treat arrhythmias and asthma ◆ Potential treatment for vitiligo

Modern research has revealed diverse uses for this herb, whose ability to relax smooth muscle, such as in the lungs and ureters, made it a traditional remedy for asthma and kidney stones.

Khella was once widely used in North Africa, but its serious side effect – liver inflammation – makes it too dangerous to take internally today. Nevertheless, its healing properties have been the inspiration for two important drugs. In the late 1940s, at Cairo University, Russian-born scientist Gleb von Anrep noticed that a colleague who used khella obtained relief from chest pain. His work led to the development of the khella-derived heart drug amiodarone for angina pectoris (chest pain caused by narrowed arteries in the heart) and later for heart arrhythmias (heart-rhythm disorders). Amiodarone is now the most widely prescribed drug in the United States for serious heart arrhythmias.

Khella also inspired the development of an important asthma medication – thanks to a daring experiment. In the 1960s, the pioneering British scientist and World War II fighter pilot Roger Altounyan developed sodium cromoglycate, an asthma drug based on the structure of khella's active ingredient, khellin, and tested it first on himself. For decades, Altounyan's discovery, sodium cromoglycate (Intal), was a popular asthma controller. Today, it has largely been replaced by more effective inhaled corticosteroid drugs.

Colour restored Meanwhile, researchers are also looking into a new twist on another traditional use for khella. The herb was once used for vitiligo, a condition in which the skin develops white, pigment-free patches. When affected skin is exposed to sunlight, khella triggers the development of new pigment. In one Dutch study from 2011, a skin cream containing khella restored 75 per cent of missing pigment for 47 per cent of participants.

As an introduced species, khella now grows worldwide. Its flowering stems can rise to a height of 80 cm (30 in).

OTHER NAMES Bisnaga, toothpickweed
ORIGIN Egypt
PART USED Dried seeds

If you have a life-threatening heart arrhythmia that's not helped by other medications, your doctor may prescribe the drug amiodarone. If you have vitiligo, it may be worth asking your doctor about the availability of treatment with topical khella preparations followed by exposure to ultraviolet light.

Lavender

What You CAN DO

NATURAL SKIN CARE

Nature offers an abundance of good-for-you substances that can be used to pamper, soothe and revive the skin, including many whose traditionally trusted healing effects are now backed up by science. These easy recipes incorporate effective, readily available ingredients.

Rejuvenating spritzer
Lavender essential oil has a relaxing scent and may help protect skin from infections, as reported by researchers at Thames Valley University in the United Kingdom, in a 2009 study. And simply inhaling the aroma of rose essential oil can strengthen the skin's ability to keep out invading viruses and bacteria when you're under stress, too, according to scientists from Japan's Tottori University Faculty of Medicine in a 2012 study.

For a rejuvenating skin treat, mix a few drops of lavender or rose essential oil with water in a small spray bottle. Spray on your face (with eyes closed, of course) whenever your skin needs a little boost.

Soothe and moisturise Bright yellow and orange calendula flowers (*Calendula officinalis*) have anti-inflammatory effects, according to a 1994 study from the University of Trieste in Italy. Comfrey (*Symphytum officinale*) is a traditional wound-healer and skin-softener, and apricot kernel oil is a mild skin moisturiser.

Fill a glass jar two-thirds full with dried comfrey leaves and calendula flowers then pour in apricot kernel oil till the jar is three-quarters full. Cap tightly. Shake once a day for one to two weeks, then strain. In a double boiler over very low heat, warm the oil and add 28 g (1 oz) of grated beeswax for every cup of oil. Keeping the heat low, stir until the wax melts. Pour into jars, cap and store in a cool cupboard.

Two-minute elbow treatment
Got rough elbows? Grab olive oil. It's rich in squalene, an unsaturated fatty acid, also found naturally in human skin, which restores suppleness and helps repair damage caused by wind and sun. Simply pour a few drops of olive oil into your palm and massage into your elbows.

ROSY PERIWINKLE

Catharanthus roseus

MEDICAL BENEFITS ◆ Treatment for leukaemia, Hodgkin's lymphoma, non-Hodgkin's lymphomas, Kaposi's sarcoma and cancers of the brain, bladder, thyroid, testes, breast and lung

Prized in folk medicine as a remedy for a range of ailments, this lovely, long-blooming ornamental is the source of some of the most effective anticancer medicines yet discovered.

For centuries, rosy periwinkle, a shrubby plant with leathery leaves and pink, pinwheel-shaped blossoms, has been tended in tropical gardens worldwide, from Africa and the Caribbean to India and Southeast Asia. In many of those realms, its bitter leaves, flowers and stems have long been used as a remedy for diabetes, digestive complaints, menstrual pain, high blood pressure and even tuberculosis.

More recently, the plant has yielded powerful cancer-fighting drugs. In particular, two compounds extracted from periwinkle's glossy foliage are used today in important chemotherapy drugs that take aim at cancers of the blood, lymphatic system, breast, bladder and more. One, vincristine, has increased the odds of surviving childhood leukaemia to 95 per cent, up from less than 10 per cent before 1963. Not bad for an unremarkable-looking plant whose life-saving potential was discovered by chance in a Canadian laboratory.

An answer to cancer? Native to the rainforests of Madagascar, rosy periwinkle first caught the attention of the Western world in 1757, when French explorers shipped samples back to the French court. American and Canadian doctors took notice during World War II, when soldiers stationed in the Philippines used periwinkle to treat diabetes during insulin shortages.

It takes 0.9 tonnes (1 ton) of periwinkle leaves to produce 1 g of vinblastine and 20 mg of vincristine.

Periwinkle became the subject of scrutiny in the 1950s, after Canadian doctor Charles Noble received an envelope in the mail containing 25 dried leaves. The leaves came from a colleague in Jamaica. Periwinkle was a popular diabetes remedy there – did Dr Noble think there was anything to it? Intrigued, Noble forwarded the leaves to his brother, Robert Noble, head of a lab at the University of Western Ontario. At this point, no-one was thinking about cancer – the doctors were hoping to find a diabetes drug that could be taken orally. As Robert Noble wrote,

What You CAN DO

If you have or a loved one has cancer, your specialist will choose the best treatment. Since vinblastine and vincristine, the cancer drugs derived from rosy periwinkle, are given as injected chemotherapy for a wide variety of cancers, they may form part of that treatment. Researchers in India, Nigeria and other countries are still exploring periwinkle's potential as a treatment for diabetes and other conditions. However, the plant should never be used without medical supervision, as it can cause a range of side effects and even death.

'The disease of cancer was certainly far from our minds when we learned of a tea made from the leaves of a West Indian shrub that was supposedly useful in the control of diabetes.'

Noble and his team fed periwinkle leaf extract to lab animals – and were surprised to find it had little effect on their blood glucose. However, at high doses a periwinkle injection nearly wiped out white blood cells. It was an important clue that this tropical plant might hold promise against leukaemia, a blood-cell cancer characterised by an overabundance of white blood cells.

Noble worked to extract periwinkle's active ingredients (in time, researchers found that the plant contains over 100 compounds called alkaloids). It was a tedious process that required large quantities of periwinkle. At first, Noble and his team relied on leaves gathered by Boy Scouts on camping trips into Jamaica's jungles and mailed north. But they needed more. So they turned to plants grown in Canadian greenhouses to get the quantities they needed. Eventually,

The island of Madagascar, particularly its eastern and southeastern districts, remains a major source of rosy periwinkle.

Of the many varieties of rosy periwinkle, pharmaceutical companies prefer those with rose-coloured flowers, as they have the highest levels of cancer-fighting chemicals.

A woman helps harvest rosy periwinkle leaves at Ranopiso, at the southeastern tip of Madagascar.

At a processing centre in Berenty, in central southern Madagascar, workers hang the leaves and flowers on racks to dry.

Noble and his colleagues extracted and tested a new plant compound – with stunning results. In lab studies, the chemical shrank tumours in bone marrow, where leukaemia begins.

Additional compounds In 1958, Noble announced the discovery of the chemotherapeutic agent vincaleukoblastine – later shortened to vinblastine. Would it work in people? Collaborating with pharmaceutical company Eli Lilly, researchers produced enough vinblastine for human clinical trials. When combined with other drugs, it had a major impact on several types of cancer. A head nurse working in the hospital where vinblastine was first tested in humans later said, 'It was quite a dramatic response. People were quite excited.'

But the discoveries weren't over. In 1961, a Lilly researcher discovered a second periwinkle compound with anticancer potential, vincristine. Vinblastine sulphate (Velban) and vincristine sulphate (Oncovin) became the first plant-derived anticancer agents ever approved by the US Food and Drug Administration – in 1961 and 1963, respectively. Today, vinblastine sulphate is used to treat lymphomas (cancers of the lymphatic system) and bladder and breast cancers. Vincristine sulphate is used

Traditional Wisdom

Rosy periwinkle has been used in folk medicine for more than 2000 years. From early times, sailors carried it from Madagascar to other realms; it grows easily in all tropical climates. One popular remedy is periwinkle tea – made from dried leaves, flowers and sometimes the whole plant – which has long been sipped in Australia, Brazil, Jamaica, Kenya, Pakistan, Thailand and the West Indies to control blood glucose. In South Africa, periwinkle tea was drunk for menstrual cramps; in the Caribbean, the flowers were used to soothe eye irritations. In India, periwinkle plant juice was applied to wasp stings, and in Hawaii it was used to stop bleeding.

Dried rosy periwinkle is shipped to processing centres, in this case the Pierre Fabre laboratories at Gaillac in France.

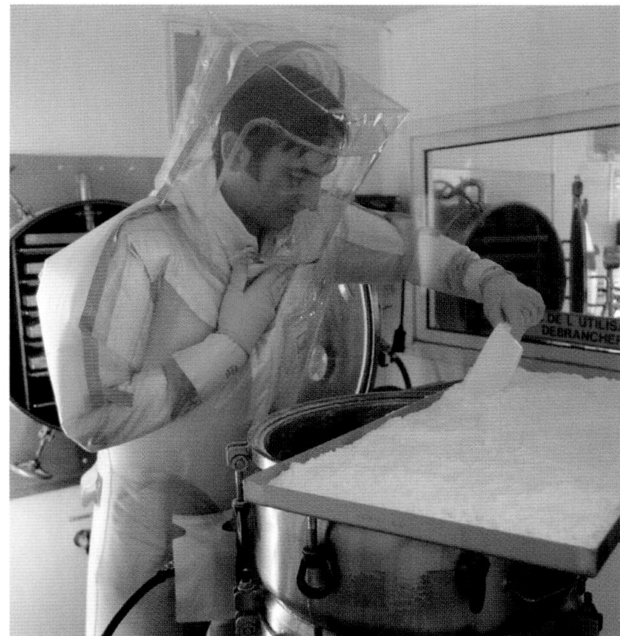

Processing and drying under airlock yields vinblastine. At Pierre Fabre, some vinblastine is used to make semisynthetic drugs.

in combination therapies deployed against acute lymphoblastic leukaemias (cancers of the white blood cells) and lymphomas.

The effectiveness of an anticancer drug is reflected in its remission rate – its ability to eradicate all evidence of cancer cells. Vinblastine and vincristine have contributed to an 80 per cent remission rate for Hodgkin's lymphoma and a 50–80 per cent remission rate for a variety of other cancers including Wilms' tumour (a rare, childhood kidney cancer), Burkitt's lymphoma (a fast-growing lymph-node cancer) and gestational choriocarcinoma, a uterine cancer that can develop during pregnancy.

Stopping cell growth Rosy periwinkle flowers contain just a tiny fraction of vinblastine and vincristine, so researchers are always exploring new ways to boost levels of the cancer-stopping chemicals in the plant, extract them more efficiently, and develop synthetic forms of the natural compounds. Recently, two synthetic derivatives of vinblastine and vincristine – vindesine and vinorelbine – have been added to the cancer-fighting arsenal. Vindesine is often used when cancers are resistant to vincristine; vinorelbine is sometimes chosen because it may cause less nerve damage than vinblastine. While all four drugs are different at a molecular level, they all work by disrupting the mechanism by which cells divide. They do this by interfering with microtubules – microscopically thin strands that pull freshly copied genes into position in new cells. When their DNA can't get where it needs to go, the new cells die off. Since cancer cells grow more rapidly and continually than normal cells, they're more affected by these drugs – though other rapidly dividing cells in the body also take a hit, causing side effects such as a higher risk of infections (due to a drop in white blood cells) and fatigue due to low iron (caused by low levels of red blood cells).

Periwinkle drugs didn't just fight cancer. They also opened the door to the development of other, even more effective drugs that hold a stop sign up to cancer in the same way, sometimes with less-severe side effects. These include the plant-based drug paclitaxel (Taxol), made from the bark of the Pacific Yew tree (see p. 42).

In 1997, Robert Noble and his colleague, a chemist named Charles Beer, were inducted into the Canadian Medical Hall of Fame for their milestone contribution to cancer care.

OTHER NAMES Madagascar periwinkle, old maid, vinca
ORIGIN Madagascar
PARTS USED Leaves; flowers, stems and bark from the roots are also used in folk medicine

FOXGLOVE

Digitalis purpurea

MEDICAL BENEFITS ◆ Treatment for congestive heart failure, atrial fibrillation ◆ Possible treatment for prostate cancer

If you are one of the many who benefit from the heart drug digoxin, you are indebted to an eighteenth-century physician who discovered one of the world's most valuable cardiac medicines in a garden flower.

Today, digoxin is still extracted from foxglove leaves, in stark contrast to most other modern medicines originally derived from plants, which are now mostly synthesised from chemical ingredients. That might please Dr William Withering, who in 1775 found a cure for what was then known as dropsy – an often-fatal fluid build-up in the torso caused by congestive heart failure – in the secret formula of a rural herbalist.

Withering wrote in his 1785 paper, *An Account of the Foxglove and Some of Its Medical Uses; With Practical Remarks on Dropsy and Other Diseases*, that the remedy 'had long been kept a secret by an old woman in Shropshire who had sometimes made cures after more regular practitioners had failed'. He suspected that the active ingredient in the 20-herb concoction was foxglove, a well-known poison, and he began experimenting with different doses of it, taken from different parts of the plant. After treating 156 patients, he concluded that small amounts of the dried leaf eased dropsy without causing toxic side effects.

His account launched foxglove as the block-buster herbal remedy of the time. For the next eight decades, physicians and healers used this herb, also called digitalis, for more than 30 other health problems including bronchitis, tuberculosis and epilepsy. It was hailed as a miracle – Charles Darwin's grandfather, a doctor, even wrote a poem extolling its virtues.

As well as being a physician, William Withering was a keen chemist and geologist and a pioneering botanist who published the first guide to British flora to adopt the Linnaean system of classification.

AN
ACCOUNT
OF THE
FOXGLOVE,
AND
Some of its Medical Ufes:
WITH
PRACTICAL REMARKS ON DROPSY,
AND OTHER DISEASES.

BY
WILLIAM WITHERING, M. D.
Phyfician to the General Hofpital at Birmingham.

—— nonumque prematur in annum.
HORACE.

BIRMINGHAM: PRINTED BY M. SWINNEY;
FOR
G. G. J. AND J. ROBINSON, PATERNOSTER-ROW, LONDON.
M,DCC,LXXXV.

Foxglove leaves hold the plant's medicinal compounds. They are usually harvested as the plant's spectacular flower spires bloom.

Your doctor may prescribe digoxin (brands include Lanicor, Lanoxin and Digitaline) for congestive heart failure or heart arrhythmia. Follow dosage instructions very carefully: too much can be toxic. Your doctor will also carefully review other medications, over-the-counter remedies and supplements you take, because many can increase or decrease the effects of digoxin. These include some antacids, antibiotics and drugs for anxiety, fungal infections, cancer and more. Never ingest foxglove leaves, or any other part of the plant, as it is poisonous.

Digoxin crystals are shown here in a polarised light micrograph image. At life size, the crystals are white and odourless.

The glove that packs a punch Foxglove's Latin name, *Digitalis purpurea*, means 'purple fingers'. The plant is rich in cardiac glycosides that sustain levels of calcium inside heart-muscle cells and slow down electrical signals within the heart. This makes heartbeats more forceful and more regular.

Between 1869 and the late 1950s, researchers in Germany, England and France isolated foxglove's heart-friendly compounds. The first, called digitalin, was identified by French pharmacist Claude Adolphe Nativelle. After World War I, the first digitalis product, a tablet called Verodigen, came on the market; it was based on another cardiac glycoside in the plant, called gitalin. In 1930, the most powerful glycoside, digoxin, was isolated by chemist Sydney Smith in England. Still sold as Lanicor, it is used to treat people with heart failure and heart arrhythmias (heart rhythm disorders). Historians say foxglove's successful evolution from rough herbal remedy to powerful modern medicine helped launch modern pharmaceutical research and drug development, too: each

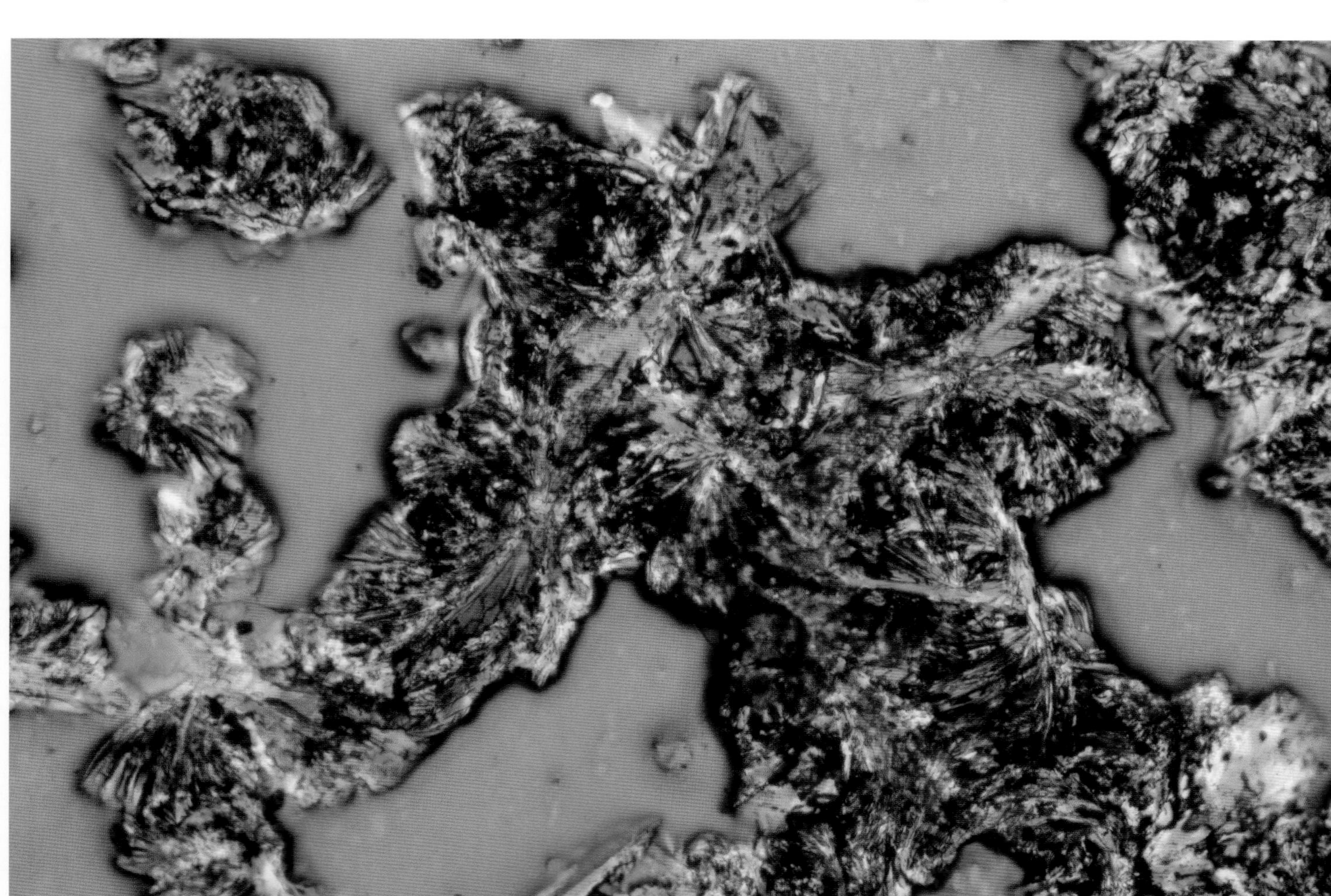

Seeing stars

Too much digitalis can trigger visual disturbances that make the world look yellow and that surround lights with a colourful glare. This effect may explain the stunning haloes in Vincent Van Gogh's painting *The Starry Night* (below) as well as the distinct yellow cast in works such as *The Sunflowers*. The artist may have taken digitalis for mania or epilepsy, and he painted a sprig of foxglove in a portrait of his doctor.

scientific and commercial success spurred more research and led scientists to look more closely at the potential locked in other natural substances as well.

But medicine moves on. Today, digoxin is not a first-line treatment for heart failure or offbeat heart rhythms. Other, more chemically based medications such as ACE inhibitors (see p. 189), diuretics, beta-blockers and calcium agonists are often used first. But because digoxin is inexpensive and effective, some experts would like to see this old heart-helper make a comeback. And researchers from Johns Hopkins Bloomberg School of Public Health recently uncovered an unexpected benefit: a 46 per-cent-lower risk for prostate cancer in men who take digoxin for 10 years or longer. This could give foxglove a powerful new role in cancer prevention.

OTHER NAMES Common foxglove, purple foxglove, fairy fingers, fairy gloves, fairy bells, floppy dock, tod-tails, witches' fingers, fairy thimbles
ORIGIN Western Europe
PART USED Leaves

ECHINACEA

Echinacea angustifolia, Echinacea pallida, Echinacea purpurea

MEDICAL BENEFITS ◆ Treatment for colds ◆ Traditional treatment for colds, flu, mumps, sore gums, venereal disease, bites, stings, burns

Used for centuries as a medicinal plant, echinacea is now more popular than ever, especially as a preventative remedy or cure for the common cold. But just how effective is it?

Before antibiotics, there was echinacea. Named for its spiky seed heads (*echinos* is Greek for hedgehog or porcupine), this North American botanical was widely used by native peoples and settlers for colds, flu, wound-healing, sore gums and even venereal disease. It fell out of favour when bacteria-vanquishing sulpha drugs burst onto the scene in the middle of the twentieth century, but a recent German-led revival in the use of echinacea as a cure for the common cold has given this herb a prominent place in health food stores and newspaper headlines.

Negative results Research in the 1990s suggested that echinacea could prevent colds and short-circuit sniffles, congestion and that run-down feeling you get if you do catch one. But many of those studies were sponsored by remedy manufacturers and not rigorously conducted, so scientists stepped in with better-designed experiments.

Alas, the results were often 'flatly negative', as one echinacea researcher from the University of Wisconsin–Madison described his own results. In 2002, a pair of National Institutes of Health studies found that the dried roots of two species, *E. purpurea* and *E. angustifolia*, didn't ease symptoms in adults and that *E. purpurea* juice didn't help colds in kids, either. A 2005 study at the University of Virginia, in which 437 brave volunteers agreed to have cold viruses dripped into their noses, sought to fix a fault critics found with the earlier study – namely that participants didn't take echinacea ahead of time, as they might in the real world. In the new study, half the volunteers took echinacea for a week beforehand and half got a placebo. They all then spent five days in hotel rooms while scientists monitored their symptoms and immune response. The verdict: echinacea was a dud.

Not all alike However, as the disappointing results mounted, herbalists began pointing out problems with the research. Higher doses or an alcohol extract of fresh echinacea flowers and leaves might have worked better. Starting to take the herbs sooner could have improved the outcome. After a University of Wisconsin study of 719 people with cold symptoms found no 'statistically significant' benefit for echinacea, the executive director of the nonprofit American Botanical Council pointed out that 'echinacea products are not all alike'.

OTHER NAMES Black sampson, cock up hat, coneflower, Indian comb, Kansas snakeroot, scurvy root, snakeroot
ORIGIN Eastern North America
PARTS USED Whole plant

There are many echinacea preparations on the market, but University of Connecticut researchers who reviewed five echinacea studies found that a liquid extract made from fresh, above-ground parts of the species *E. purpurea* consistently reduced chances for catching a cold. Follow the package directions carefully, and skip this herb if you are allergic to ragweed, chrysanthemums, marigolds or daisies.

Echinacea flowers consist of a conical orange spiky head surrounded by pale pink to purple petals – a striking colour contrast.

It was a valid point. Levels of active ingredients that seem to boost immunity vary in different echinacea species and in different parts of the plant, and in fresh versus dried plants. Doses vary, too. That means the healing potential of different echinacea products may vary widely, as well. Underlining this, a 2007 University of Connecticut review of 14 echinacea studies found glimmers of hope. The researchers concluded that taking echinacea at the start of a cold could shorten its duration by 1.4 days, while taking it regularly during cold season could cut your risk for catching a cold in half.

in CLOSE-UP

To find the best alcohol-based echinacea tincture – or to judge the freshness of one that's been sitting in your medicine cabinet – put a drop on your tongue. A tingling or numbing sensation means you've got a winner. Scientists say the 'tingle test' reveals the presence of compounds called isobutylamides. Found in echinacea leaves, flowers and roots and in high-quality remedies, isobutylamides help white blood cells in the body engulf and destroy invading viruses and bacteria.

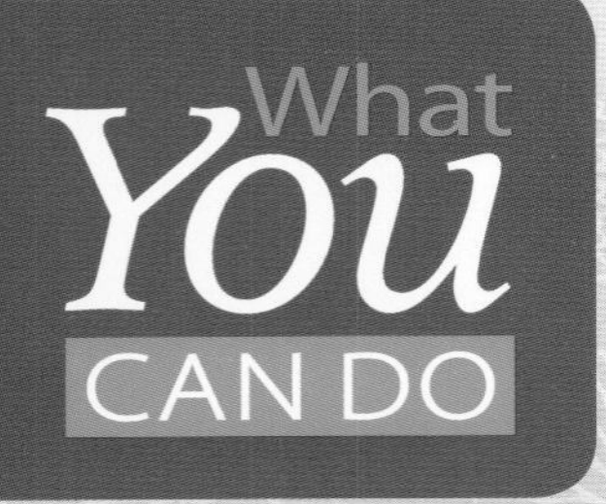

KEEPING COLDS AT BAY

Science has sent men to the Moon, decoded the human genome and cloned sheep, but has yet to conquer the common cold. However, help from nature is at hand.

Caused by more than 100 different viruses, the common cold is humankind's most-caught infectious disease. And although not serious, the illness can be unpleasant and exhausting. Most adults catch a cold two to four times a year, but you can reduce your cold count – and keep the ones you do get short – using a range of natural, plant-based strategies.

Herbs that protect In addition to natural therapies covered elsewhere in this book, such as echinacea, garlic, green tea and probiotics, two notable botanical remedies have been shown in preliminary medical studies to boost your defences against colds. American ginseng (*Panax quinquefolius*; see also p. 97), which is widely available in tincture or capsule form, contains unique compounds called polysaccharides and oligosaccharides that seem to strengthen the body's ability to fight off viruses. In research studies, people who took 200 mg twice a day for 12–16 weeks were 89 per cent less likely to develop an upper respiratory tract infection and 25 per cent less likely to catch a cold. The extract contained 80 per cent poly-furanosyl-pyranosyl-saccharides.

Used by Chinese healers for more than 2000 years to boost immunity, astragalus (*Astragalus membranaceus*) – available as a tincture, capsules or tea – has shown immune-enhancing effects in lab and test-tube studies. In one 2011 study by researchers at China's Zhejiang University, astragalus stimulated macrophages, the immune-system cells that engulf invading viruses and bacteria. In another Chinese study, the herb boosted activity of virus-fighting T cells, too.

Herbs that soothe Runny nose? Sneezing? When a cold's coming on, don't just grab the tissues. Botanical strategies can cut discomfort short. Popular in Scandinavia as a cold and flu treatment, andrographis (*Andrographis paniculata*) is fast developing a reputation as a major-league cold-fighter. In a 2003 study conducted at Chile's Southern University, of 158 adult cold sufferers, those who took andrographis were 28 per cent less tired after two days than those who took a placebo; they were also 50 per cent less congested and their noses 50 per cent less runny. After four days, symptoms improved even more. If you want to try it, take 400 mg of the extract three times a day for five days.

Compounds in South African geranium (*Pelargonium sidoides*) appear to boost immunity and also help tiny hairs called cilia in your sinuses whisk mucus and viruses out of the body. In a 2007 study at the National Medical University in the Ukraine, 79 per cent of cold sufferers who took an extract were symptom-free after 10 days, compared to just 31 per cent of those on a placebo. The recommended dose is 30 drops three times a day for seven to ten days.

Long used in Europe as an expectorant to thin mucus and ease coughing, ivy leaf extract (*Hedera helix*) nearly eliminated cough and cold symptoms in one 2012 study by the group HerbResearch Germany of 268 children. A typical dose is 50 drops per day for an adult and 25 for children.

South African geranium

FOUR FEEL-BETTER HOME REMEDIES

1 Spoon up some chicken soup Grandma was right: a comforting bowl of chicken soup has proven powers to ease cold symptoms. In a 2000 study at the Nebraska Medical Center in Omaha, this classic comfort food inhibited the ability of virus-fighters called neutrophils to cause inflammation and congestion by about 75 per cent. Homemade and canned soups both worked.

2 Create a eucalyptus steam treatment Add a few drops of eucalyptus essential oil or a small handful of fresh eucalyptus leaves to a large bowl or pot of steamy water. Breathe in the steam to help relieve congestion.

3 Sip elderflower tea In Germany, this drink is widely used for colds with a fever. Steep one tea bag or about a teaspoon of dried flowers in hot water and sip. Repeat several times a day.

4 Soothe a sore throat Give a scratchy, raw throat a little TLC with a tea made with soothing herbs such as slippery elm bark (*Ulmus rubra*), marshmallow root (*Althea officinalis*), liquorice root (*Glycyrrhiza glabra*) and/or Chinese liquorice root (*Glycyrrhiza uralensis*). Use a teaspoon or two of one of these (in a tea strainer or tea bag) in a cup of just-boiled water, or keep a cold-care tea on hand that contains a combination of these proven throat protectors.

South African geranium extracts have been shown to be effective as a treatment for bronchitis.

EYEBRIGHT

Euphrasia spp.

MEDICAL BENEFITS ◆ Possible treatment for inflammation of the eyes and for respiratory allergies and infections ◆ Traditional treatment for vision problems

Although the longstanding use of this group of 20 related species for improving eyesight has found little scientific support, its anti-inflammatory properties make it a useful gentle treatment for minor infections and irritations.

Eyebright flowers

Like the eye-catching label on a fancy beauty cream, the purple stripes and yellow spots on eyebright's flower petals 'told' medieval herbalists this was the herb for eye disorders and vision problems. Under a widely practised system called the Doctrine of Signatures, the markings, which resembled bloodshot eyes, were considered a divine sign.

By the 1300s, this meadow flower and its leaves were seen as cures for 'all evils of the eye' and as the source of 'a precious water to clear a man's sight'. Teas, eyewashes and an English 'Eyebright Ale' were popular from the 1600s on. The herb, also called euphrasia, even earned a place in John Milton's *Paradise Lost*, when Adam's vision is 'purged with euphrasine' by the Archangel Michael.

Light relief But does this semiparasitic plant really improve vision? Germany's Commission E, a respected scientific panel appointed by the government in the 1970s to review the evidence for 300 popular herbs, said no. 'The effectiveness of the herb for its claimed uses is not documented', the group reported. On the other hand, while there's little research on this herb's chemical constituents, herbalists say that, based on traditional use, eyebright seems to have inflammation-easing properties that make it useful in relieving nasal and sinus congestion caused by respiratory allergies and infections, as well as minor inflammation of the eyes, such as mild conjunctivitis.

OTHER NAMES Euphrasia, *casse-lunette* (French), *Augentröst* (German)
ORIGIN Europe
PARTS USED Leaves, flowers

Eyebright is sold in tinctures, tablets, capsules and teas, often in combination with other herbs considered helpful for eye or respiratory problems; it is also available as a dried herb. Eyebright eyewashes are regarded as gentle and safe. If you'd like to make one from a commercial powdered mix, start with sterilised water (boil and cool) and be sure there are no particles in the wash that could irritate or even infect your eyes. Then simply follow the package directions.

HOODIA

Hoodia gordonii

MEDICAL BENEFITS ◆ Potential weight-loss aid

Extracts from this succulent have been developed as a weight-loss drug by a major government-affiliated research organisation and sold widely online. But the jury is still out on whether it's safe to take.

To quench hunger and thirst on long hunting trips, the San people of Africa's Kalahari desert have traditionally chewed the pulp of the hoodia plant. South Africa's Council for Scientific and Industrial Research (CSIR) says it discovered hoodia's active ingredient, an appetite-taming substance called P57, in 1977. Since then the group has patented P57 – angering the San people, who ultimately won an agreement entitling them to royalties (see p. 69) – and numerous commercial hoodia extract products have been manufactured and touted worldwide as a 'wonder weight-loss drug'.

Questions raised So are the claims true? Herbal-medicine experts say there's no proof. What's more, concerns have been raised about safety. A 2011 study by consumer goods company Unilever found no benefits, but plenty of side effects including vomiting and elevated blood pressure and heart rate.

That hasn't stopped online marketers, who continue to call hoodia a 'worldwide sensation'. And it hasn't stopped the CSIR, which is looking into other varieties of hoodia, like a wild variety called *Hoodia pilifera*. Could this be the 'real' hoodia? Locally known as *ghaap*, it's preferred over *Hoodia gordonii* by the people of the Kalahari according to the researchers. And it contains two chemicals, called pregnane glycosides, which in rat studies reduced food intake and body weight.

OTHER NAMES Kalahari cactus, xhoba
ORIGIN Kalahari Desert of southern Africa
PART USED Stems

Given the lack of scientific evidence plus concerns about side effects, it's best to skip this herb at this point and wait to see if any further benefits emerge. Note that some hoodia products contain other substances that can be dangerous. Indeed, in 2011, the US Food and Drug Administration advised consumers to stop buying P57 Hoodia, made by Huiking Pharmaceutical, because it contained the banned diet drug sibutramine, which can increase pulse rate and blood pressure and be a serious health risk for people with coronary artery disease, congestive heart failure, arrhythmias or stroke.

A protected species, hoodia grows in arid, rocky areas and has large orange flowers.

CLUB MOSS

Huperzia serrata

MEDICAL BENEFITS ◆ Potential treatment for Alzheimer's disease and dementia ◆ Traditional treatment for fever, swelling and blood disorders

Though it resembles little more than a scrawny evergreen branch, this unprepossessing Asian plant might yet yield an effective treatment for Alzheimer's disease and other forms of dementia.

In China, where it is most widespread, *Huperzia serrata* has been employed for medicinal purposes for thousands of years. Known there as *qian ceng ta*, it is made into a tea that is used to cool fevers, ease swelling and even to treat schizophrenia. In the 1990s, Chinese researchers announced that this traditional remedy harbours an alkaloid, huperzine A, with a striking resemblance to a class of breakthrough Alzheimer's disease drugs called cholinesterase inhibitors. Those drugs – donepezil (Aricept), rivastigmine (Exelon) and galantamine (Razadyne) – delay by six to twelve months the decline in memory and thinking skills that come with this progressive brain disease. Could huperzine A do as well, or better?

A series of small studies from China – the source of most of the world's huperzine A – said yes. A large, well-designed 2011 study from the University of California, San Diego, was less enthusiastic, but still raised a glimmer of hope.

Keeping brain cells chatting Alzheimer's disease is thought to be caused by sticky plaques and protein tangles forming around

A wide range of club mosses are now being tested for promising medical compounds.

Searching for huperzine

Right now, most of the world's supply of huperzine A extract comes from Chinese-grown *Huperzia serrata* plants. That's a problem because *Huperzia serrata* takes decades to grow and wild plant colonies are in danger of extinction due to overharvesting. But science has turned up two new sources. At Yale University, chemists recently developed a quicker way to create huperzine A in the lab; the new process could slash the price tag for pure huperzine A from nearly US$1000 per milligram to 50 cents. Meanwhile, researchers at Auburn University in Alabama reported in 2012 that they had found huperzine in two other types of club moss, both of which grow in Panama: *Huperzia* cf. *chamaeleon* and *Huperzia reflexa*.

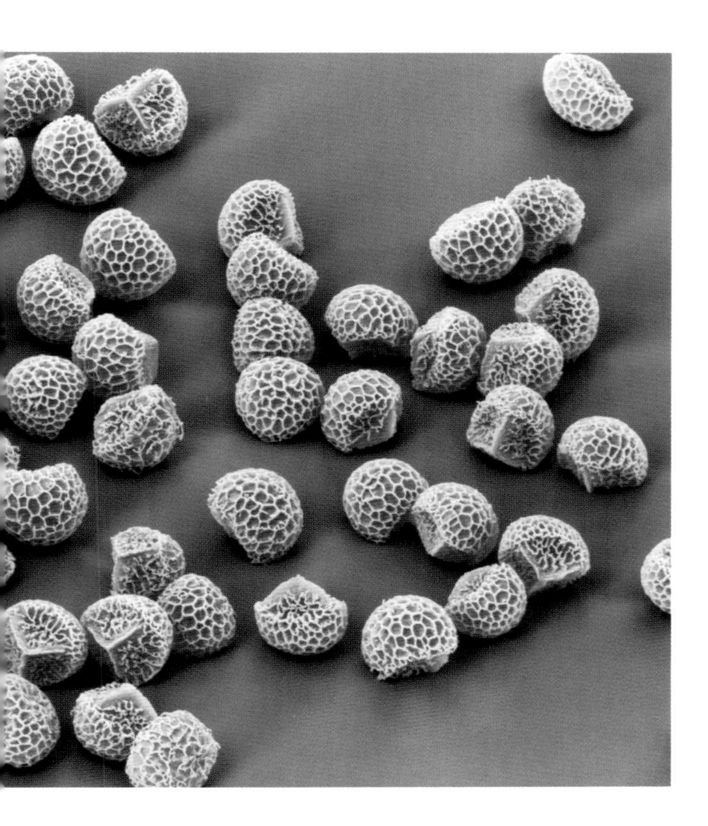

Highly flammable, dried club moss spores (seen here greatly magnified) have been used in fireworks, flash guns and explosives.

and within brain cells (neurones). Cholinesterase inhibitor drugs don't directly affect these changes, but by topping up levels of the neuro-transmitter acetylcholine – one of the chemicals that neurones use to send signals to each other inside the brain – they allow the affected brain to think, remember and function a little longer. They buy time, in other words. Recently, Israeli researchers discovered that huperzine A works in a similar way, at least in lab studies.

> One in eight adults aged over 65 has Alzheimer's disease.

However, when University of California, San Diego, researchers put 177 people with mild to moderate Alzheimer's disease on huperzine A, the results were mixed. Those who took 200 micrograms a day for 16 weeks saw no improvement in memory or thinking skills. But volunteers who received 400 micrograms daily saw a small improvement. And although there were no serious side effects, 11 per cent of study volunteers could not tolerate huperzine A, usually because it made them feel nauseous. Now, the researchers say, further investigations are required to find out if the higher dose really is effective.

Huperzine A is also attracting research interest from the US Army for its potential to block the effects of chemical warfare agents and from researchers elsewhere who are looking into its potential benefits in improving schizophrenia, cocaine addiction and traumatic brain injury.

OTHER NAMES Toothed club moss, fir moss, fir clubmoss, *qian ceng ta*
ORIGIN China and other parts of Asia
PARTS USED Stems, leaves

Huperzine A extract is available as an over-the-counter health supplement, but if you or a loved one has been diagnosed with Alzheimer's disease it's best to talk to your doctor about the most promising currently approved medications. If you'd like to try huperzine A, experts recommend taking 30 micrograms twice daily to support healthy brain function or 50–200 micro-grams twice daily as a potential buffer against brain changes associated with dementia. Studies show that huperzine A is generally safe at those doses. Don't take it if you're already using a medication for Alzheimer's disease; the combination could cause nausea, vomiting, diarrhoea, dizziness and muscle cramps. And use it cautiously if you have asthma, emphysema, epilepsy, a gastrointestinal blockage, heart disease or a peptic ulcer.

Various types of club moss are dried to make herbal teas.

ST JOHN'S WORT

Hypericum perforatum

MEDICAL BENEFITS ◆ Treatment for mild depression ◆ Traditional treatment for nerve pain, wounds, burns, insect bites

While the excitement that surrounded the use of this flower as an antidepressant in the 1990s has waned, St John's wort still offers moderate mind-enhancing benefits for some.

St John's wort was traditionally harvested on St John's Day, 24 June, hence its name.

When soaked in alcohol, the sunshine-yellow flowers of St John's wort release a burgundy-hued extract rich in hypericin. In the 1990s, the apparent mood-boosting effects of this compound earned the ancient herb a new image as a depression-conquering superstar. Television shows and magazines hailed it as 'Nature's Prozac' and the 'most-used antidepressant in the history of humanity'.

In demand Small wonder then that sales soared from $20 million in 1995 to nearly $315 million in 1998 in the United States alone, while in Germany the herb was prescribed 20 times more often than conventional drugs for depression. Supplies even ran short, particularly as word spread about a blockbuster *British Medical Journal* review of 23 studies involving 1757 people with mild to moderate depression. It compared the effects of St John's wort, standard antidepressants and a placebo – and

Spreading itself around

Despite its healing properties, St John's wort is considered a noxious weed in 20 countries including Australia, France, Italy, Turkey, Sweden and the United States. This hardy plant crowds out native species and can trigger severe sunburns if eaten by livestock. The sticky seeds stay viable in soil for up to 10 years and can hitch rides on fur, feathers, clothing, tyres and even machinery. The plant thrives in almost any conditions and also spreads via underground runners called rhizomes.

concluded that the herb had a depression-lifting effect similar to drugs, but with less than half the side effects.

Hypericum hype, or wort wisdom? But then the tide turned. The ultrapopular botanical was knocked off its pedestal in 2002, when a study sponsored by the US National Institutes of Health found a 'complete absence' of improvement in people with moderately severe depression. Reports of potentially serious herb–drug interactions followed, including birth-control pills that didn't work as well, reduced levels of chemotherapy drugs in people undergoing cancer treatment, and rising cholesterol levels in people taking some types of statin drugs while also using St John's wort.

Two-fifths of adults with depression use alternative treatments; most don't tell their doctors.

Sales fell to $100 million by 2003 in the United States. But the story wasn't over. Instead, a clearer picture of this remedy's best uses – and real-world risks – was emerging. Herbalists say St John's wort's traditional uses for nerve pain and to soothe wounds, burns and insect bites are still sound. And while we now know it isn't a miracle cure for the low moods that affect 121 million people worldwide, it may help some. The same scientists who first sang the herb's praises in 1996 reported recently that both St John's wort and antidepressants are 'similarly effective'. And in a review of 29 studies involving 5489 people, researchers from Germany's Technical University of Munich reported that one in four taking the herb halted treatment as a result of side effects compared to one in two taking a mood-lifting drug.

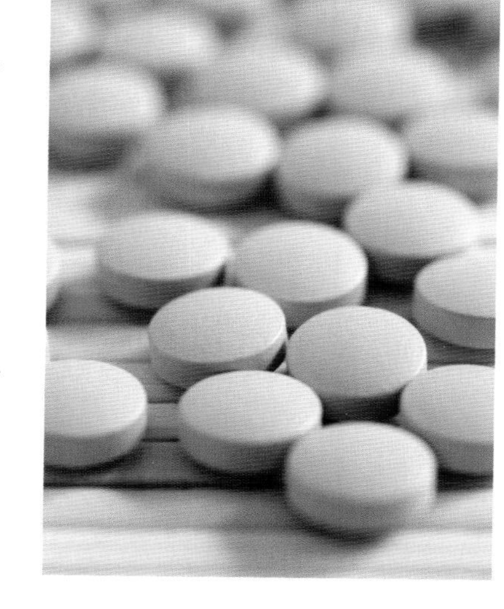
St John's wort tablets

Research frontiers

St John's wort contains at least seven substances – including hypericin – that counter depression. One, hyperforin, seems to function like popular selective serotonin reuptake inhibitor drugs (such as Prozac), by inhibiting the reuptake of a number of mood-elevating brain chemicals, including serotonin, dopamine, norepinephrine and gamma-aminobutyric acid, by brain cells. The longer these neurotransmitters are in play, the better you feel.

Now scientists are looking more closely at other uses for compounds found in St John's wort. In lab studies, two of these, hypericin and pseudohypericin, have knocked back many types of viruses including influenza A and hand, foot and mouth disease, a highly contagious but usually mild, blister-raising infection in people.

OTHER NAMES Hypericum, Klamath weed (or klamathweed), goatweed, amber, rosin rose, tipton weed
ORIGIN Europe, western Asia and North Africa
PART USED Flowering tops

If you'd like to try St John's wort for depression, choose a product standardised to 0.3 per cent hypericin or 2–4.5 per cent hyperforin, and take 300 mg three times a day. Consult your doctor first, though. This herb can interact with other antidepressants, birth-control pills, the organ-transplant drug cyclosporine, the heart medicine digoxin, indinavir and possibly other HIV drugs, and some cancer drugs, as well as seizure and anticlotting drugs. Stay in touch with your doctor; if depression does not improve in two to four weeks, explore other treatments.

FLAX

Linum usitatissimum

MEDICAL BENEFITS ◆ Treatment for constipation ◆ May help lower cholesterol and blood glucose and reduce cancer risk ◆ Traditional treatment for coughs, colds, constipation, skin irritations

Plenty of laxative products promise to put an end to constipation, but one millennia-old botanical remedy, flaxseed, has unique, natural advantages.

The tiny, golden-brown seeds of the flax plant are very effective at getting things moving again. They're high in fibre – 16 g of whole seeds packs 3–4½ g. Moreover, they are rich in insoluble fibre, which provides bulk and in turn stretches the intestinal walls, triggering contractions and bowel movements. They also contain a soluble fibre called mucilage, which binds with water to create a gel that keeps movements soft.

Fixing constipation is only one of the benefits of flax, however. In ancient times, it was grown for clothing, as well as for food and as medicine. Flaxseed is also rich in good-for-you omega-3 fatty acids and in beneficial plant compounds called lignans. Research suggests that these may play a role in reducing risk for heart disease, brittle bones (osteoporosis) and putting the brakes on growth of breast, prostate and skin cancers – a 2008 University of Texas study showed prostate cancer growth slowing by approximately 50 per cent in men who received 2 tablespoons of flaxseeds daily for three weeks before surgery.

The biggest producer of flaxseed is Canada, yielding about 40 per cent of global output.

Healthy reductions Flaxseed also appears to lower cholesterol and blood glucose levels. In a 2012 study from the University of Copenhagen in Denmark, flaxseed lowered total cholesterol 12 per cent and heart-threatening LDL cholesterol by 15 per cent, while in a 2008 study from the Chinese Academy of Medical Sciences, 55 people who took flaxseed extract daily for eight weeks saw their fasting blood glucose levels fall 25 per cent.

OTHER NAMES Flaxseed, linseed
ORIGIN Egypt
PARTS USED Seeds

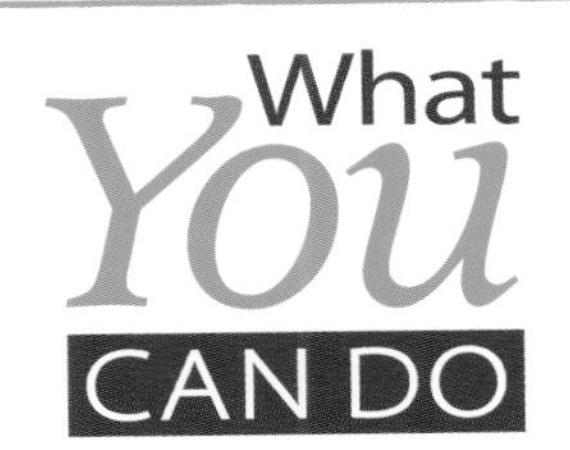

To use flaxseed as a laxative, mix 12 g ground flax (1½ tablespoons) into 150 ml (5 fl oz) of water, milk or fruit juice, and drink. Take two to three times a day and be sure to sip more fluids to avoid intestinal discomfort. Expect results in 12–24 hours. Flaxseed may interfere with absorption of medicines, so don't use it within one hour before or after taking any drugs.

DAFFODIL

Narcissus spp.

MEDICAL BENEFITS ◆ Treatment for Alzheimer's disease symptoms

Introduced by Roman soldiers stationed in the British Isles 2000 years ago, the daffodil became a national emblem of Wales. And now it's being grown there for another reason – as a promising new source of the drug galantamine, a treatment for Alzheimer's.

Recently, galantamine has been heralded for its ability to temporarily improve memory and thinking skills in people with mild to moderate dementia. But it has a much longer history of medicinal use that ultimately inspired today's research.

Galantamine is also found in the snowdrop (*Galanthus nivalis*), a close relative of the daffodil, and that's where the story begins. In Homer's classic tale *The Odyssey*, a snowdrop potion restores memory and stops hallucinations when Odysseus' crewmen are put under a spell by the witch Circe. In the 1950s, Bulgarian pharmacologist Dimitar Paskov investigated snowdrops after noticing a widespread Bulgarian folk-medicine custom in which snowdrop leaves and bulbs were rubbed on the forehead to ease pain. Paskov extracted the compound galantamine; after it was found that it could restore communication between nerves damaged by polio, it became the major treatment for the symptoms of the disease in Eastern Europe for decades, under the brand name Nivalin. The drug was also sometimes prescribed for other medical conditions involving the nervous system and muscles of the human body, such as muscular dystrophy.

Buying time But it was not until the 1990s that Alzheimer's researchers turned their attention to this snowdrop substance. Scientists were searching for new compounds that worked like the breakthrough drug tacrine (Cognex), discovered in 1993. It appeared to improve memory and thinking skills in people with mild to moderate Alzheimer's disease, buying them and their families a better quality of life for several months; but it also had a dark side, such as dangerous, liver-harming side effects. Could a similar compound take its place and be safer?

In Wales, daffodils are traditionally worn on St David's Day (1 March) to honour the nation's patron saint.

Medical researchers at England's Newcastle University cultivate daffodils hydroponically.

Galantamine soon emerged as a contender. Thanks to earlier research in Eastern Europe, scientists knew it worked like tacrine in the body but without the liver side effects; in the 1990s, some German and Swiss studies suggested it held promise against Alzheimer's. In 2001, the galantamine-based drug Reminyl was approved by the US Food and Drug Administration for Alzheimer's disease and in 2005 it was renamed Razadyne.

If you or a loved one is diagnosed with Alzheimer's disease, ask your doctor about drugs approved to slow the progression of the disease such as donepezil, rivastigmine – and galantamine.

in CLOSE-UP

Galantamine is an acetylcholinesterase inhibitor. In the brain, it increases the effectiveness and boosts levels of acetylcholine, a neurotransmitter that helps brain cells communicate with each other. In this role it improves memory and sharpens thinking skills for people suffering from Alzheimer's, keeping the disease at bay. However, acetylcholinesterase inhibitors cannot prevent Alzheimer's or treat the root causes of the disease.

Land of promise Initially, Razadyne was manufactured using synthetic galantamine because by the early 2000s the main natural source of the compound – snowdrops – was fast disappearing from the hills and valleys of Bulgaria, due to habitat destruction and decades of extensive harvesting for use in drugs and folk remedies. However, synthetic galantamine is expensive to produce, so researchers looked once again to the natural world.

After examining a range of potential sources, they found respectable levels of galantamine in daffodils. And it turned out that conditions in Wales's rugged Black Mountains produced daffodils with high levels of the compound. Welsh growers are therefore hopeful that galantamine from their daffodil bulbs will soon help fight Alzheimer's around the world.

Meanwhile, scientists elsewhere in Europe are also showing strong interest in galantamine from those yellow, springtime blooms. In 2011, separate research teams from the University of Barcelona in Spain and Leiden University in the Netherlands published preliminary studies of galantamine levels in daffodils. As the world's population ages steadily over the next few decades and rates of Alzheimer's disease inevitably increase, daffodils could help meet an important medical need.

OTHER NAMES Jonquille, Lent lily, narciso, narcissus
ORIGIN Spain and Portugal
PART USED Bulb

EVENING PRIMROSE

Oenothera biennis

MEDICAL BENEFITS ◆ Possible treatment for eczema, diabetic neuropathy, Sjögren's syndrome, breast pain ◆ Traditional remedy for allergies

The tiny seeds of the evening primrose flower yield a fat-rich oil that could be good news for sufferers from cyclical breast tenderness, eczema, diabetes-related nerve damage or dry eyes.

The minuscule seeds of the evening primrose (shown at right much enlarged) grow inside a seed pod attached to the flower.

How could one substance help so many different conditions? The answer is that the body converts a fat in evening primrose seeds – gamma-linolenic acid, or GLA – into a chemical that soothes inflammation in many different types of tissue, from breasts to eyes and beyond.

Hit and miss But verdicts from scientific studies of evening primrose oil's effects aren't unanimous: some have confirmed benefits, others haven't. Experts say it could be that you have to take the oil for several weeks or months to see results, or that it simply helps some people more than others.

For example, evening primrose oil may reduce the breast tenderness and swelling that happens in the second half of the menstrual cycle – it seems to help by protecting breast tissue from the effects of shifting hormone levels. But it doesn't seem to help breast discomfort that's not related to menstrual-cycle hormone shifts.

The oil also seems to boost levels of soothing, anti-inflammatory compounds in natural tears. And in two studies from the University of Glasgow and Guy's Hospital in London, both conducted in 1993, people with diabetes-related nerve damage obtained some relief with daily doses of evening primrose oil – but only if their blood glucose was under control.

Evening primrose supplements reduced the swelling, itching, crusting and redness of eczema in some tests as well – but, again, not all studies have found a benefit. And taking capsules of the oil eased eye problems such as burning, dryness and light sensitivity in people with Sjögren's syndrome (an auto-immune disorder) in one Italian study from the University of Messina, carried out in 2005.

OTHER NAMES Sun drop, night willow herb, fever plant, king's cure-all
ORIGIN North America
PARTS USED Seeds

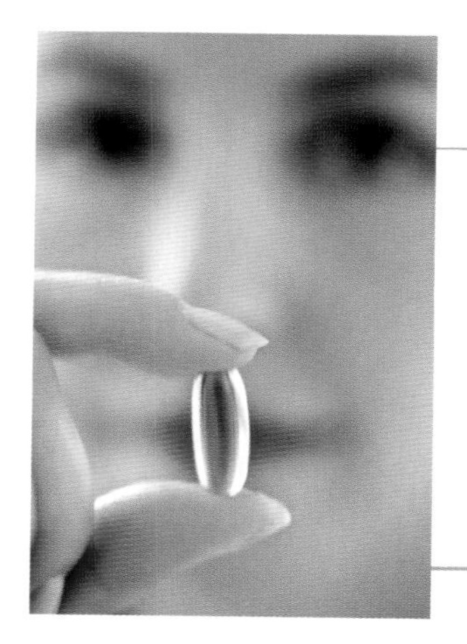

Evening primrose oil is available in health food stores and on prescription. The daily dose depends on why you're taking it: for breast tenderness try 3000–4000 mg a day; for dry eyes due to Sjögren's syndrome, 15 mg twice a day; for diabetes-related nerve damage, 360–480 mg a day; for eczema, 3000 mg a day. Maintaining a healthy diet rich in magnesium, zinc and vitamins C, B3 and B6 will help your body use GLA.

GINSENG

Panax ginseng

MEDICAL BENEFITS ◆ Potential treatment to improve stamina, memory and mental focus ◆ Traditional treatment for bronchitis, insomnia, recovery after illness and to improve stamina, memory and mental focus

This ancient Eastern health elixir's reputation for boosting vitality and memory make it a best-selling twenty-first-century botanical. But will it really make you feel sharper and stronger?

The year was 1709. The place, a remote Chinese forest close to the Korean border. There, an adventurous Jesuit missionary named Petrus Pierre Jartoux ingested a root known locally as *ren shen* – meaning literally 'the essence of the earth in the form of a man' – that had long been used in traditional Chinese and Korean medicine to increase strength and vigour. Almost at once, Jartoux felt a rush of energy. In his account of the experience, published by the Royal Society of London in 1713, he declared, 'I am persuaded that it would prove an excellent medicine in the hands of any European who understands pharmacy.' Thus the Western world was introduced to *Panax ginseng*.

In demand Four hundred years later, ginseng is one of the world's most sought-after herbs, according to the World Health Organization.

This quirky statue is in Geumsan, South Korea, a major centre of ginseng production.

And for much the same reasons. It's even said that it can help your body (and mind) withstand a modern-day threat: chronic stress. Ginseng turns up in capsules, tinctures and teas; as a flavouring in beverages; as gnarled roots dug from the earth, dried and sold in marketplaces; and even, in one interesting Spanish experiment, in a fortified milk researchers hoped would enhance the memories of older people (no word yet on the results!).

Memory magic? So, are the claims true? Could ginseng help you score top marks in an exam or remember the names of new clients on the job? Research suggests the answer is a qualified yes. In one study from the United Kingdom's University of Northumbria, people who took one 400-mg dose of ginseng improved

Though it is difficult to grow, ginseng is now cultivated all over Asia. The preserved roots are widely sold at food markets.

their speed and accuracy on mental-skills tests. They even got better at subtraction problems, compared to their pre-ginseng scores. It's interesting to note that in a follow-up study the same ginseng researchers found that bigger doses weren't any more effective, and even slowed thinking skills slightly.

This root remedy may give brain power a temporary nudge by dilating blood vessels, which could boost blood flow to the brain. But that's just part of the story. Ginseng contains dozens of active ingredients, most notably compounds called ginsenosides, which seem to work together to 'revitalise the functioning of the (body) as a whole', according to scientists who reviewed ginseng research for Germany's Commission E.

Vitality and strength Ginseng's invigorating effects may have led to its reputation for improving circulation. While few studies suggest it really does this – and some experts warn that it may actually raise blood pressure if you also consume a lot of caffeine – plenty do confirm ginseng's age-old, total-body wellbeing benefits. Or, as the World Health Organization puts it, research confirms ginseng's use as 'a restorative agent for enhancement of mental and physical capacities, in cases of weakness, exhaustion, tiredness and loss of concentration, and during convalescence'.

Ginseng supplements helped night-shift nurses in a French hospital reduce fatigue and improve their moods and mental focus in one study conducted by British researchers in 2003. And renewed vitality could include renewed intimate vitality: in a 2008 report from the Korea Food Research Institute, in South Korea, researchers reviewed seven ginseng studies involving 349 men with erectile dysfunction and found that the remedy significantly improved sexual functioning, desire and satisfaction.

OTHER NAMES Asian Ginseng, Chinese Ginseng, Korean Ginseng, *ren shen* (Chinese)
ORIGIN China, Korea, eastern Russia
PART USED Root

Ginseng's New World cousin

Another ginseng, *Panax quinquefolius*, grows wild in North America. Prized in Native American medicine, it was used, like Asian ginseng, to restore vitality. Often, it was saved for the elderly; some groups also used it to boost female fertility, improve mental powers or even as a general tonic. Science backs up some of these claims: a 2010 study of 32 women and men by Swinburne University of Technology in Melbourne, Australia, found that American ginseng improved working memory.

If you want to use ginseng to boost stamina, take 100 mg of a ginseng extract (such as a tincture, fluid extract or capsules), standardised so it contains 4 per cent ginsenosides, twice daily. Or make a tea using 1–2 g of ginseng root and sip daily. Consult your doctor if you plan to take ginseng for more than three months; if insomnia or anxiety develops, stop at once. Skip it if you take blood thinners, the heart medicine digoxin or antidepressants; diabetics should be aware that ginseng may lower blood glucose levels.

OPIUM POPPY

Papaver somniferum

MEDICAL BENEFITS ◆ Treatment for moderate to severe pain

For centuries, humans have used opium to ease pain, invite slumber and induce highs. And while some opium-derived substances are among the most abused drugs, others continue to ease suffering and save lives.

Raw opium is a sticky, brown resin harvested by slashing immature poppy seed pods and collecting their sap. It was a mainstay of ancient Egyptian, Greek, Roman, Indian and Chinese medicine – in 1993, archaeologists discovered fossilised poppy seeds at the site of a 7700-year-old city now submerged in a lake north of Rome. Today opium poppies are cultivated in Afghanistan, Myanmar, Mexico and a few other countries. Most of the 7000 tonnes (7700 tons) or so of opium produced globally each year is used to make heroin, but part of the harvest becomes raw material for the painkillers morphine, codeine and oxycodone.

Illicit drugs and patent medicines Trade in opium flourished in the 1600s and 1700s, leading to the mid-nineteenth-century Opium Wars between China and Britain. In the West, the drug's popularity soared after the introduction of an opium-based drink called laudanum in the mid-1600s. Made by mixing powdered opium with wine, it was often used by patients facing grisly surgeries without anaesthesia. One famous recipe, created by British physician Thomas Sydenham, called for 1 lb (0.5 kg) of sherry wine and 2 oz (57 g) of opium, flavoured with saffron, cinnamon and cloves. Sydenham wrote in 1680, 'Among the remedies which pleased Almighty God to give man to relieve his sufferings, none is so universal and so efficacious as opium.' With names like 'A Penny's Worth of Peace' and 'Mrs Winslow's Soothing Syrup', laudanum preparations and opium-laced patent medicines were the aspirin of the late nineteenth century on both sides of the Atlantic – widely used and considered genteel even for teetotal ladies.

Rise of the super drugs A more scientific and methodical investigation of opium and its properties was also taking place. In about 1803, a young German pharmacy assistant named Friedrich Sertürner decided to solve the mystery of raw opium's unpredictable quality and effects. Working at night, he experimented with opium, dissolving it with acid, neutralising it with ammonia and finally isolating what he

The main source of illicit opium is Afghanistan. Opium poppies are grown legally in countries including India, France, Japan and Australia.

When cut, an opium poppy seed pod exudes a milky liquid latex. The latex dries to form a brown resin, which is subsequently collected.

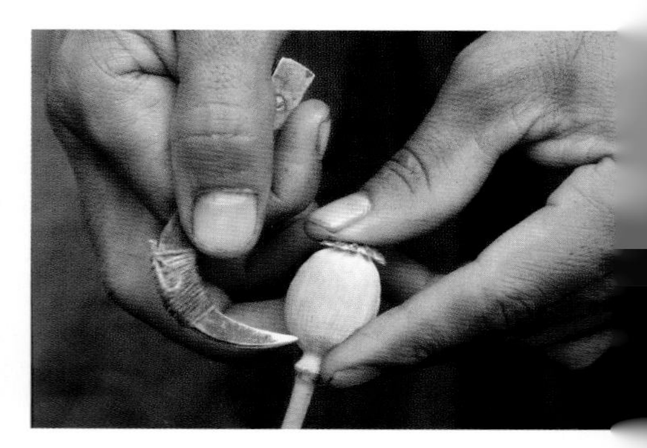

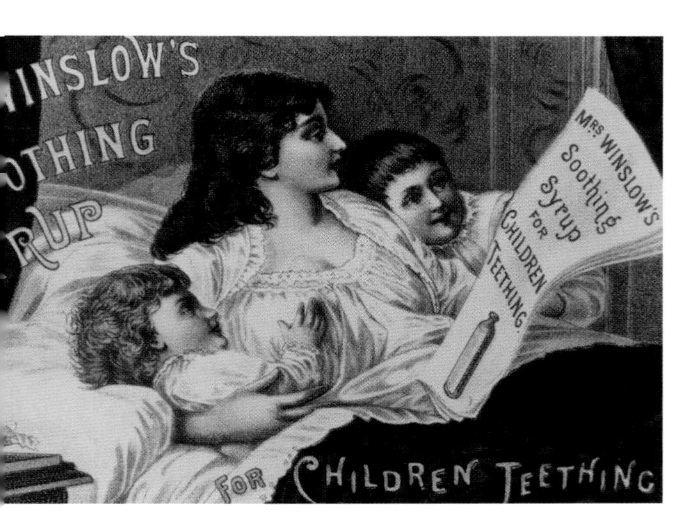

First sold in 1849, Mrs Winslow's morphine-based syrup caused many infant deaths.

Opium dens, for smoking the drug, spread from China to the West in the mid-1900s.

suspected was its active ingredient. Named morphine, it was 10 times stronger than opium. It, too, was widely used, at first to treat opium and alcohol addiction.

Another active opium compound, codeine, was first isolated from morphine in 1832 by French chemist Pierre Robiquet, and in 1874, in a failed effort to eliminate morphine's habit-forming properties, English chemist C Alder Wright developed a derivative called diacetylmorphine, better known today as heroin. Two to three times more potent than morphine, it was marketed in 1889 by Bayer in Germany as a new painkiller – and was soon widely abused.

Today, of course, heroin is an outlawed street drug. But pain relievers derived from opium or morphine or synthesised from other chemicals to mimic opiate molecular arrangements – including codeine, hydrocodone (Vicodin, Lortab), hydromorphone (Dilaudid), oxycodone (Percocet, Percodan, OxyContin) and oxymorphone (Opana) – have taken centre stage in the management of severe, tough-to-treat and chronic pain.

in CLOSE-UP

Why are opium and its derivatives so effective at killing pain yet so highly addictive? In 1972, two Johns Hopkins University scientists, Solomon Snyder and Candace Pert, stumbled upon the startling answer. Opiate drugs have a chemical structure similar to that of endorphins – natural, feel-good chemicals produced by the brain during exercise, laughter, physical intimacy and eating certain foods (yes, including chocolate!), which in turn create feelings of wellbeing and reduced pain. Opiates latch onto endorphin receptors and trigger the same sensations, but are more powerful (and dangerous) because they can be taken at any time and in any dose.

ORIGIN Western Asia
PART USED Latex sap from seed pods

If you have moderate to severe pain that's not helped by other pain relievers, your doctor may prescribe an opiate-based drug such as codeine, morphine or oxycodone. It may make you drowsy, so don't drive or drink alcohol; it can also cause constipation, so your doctor may suggest using a laxative. Bear in mind that these drugs can lead to dependence and addiction in about 1 per cent of people who use them for pain – causing unpleasant withdrawal symptoms when users try to quit.

BUTTERBUR

Petasites hybridus

MEDICAL BENEFITS ◆ Prevention of migraines ◆ Treatment of respiratory allergies (such as hay fever) ◆ Traditional use for digestive disorders, lung disease, headache

Migraine and seasonal allergy sufferers alike are finding relief in a purple-flowered herb once used as a butter-wrapper; today, even conventional medicine hails it as a remedy as effective as some pharmaceutical drugs.

Butterbur's spectacularly oversized leaves measure up to 60 cm (2 ft) across. They were used hundreds of years ago in Europe to wrap butter in warm weather to discourage melting, and in some parts of the world children still fashion the enormous leaves into hats. This echoes the Greek physician Dioscorides' 2000-year-old observation that leaves resembled rain hats, the word for which in Greek was *petasos*, in turn the source of this marsh-dwelling plant's scientific name, *Petasites*. Today, however, the attention of scientists and supplement makers has turned to butterbur for a new kind of protection – against recurrent migraine headaches and the annoying symptoms of seasonal allergies.

Giant butterbur, *Petasites japonicus*, which is native to Japan, is being investigated for its antioxidant and anti-inflammatory effects.

In a 2002 Swiss study, nasal airflow increased nearly 100 per cent in people who took butterbur to treat congestion due to hay fever.

Preventing head pain Around the world, about one in twelve men and one in seven women experience the pulsing, throbbing pain of migraine headaches. For more than half, these big headaches return with frightening regularity. In Europe, butterbur has long been a folk remedy for headaches, and today scientific research and even mainstream medical groups such as the American Academy of Neurology are endorsing the plant's effectiveness against migraines. In one 2004 study from the Albert Einstein College of Medicine in New York, 222 people who experienced two to six migraines each month stopped their regular medications and took 50–75 mg of butterbur or a placebo twice daily for 16 weeks. The butterbur group reported a reduction of between 36 and 48 per cent in the number of migraines they experienced. And German researchers from the University of Duisburg-Essen reported in 2004 that 45 per cent of volunteers experienced a 50 per cent or greater reduction in migraines.

Clearing the airways Congestion, sneezing and itchy, watery eyes are the hallmarks of respiratory allergies such as hay fever and allergies to mould and pets. Could butterbur conquer these, too? Published studies say yes. In one large 2005 study conducted at the Allergy Clinic in Landquart, Switzerland, of 330 people with allergies, a butterbur extract was as effective as a commonly prescribed antihistamine at easing all of those annoying symptoms. The bonus? Butterbur users didn't feel sleepy or sedated the way those who took this type of antihistamine did.

In another Swiss study of 580 allergy sufferers, 90 per cent enjoyed symptom relief while taking butterbur for two weeks during allergy season. And eight in ten said the herb made everyday life easier as a result.

in CLOSE-UP

A family of multitasking chemicals in butterbur accounts for this herb's ability to dry up seasonal allergy symptoms and stop strong headaches before they start. This includes a compound called petasin that helps relax smooth muscle, such as the muscle in artery walls, which can help prevent the blood-vessel constrictions that lead to migraine pain, say researchers from the University of Rhode Island, in the United States. Petasin also soothes inflammation, which helps ease allergy symptoms such as swollen nasal passages. Moreover, two related compounds called isopetasin and oxopetasin reduce the body's production of leukotrienes, molecules that cause congestion, excess mucus production and tightened airways in response to triggers such as pollen, according to German researchers reporting in the journal *European Neurology* in 2004.

To put a stop to recurring migraines or clear congestion due to respiratory allergies (such as to pollen, mould or pet hair), the Natural Standard – a highly regarded international research collaboration that reviews the scientific evidence for alternative remedies – recommends butterbur supplements containing standardised levels of the active ingredient petasin. You should follow the dosing directions for the individual product, but in general a good adult dose is 100–150 mg of butterbur a day that provides 15–32 mg of petasin. Only buy butterbur extracts labelled 'PA-free'; this means that harmful toxins called pyrrolizidine alkaloids, which raise risk for liver damage and even cancer, have been removed. Butterbur is related to ragweed, so avoid this herb if you're allergic to ragweed, marigolds, daisies or chrysanthemums.

Conventional antihistamines are effective at suppressing allergy symptoms, but can cause drowsiness and interact with other drugs.

OTHER NAMES Petasites, purple butterbur, butter dock, bog rhubarb, exwort
ORIGIN Europe, southwestern Asia, North Africa
PARTS USED Leaves, rhizomes (underground stems), roots

SNAKEROOT

Rauwolfia serpentina

MEDICAL BENEFITS ◆ Treatment for high blood pressure ◆ Potential treatment for agitation in mental disorders such as schizophrenia ◆ Traditional treatment for insect stings, bites of poisonous reptiles

Nowadays, as soon as high blood pressure is diagnosed, it can be treated with medications. But before 1949, the year a plant extract from India revolutionised blood-pressure care, there was little doctors could do.

Powdered root of *Rauwolfia serpentina* is traditionally used to make a medicinal paste.

The extract came from snakeroot, a herb that had been used in Indian Ayurvedic medicine for centuries to treat snakebites, insect stings, insomnia and – thanks to its calming effects – even mental disorders (in the northern Indian state of Bihar, snakeroot is known as Pagal-ka-dawa, 'insanity drug cure'). Through modern times, snakeroot has continued to be sold in rural markets in India in powdered form. But it was after one Indian drug maker released a tablet version, called Serpina, in the 1930s, that intense interest from Indian researchers turned this traditional remedy into the world's first breakthrough high-blood-pressure medication.

Early lab studies revealed that snakeroot contained a rainbow of bitter-tasting alkaloids, and that these compounds could slow heartbeat, depress the central nervous system, relax smooth muscle in artery walls and lower blood pressure. In 1940, a pioneering Indian cardiologist named Rustom Jal Vakil published the first research documenting snakeroot's effects in people. He noted, 'After a trial of this preparation, one finds it useful in a percentage of cases of hypertension only; the indications and suitability of the case for the drug have not as yet been worked out'. Nevertheless, by 1949, 90 per cent of Indian doctors were prescribing it and approximately 50 million tablets had been sold by one company alone.

in CLOSE-UP

Bitter-tasting alkaloids in snakeroot, including reserpine, isoajmaline, neoajmaline and serpentinine, calm blood pressure by slowing down the nervous system. Arteries relax and the heartbeat slows. According to one drug maker, reserpine works at a cellular level by reducing levels of catecholamines, hormones that control the activity of the sympathetic nervous system, which regulates circulation.

In a study at Georgetown University, Washington DC, in 1956, reserpine reduced blood pressure by up to 35 per cent.

From India to the world In 1949, Vakil published the first clinical news about the medicinal properties of snakeroot to appear beyond India's borders, in the *British Heart Journal*. It fired the imagination of doctors and researchers around the world, who until then had no effective medications for high blood pressure. Vakil's study of 50 volunteers with hypertension showed that 85 per cent of those who took the extract showed an average 21-point drop in systolic pressure (the top

Snakeroot flowers are pink and white. The roots are harvested after two to four years.

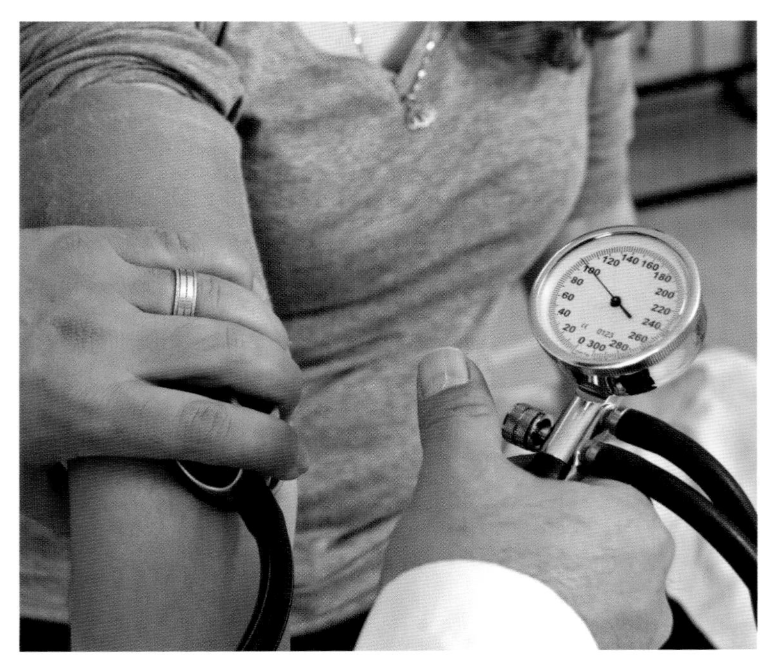

The blood pressure meter was invented and first used in Austria in the early 1880s.

number in a blood pressure reading), while 81 per cent had an average drop of 11 points in diastolic pressure (the bottom number).

The paper launched a flurry of international research. More than 100 studies of snakeroot were published in the next five years as scientists looked into the extract's potential as a sedative and antipsychotic drug as well as a blood pressure medicine. A breakthrough came in 1952, when Swiss researchers discovered that a previously unknown compound in the herb, reserpine, was responsible for 50 per cent of its activity. Soon, the reserpine-based drug Sarpasil was released on the market for high-blood-pressure control.

A life-saving connection Reserpine-based drugs made history again in the 1960s. A Veterans Administration trial in the United States, of 143 men, proved for the first time that lowering high blood pressure really did reduce risk for deadly heart attacks. That's a benefit we take for granted today, but it was unproven before this 1964 study. The study was also the first to show that treating high blood pressure, using reserpine, lowered risk for stroke, congestive heart failure and kidney damage.

Today, reserpine is rarely used to treat high blood pressure. Newer drugs with fewer side effects are usually chosen first by doctors. However, reserpine deserves credit for ushering in a new and effective way of dealing with high blood pressure, as a serious medical condition that can be treated successfully – thus saving lives. No wonder the US Surgeon General once described the discovery of reserpine as 'trailblazing and epoch-making'!

OTHER NAMES Indian snakeroot, sarpagandha
ORIGIN India, Borneo, Sri Lanka, Sumatra
PART USED Root

Due to side effects such as sedation, depression, Parkinson's-like tremors and constipation, reserpine is rarely a first-choice drug today, but it is still occasionally used in combination with diuretics for blood pressure problems. Reserpine is available as a generic drug and under brand names including Demi-Regroton, Regroton and Hydropres. The usual dose of this drug is 0.1–0.25 mg once a day. Don't use reserpine, however, if you have depression or a peptic ulcer.

CASTOR BEAN

Ricinus communis

MEDICAL BENEFITS ◆ Potential cancer treatment ◆ Traditional use for constipation and as general health tonic

Inside every shiny, brown castor bean lurks a poison so deadly it's considered a potential biological weapon – and an assassin's toxin of choice. Yet this lethal substance, called ricin, also shows promise as a tumour-destroying therapy.

The castor bean plant has been prized for millennia for its oil, which was used in lamps 4000 years ago in Egypt and is incorporated today in aircraft lubricants, paints, inks, soap and electrical insulation. In the first half of the twentieth century, castor oil was also a popular home remedy. But the bean's most insidious constituent, ricin, has a deadly claim to fame. In a headline-grabbing 1978 assassination in London, a killer shot a ricin-packed pellet into the thigh of Bulgarian dissident Georgi Markov – using an umbrella equipped with a firing device and silencer. Markov died several days later.

Georgi Markov was poisoned with ricin.

As yet, there's no antidote for ricin poisoning, but scientists are testing a vaccine that protects against its effects – of particular interest to national security services concerned about biological attacks. At the same time, researchers are also investigating ricin's potential as a killer of cancer cells.

A guided missile Ricin works by shutting down the production of proteins inside cells. Without these important building blocks, cells die. But how do you kill only cancer cells – while protecting the rest of the human body? That was the challenge facing scientists who discovered ricin's anticancer properties in the 1970s. Injected into tumours in mice by National Taiwan University researchers in a 1971 lab study, ricin reduced tumour size by 90 per cent within 48 hours – and suppressed new growth with just four days of treatment.

In a 2011 Chinese study, ricin gel inhibited the growth of breast cancer tumours by 61 per cent.

In the early 1980s, scientists at the University of Texas were ready to try a 'guided missile' approach. They attached ricin molecules to particular antibodies that cling only to leukaemia cells, with the result that the 'immunotoxins' reduced tumour cells by 80 per cent or more in mice.

Ricin immunotoxin therapy is still experimental and so not widely available as a cancer therapy. If you're tempted to try castor oil as a laxative, go easy. It's a strong, fast-acting stimulant, causing powerful intestinal-wall contractions that can relieve constipation in just two to six hours. But it can also cause nausea, diarrhoea and cramping. Therefore you should follow package directions carefully and use the oil only occasionally; regular use can make chronic constipation worse, by making your digestive system dependent on the oil. Castor oil might be worth trying for knee osteoarthritis, too: in a study involving the All India Institute of Medical Sciences, people who took a 0.9 ml capsule three times a day for four weeks said it soothed their knee pain.

Grown as an ornamental plant in warmer climates, castor bean often has striking purple leaves and spiky red female flowers.

But concerns about ricin's toxicity remained. After genetically modifying ricin to make it less dangerous, researchers began human trials. In a 2003 study of 35 people with Hodgkin's lymphoma, ricin therapy put three volunteers into partial remission, reduced the number of cancer cells slightly in two others, and stopped progression of cancer in seven study participants. But there was an unwanted side effect: most participants developed vascular leakage syndrome, in which fluid leaks from blood vessels, especially in the lungs. And in other human studies, ricin provoked immune-system reactions that forced researchers to halt treatment.

Future directions To date, ricin is not an approved cancer therapy. Researchers are still trying to develop new ways to deliver it to cancer cells while disarming its troubling side effects. In 2010, scientists at the University of New Mexico engineered a silica-and-fat nanoparticle just one-billionth of a metre in size that delivered ricin directly to liver cancer cells.

And at least one new clinical trial of ricin is underway, this time in adults with either leukaemia or lymphoma, at the Albert Einstein Cancer Center in New York City. Meanwhile, cancer experts at Tel Aviv University reported in a 2012 review that even if ricin's side effects mean it never becomes a cancer drug, its role in 'guided missile' cancer therapies will one day yield newer, better, safer treatments.

Traditional Wisdom

Castor beans are rich in foul-tasting castor oil. Used as a medical remedy by many cultures for thousands of years, the oil was especially popular in the West in the first half of the twentieth century, both as a general health tonic and to reverse constipation. Still available in health food stores, it turns out to be rich in ricinoleic acid, researchers from Germany's Max Planck Institute for Heart and Lung Research reported in 2012. And this acid really does bind to receptors in intestinal walls, possibly explaining the oil's effectiveness as a laxative.

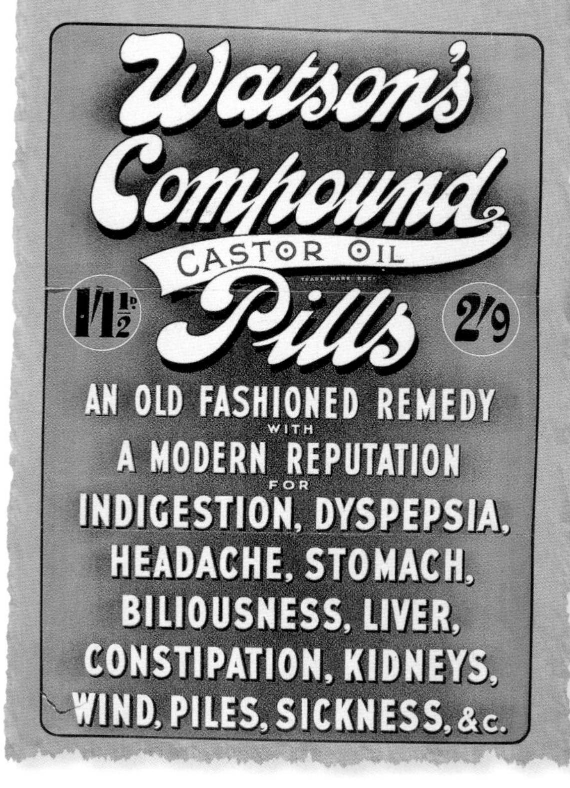

OTHER NAME Castor seed
ORIGIN Africa, Asia
PARTS USED Seeds

PLANT-DERIVED CANCER DRUGS

Will the next blockbuster cancer drug come from a field, rainforest or backyard vegetable garden? The concept isn't as far-fetched as it may sound – nearly 60 per cent of cancer treatments in use today were derived or modelled on compounds originally found in plants.

Several articles in this book recount stories of breakthrough cancer drugs derived from plants, ranging from lymphoma-fighting vincristine from rosy periwinkle (see p. 74) to the breast, lung and ovarian cancer drug paclitaxel from the Pacific yew tree (p. 42). Many other plant-sourced drugs are part of the pharmaceutical armamentarium wielded by cancer specialists daily as mainstream chemotherapies. And with just 15 per cent of the world's 320,000 plant species having so far been investigated for medical uses, many, many more plants are being or have yet to be investigated for their potential in the fight against cancer. Here's a glimpse of some of the most exciting recent developments in this field.

A felicitous discovery The ovarian cancer drug topotecan and the colorectal cancer drug irinotecan have chemical structures inspired by a compound from an ornamental Chinese tree called *Camptotheca acuminata* – known in China as *xi shu*, 'happy tree'. It contains a life-saving cancer-fighting compound, called camptothecin, that works in a way scientists had never before seen, trapping an enzyme involved in cell division so that cancer cells cannot reproduce. The medication was nearly derailed in the 1970s due to severe bladder-damaging side effects that halted studies, but extensive research resumed, allowing scientists to develop synthetic forms of camptothecin that became available in the 1990s.

Cousins join the fight The compound podophyllotoxin, derived from a rare Himalayan plant called *Podophyllum hexandrum*, is used to make etoposide, a drug that is used alone to treat cancer and is an ingredient in other anticancer medications including teniposide and etopophos. Over-harvesting of *P. hexandrum* for its use in these drugs led scientists to take a closer look at related plants like the American May apple (*P. peltatum*). In 2009, Mississippi State University researchers announced that leaves of this botanical cousin contain high levels of podophyllotoxin, and could be an alternative source of this important compound.

South African strangler In the 1970s, researchers from the Botanical Research Institute of South Africa and the National Cancer Institute (US) gathered traditional medicinal

SMALL BUT POTENT

Inside the tiny first leaves to emerge from radish seeds, a compound called olomoucine has been found. In lab studies this chemical halted the normal life cycles of cells – leading scientists to develop synthetic versions with anticancer potential. The first, called roscovitine, showed promise against breast and lung cancer, and an even more potent derivative, called purvalanol, is now being studied. A 2010 paper published by researchers from Japan's Osaka University noted that purvalanol's effects could make it an important drug for suppressing the progression of cancer.

Above: The Chinese 'happy tree' yields a compound that led to the drugs topotecan and irinotecan.

Right: US researchers have found that at least 14 compounds in the native wild tomatillo plant have potent anticancer effects.

Left: In cell-line studies, Peruvian researchers shrank tumours using extracts from a native plant called cat's claw.

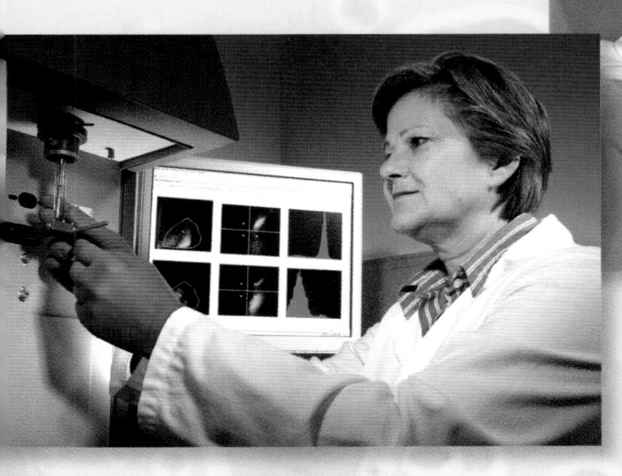

Above: This US biologist is testing the antileukaemia properties of compounds in strawberries.

Right: Large pale pink flowers crown the Himalayan plant *Podophyllum hexandrum*.

plants in South Africa for further study. One, known as the bush willow (*Combretum caffrum*) subsequently surprised researchers. Used in African traditional medicine for hepatitis and malaria, it contains a compound called combretastatin A4 phosphate (CA4) that attacks cancer in a very particular way. In lab studies, CA4 caused the linings of the blood vessels that supply tumours with nutrients to swell up, with the result that the blood vessels withered and died. According to a 2010 paper from West Virginia University, CA4 is the most promising compound to emerge from this new approach to stopping cancer. In one 2011 study from the Mount Vernon Cancer Center in Middlesex in the United Kingdom, adding CA4 to other cancer drugs improved results for women whose ovarian cancer had relapsed.

SPHAGNUM MOSS

Sphagnum spp.

MEDICAL BENEFITS ◆ Possible treatment for dressing wounds, fighting bacteria ◆ Traditional treatment for nappy rash, wounds

This bog-loving, low-growing plant could teach household sponges a trick or two, as it's capable of absorbing 20 to 30 times its weight in water. That has made it highly useful for millennia and could provide benefits in the future.

Sphagnum moss's absorbency led to it being used as a natural baby nappy among the Cree people of North America and the Inuit of the Arctic. It was also used as a wound dressing by Native Americans and early Europeans – perhaps because it also has natural antibacterial and antifungal properties thanks to its high acidity levels, as shown in a 2009 analysis from Queens University in Canada.

In 1963, when four Bronze Age burial sites were found near Ashgrove in Fife, Scotland, researchers from the University of St Andrews investigated – and found sphagnum moss tucked in with one man's skeleton. It's thought the moss might have been used to dress a chest wound. Ötzi, the prehistoric 'Iceman' discovered in 1997 in a melting mountain glacier in northern Italy, also carried sphagnum moss, probably as an ancient first-aid remedy.

Moss goes to war This was a use that soldiers of World War I would have understood. During that war, with supplies of cotton for bandages growing scarce and expensive, the British Red Cross turned to this old-time alternative dressing, with good results. Harvested in northern Canada and Scotland then cleaned, dried and

OTHER NAMES Bog moss, peat moss
ORIGIN North America, United Kingdom, northern mainland Europe
PARTS USED Above-ground parts of plant

Sopping mats of sphagnum moss often provide water for other plant species.

packed into fabric casings, sphagnum moss appeared to improve survival times for soldiers injured by bullets and mortars. According to contemporary accounts, its antibacterial properties may have discouraged infection – a boon in a time before antibiotics. At the height of the war, Allied volunteers were fashioning between 200,000 and 300,000 dressings per month.

Moss is no longer used as a battlefield dressing, but it hasn't gone into retirement. One personal-products maker, Johnson & Johnson, used it as an absorbent layer in sanitary napkins in the 1980s. Around the same time, Terence J Painter from the Norwegian University of Science and Technology studied the plant's preservative powers, pinpointing a sugar in cell walls, called 5-KMA, that show promise for food conservation. And in 2009, Chilean researchers found that *Sphagnum magellanicum* displayed antibiotic activity against disease-causing bacteria – including *Staphylococcus aureus*, group B *Streptococcus* and *Escherichia coli*.

in CLOSE-UP

Sphagnum moss's ability to hold many times its weight in water is due to the structure of its leaves. Its living cells are interspersed with very large, dead, empty structures with pores in their thickened walls. These 'hyaline' cells act like super sponges. In some species, hyaline cells even twist up the outside of the stem, wicking water to the leaves.

FEVERFEW

Tanacetum parthenium

MEDICAL BENEFITS ◆ Potential treatment for prevention of migraine headaches ◆ Traditional treatment for headaches, fevers, stomachaches, toothaches, insect bites, infertility and problems with menstruation and with labour during childbirth

Feverfew belongs to the daisy family and has typical yellow-and-white flowers.

If you're prone to migraines, you may have fewer with feverfew. It has long been considered a go-to remedy for head pain – and researchers now know why.

An English herbal medicine guide from 1633 noted that feverfew is 'very good for them that are giddie in the head'. Nevertheless, feverfew fell into relative obscurity in the 1800s and 1900s – until a 1985 study in the *British Medical Journal* put it back in the spotlight. Researchers at the City of London (now National) Migraine Clinic asked migraine sufferers already using the herb to stop; some then started taking the herb again while others were given a placebo. The placebo group experienced more migraine headaches and more intense pain. A larger, 1988 study from the University of Nottingham, published in the journal *The Lancet*, confirmed feverfew's ability to reduce the severity and frequency of migraines – by about 24 per cent.

Leafy chemicals How does feverfew do this? It may be its effect on serotonin, a chemical that occurs naturally in the body. Abnormal levels of serotonin are associated with migraines. Test-tube studies conducted in 1985 at the University Hospital in Nottingham, England, showed that an active ingredient in feverfew, parthenolide, inhibits the clumping-together of platelets in the bloodstream, which in turn discourages the release of excess serotonin.

Meanwhile, researchers from Case Western Reserve University in Cleveland, in the United States, found in a 2007 test-tube and mouse study that parthenolide's anti-inflammatory action could one day be harnessed to ease the excessive inflammation that leads to lung destruction and death in people with cystic fibrosis. Parthenolide inhibited the release of an inflammatory chemical called interleukin-8 – and might in the future be the basis for a safe, effective drug for this serious medical condition.

OTHER NAMES Altamisa, featherfew, featherfoil, febrifuge plant, midsummer daisy, bachelor's buttons
ORIGIN Balkan Mountains of Eastern Europe
PARTS USED Leaves

If you decide to try feverfew for migraine prevention, look for a product with a standardised amount of parthenolide, the herb's active ingredient. Follow package directions. If you are allergic to plants in the daisy family (which includes ragweed and chrysanthemums), be careful, as you could be allergic to feverfew. Make sure you store feverfew capsules in a cool, dry place, as levels of parthenolide can drop as much as 25 per cent at room temperature in six months. People who take feverfew for a long time and then stop taking it may experience difficulty sleeping, headaches, joint pain, nervousness and stiff muscles.

RED CLOVER

Trifolium pratense

MEDICAL BENEFITS ◆ Potential treatment for menopausal hot flushes and night sweats ◆ Traditional treatment for whooping cough, bronchitis, asthma

Hot flushes. Night sweats. Mood swings. Over half of women experience these life-disrupting symptoms during menopause – and 70 per cent never find relief. Could plant hormones from red clover flowers help?

Red clover can grow to 1 m (3 ft) high and has round, pink, purple or white flower heads.

Discovered by Australian researchers during the 1930s when sheep grazing on large quantities of red clover developed infertility, the plant hormones in clover flowers are weak oestrogens called daidzein, genistein, formononetin and biochanin A. They are similar to the 'phyto-estrogens' in soy – a common food in Asian countries, where, intriguingly, women report less menopausal discomfort than in the West.

Flower power There is some evidence that Native American Iroquois women used red clover during the change of life, and recent research has shown benefits, too. When scientists from the Universities of Exeter and Plymouth in the United Kingdom reviewed five well-designed red clover studies in 2007, they reported a 'marginally significant effect' against hot flushes.

In 2005, scientists from Ecuador's Foundation for Health and Well Being in the Climacteric gave 60 menopausal women a red clover extract or placebo daily for three months; women taking clover saw an 80 per cent reduction in menopausal symptoms. And when 25 menopausal women with severe hot flushes and night sweats took a red clover extract for 12 weeks, symptoms eased by 46 per cent, in a 2005 study conducted at the Functional Medicine Research Center in Gig Harbor, Washington State.

Given these mixed results, it may be that red clover simply works for some women and not for others. Meanwhile, the plant could yet have another application: there's early evidence from a 2009 lab study at Japan's Biokenkyusho Research Laboratory that red clover may also maintain bone density.

OTHER NAMES Cow clover, meadow clover, wild clover
ORIGIN Southeastern Europe
PARTS USED Flowers

Many red clover supplements are available, some with standardised levels of 'isoflavones', the weak plant oestrogens that are clover's active ingredients. Aim for 80 mg of isoflavones a day, the amount used in many menopause research studies. Studies lasting up to one year have found red clover to be generally safe to take, but it is not known whether it is safe for women who have had breast cancer or other hormone-sensitive cancers, or whether use for more than a year raises any health risks. If you have any concerns, discuss red clover supplements with your doctor first.

VALERIAN

Valeriana officinalis

MEDICAL BENEFITS ◆ Potential treatment for anxiety and insomnia ◆ Traditional treatment for insomnia, anxiety, epilepsy

The ancient Greeks called valerian root 'Phu' (as in *phew!*) because it smells like nothing other than a stinky old sock. But this substance may be a boon if you're stressed or unable to sleep.

In contrast to the plant's roots, valerian flowers have a sweet and delicate scent.

Valerian root's distinctive aroma comes from isovaleric acid, one of several calming compounds it contains. Traditional use of the plant for insomnia and anxiety dates back thousands of years, to Greece, Rome and China. It became popular in Europe in the 1600s, and until the 1940s was even listed in the US National Formulary as a sleep aid and anxiety remedy. And today valerian is enjoying a resurgence in popularity, as researchers document its sedative properties. The latest news about this age-old botanical? It works well as a calming herb for some people – but not for all.

Sedative science Nightly tablets of valerian root extract helped about 1 in 13 insomniacs enjoy a longer night's sleep, with fewer middle-of-the night wake-ups, in a 2007 study conducted by the Norwegian Knowledge Centre for the Health Services. The researchers concluded: 'A small number of people with insomnia are likely to experience a noticeable improvement attributable to valerian.'

Valerian's reputation for easing agitation has also been put to the test in a number of studies, with mixed results. In laboratory experiments, it appears to relax mice, rats and even zebrafish. And in 2008, University of Zurich scientists discovered that valerian compounds enhanced the effects of GABA, a brain chemical that eases fear and anxiety by calming excited brain cells. Yet valerian didn't soothe anxiety in women volunteers during a 2007 study held at the University of Illinois; and in a 2006 review of studies of the use of valerian to treat anxiety in people, researchers from Brazil's Federal University of São Paulo concluded that there's not yet enough evidence to prove that this herb is effective. Combining valerian with lemon balm (*Melissa officinalis*), another calming herb, did, however, ease stress in one 2006 study at the University of Northumbria in England.

OTHER NAMES All-heal, common valerian, fragrant valerian, garden heliotrope
ORIGIN Europe and Asia
PART USED Root

What You CAN DO

If you'd like to try valerian to ease mild insomnia, take 400–900 mg of valerian extract in tablet or capsule form or 20–60 drops of valerian tincture in warm water between half an hour and two hours before bedtime. Valerian tea (2–3 g of dried, powdered valerian steeped in a cup of just-boiled water) may also help; mask the unpleasant taste by also steeping a cinnamon stick or star anise in the cup. Extracts containing lemon balm as well as valerian – effective against anxiety in one study – are also available; follow label directions.

HERBAL STRESS RELIEF

Stressed out? Mother Nature's got a serene solution: Four herbs proven to tame tension and ease anxiety. Keep them handy to create soothing teas you can turn to when you need to relax. Brew a comforting cuppa, put your feet up, sip and unwind.

You can choose and use as many of the soothing herbs described here as you like. Buy them in loose, dry form (not in tea bags) at a natural foods store or online. Mix equal parts together. Then add natural flavour-enhancers such as dried peppermint, dried orange peel (in small pieces) or small pieces of cinnamon bark. Store in a jar with a tight-fitting lid. At teatime, place 2–3 teaspoons of your blend in a tea strainer, infuse in a cup of just-boiled water for five to ten minutes, and enjoy!

Calming chamomile The tiny, daisy-like flowers of this herb (*Matricaria recutita*) have a long history as traditional stress-busters. The modern twist: in 2009, University of Pennsylvania researchers tested a concentrated chamomile extract in 61 people with generalised anxiety disorder. The study volunteers took a 'pharmaceutical grade' capsule containing 220 mg of chamomile or received a placebo. Those who got the real thing saw anxiety ebb significantly. According to the researchers, credit for the effect belongs to a compound called apigenin, which acts as a mild sedative.

Passionflower power This stress eraser helped volunteers in a 2012 Turkish study at Ankara Training and Research Hospital quell tension before surgical procedures. Those who received a passionflower (*Passiflora incarnata*) extract before receiving spinal anesthesia prior to surgery had fewer signs of anxiety than those who didn't take this herb. According to research carried out at Germany's VivaCell Biotechnology company in 2011, passionflower makes brain cell receptors more responsive to the calming effects of the natural brain chemical gamma-aminobutyric acid (GABA).

Soothe with lemon balm
When volunteers took 300 or 600 mg of lemon balm (*Melissa officinalis*) or a placebo, then performed stress-inducing tasks during a study at the University of Northumbria in England, researchers found that those who received the highest dose of lemon balm stayed calm while the others grew tense. In a 2009 study conducted at the University of Ottawa, researchers noted that a chemical called rosmarinic acid is not only partly responsible for the lemony aroma and flavour of

Passionflower tea

Chamomile flowers

this herb but also, like passionflower, acts on brain receptors to enhance the calming effects of the brain chemical GABA.

Skullcap to relieve tension In a 2010 University of Westminster survey of highly trained herbalists in the United Kingdom and Ireland, 100 per cent said they would recommend this mint-family herb for anxiety and stress. Skullcap (*Scutellaria lateriflora*) ranked number one in the survey ahead of 14 other herbs used for tamping down tension. Despite its popularity among herbalists and a long history as a stress-soother, there's actually little research on the effects of skullcap in people. However, in one 2003 American study, 10 volunteers who took between 100 and 350 mg of freeze-dried skullcap saw a marked reduction in tension. Skullcap contains high levels of an amino acid called glutamine, which seems to work on the brain's GABA receptors in ways similar to those described above for lemon balm.

QUICK FIXES

These easy strategies can help you bust stress fast:

Keep chamomile teabags in your desk: Make a quick cup of soothing tea when work gets stressful.

♦ ♦ ♦

Sprinkle lemon balm essential oil into the bathtub: Add 15 drops to a hot bath then enjoy a soak.

♦ ♦ ♦

Buy a stress-reducing herbal formula. Look for a tincture or capsules that contain some of the herbs mentioned here, keep it with you and take as directed.

GARLIC

Allium sativum

MEDICAL BENEFITS ◆ Potential prevention of cancers of the colon, prostate, stomach, bladder, rectum ◆ Potential treatment and prevention of high blood pressure, upper respiratory tract infections

As far back as 1858, Louis Pasteur discovered that garlic cloves killed bacteria in a petri dish, and recent studies indicate that this popular seasoning could help fight major diseases such as high blood pressure and cancer.

Garlic is remarkably odour-free until you slice or press it. What happens next sounds like something straight out of a science-fiction movie. At blinding speed, an enzyme within garlic cloves called alliinase interacts with garlic's active ingredient, allicin – dubbed 'the world's most powerful antioxidant' by researchers at Canada's Queen's University – releasing the bulb's signature aroma and flavour and turning it into powerful sulphur compounds that, when eaten, neutralise any harmful free radicals in the body in nanoseconds. But does this speedy antioxidant action justify garlic's millennia-old reputation as a super-healer?

From colds to cancer In a study by the United Kingdom's aptly named Garlic Information Centre in 2001, people who took a garlic supplement daily for three months had just one-third as many colds as those who received a placebo. And their colds lasted for an average of just 1½ days, versus five days in the placebo group.

Meanwhile, the long-held notion that garlic may help prevent cancer is also gaining research support. Clues come from major population studies such as the 1994 Iowa Women's Health Study, in which University of Minnesota researchers tracked the health of 41,387 Iowa women for five years and asked about their intake of 127 common foods. Those who ate garlic (fresh or powdered) at least once a week were 35 per cent less likely to have developed colorectal cancer – a leading cause of death in the United States, Australia and Europe.

Thirteen years later, University of South Australia researcher Suong NT Ngo reviewed 20 lab and human studies looking at garlic and colorectal cancer and concluded that a high intake of raw or cooked garlic may, indeed, have a protective effect. Bolstering the good news: 11 lab studies that illuminated garlic's anticancer abilities, which include blocking cell growth, encouraging cancer cells to die off, boosting the activity of cancer-fighting enzymes and suppressing cancer-promoting enzymes. Lab studies also suggest garlic may slow or stop tumours in prostate, stomach and bladder tissue according to the American Institute for Cancer Research.

There's a long tradition of using garlic to repel evil spirits. Ancient Greeks tied cloves round newborns' necks to protect them.

Shown here for sale in a market in southern France, garlic has long been a mainstay of the healthy Mediterranean diet.

The heart of the matter In the 1990s, advertisements on TV and radio and in magazines and newspapers claimed that garlic supplements were 'clinically proven to lower cholesterol' – a promise disproven by later US government-sponsored research that compared raw, powdered and aged garlic extracts against a placebo and found no improvements. But if you have high blood pressure, a daily clove – or the equivalent in supplements – could nudge down your numbers by between two and five points. That's not enough to stop taking blood-pressure drugs, but everyone adopting a regular garlic habit could lower overall risk for blood-pressure-related deaths by 8–20 per cent, says researcher Karin Ried of the University of Adelaide. Well worth a little garlic breath!

OTHER NAME Stinking rose
ORIGIN Central Asia
PART USED Bulb

Traditional Wisdom

Pungent garlic's prowess as a remedy dates back at least 3500 years to the Ebers Papyrus, one of the oldest medical texts in existence – which lists garlic 22 times as an ingredient in curative recipes. Early Greeks used garlic as performance-enhancing supplements before going to war and before the original Olympic Games. Other medicinal uses for garlic through the ages include:

- Improving sexual desire and performance, according to the Talmud
- Curing ulcers and healing bites from dogs, snakes and spiders, according to the 1652 guide *The English Physician* by British herbalist Nicholas Culpeper (pictured right)
- Boosting immunity during Europe's plague of 1348–50
- Preventing stomach cancer, according to Native American healing traditions
- Increasing longevity, according to the 1609 book *The Englishman's Doctor*, which noted that garlic also has a downside: 'Bear with it though it maketh unsavory breath.'

What You CAN DO

Chop or press a clove of fresh garlic into a dish during cooking at least once a week – that was the 'dose' associated with lower risk for colon cancer in the Iowa Women's Health study. But to really harness this plant's blood-pressure-lowering potential, have a clove a day. Garlic supplements with standardised levels of allicin may be a good alternative if you'd like to avoid garlic breath. But be wary: reviews by the US watchdog group Center for Science in the Public Interest found that many supplements deliver far less allicin than their labels promise.

PINEAPPLE

Ananas comosus

MEDICAL BENEFITS ◆ Treatment for digestive problems, joint pain ◆ Potential supplementary treatment for allergy-induced asthma attacks, inflammatory bowel disease

Among some aboriginal groups in Central and South America, juicy pineapple is called *ananas,* meaning 'excellent fruit'. But this sweet, tropical treat is more than just excellent eating, thanks to a multitasking enzyme called bromelain.

Pineapple has been used as a folk remedy for indigestion for hundreds of years. In one 1605 history of the Caribbean region, historian Charles de Rochefort reported that pineapple 'fortifies the Stomack, cureth quesiness and causeth Appetite'. The active compound behind this use, bromelain, was first isolated in a Venezuelan laboratory by chemist Vicente Marcano in 1891. In the 1950s, researcher Ralph Heinecke of the Dole Pineapple Company opened the door to more extensive bromelain research when he discovered higher concentrations in pineapple stems than in the fruit. This led directly to the commercial production of bromelain supplements for therapeutic uses by 1957. By the early 1960s, several research teams were publishing studies looking at bromelain's potential to treat inflammation and fluid build-up (oedema). The work would lead in surprising directions.

Bromelain and cancer

Despite the claims of some alternative-medicine experts, bromelain is not a cancer cure. However, there's evidence that taking it (under a doctor's guidance) may help ease the painful side effects of standard cancer treatments, especially radiotherapy. In a 2001 study conducted by India's SGPT Cancer Hospital, people with head and neck cancers treated with radiation who took proteolytic enzymes such as bromelain reported less difficulty swallowing and less inflammation and ulceration of the mouth and digestive system.

Digestive benefits and more Bromelain's best-known talent is its ability to break down proteins – one reason this enzyme is a popular digestive aid. In a 2001 study at Chicago's Northwestern University Medical School, bromelain supplements even improved digestion in people who needed feeding tubes. And in a 2006 rat study at the University of Technology in Sydney, Australia, bromelain also improved gastrointestinal 'motility' – getting the digestive system moving again.

In laboratory studies, the pineapple enzyme (really a collection of enzymes) also demonstrates anti-inflammatory and pain-relieving effects, in large part, according to a 1988 study at Japan's Tohoku University, by reducing levels of bradkykinin, a peptide that makes blood

Leading producers of pineapple include the Philippines, Thailand, Costa Rica and Brazil.

vessels swell. As a result, bromelain is a widely used alternative remedy for people with osteo-arthritis and soft-tissue injuries, such as from playing sports.

In one 2000 study sponsored by Germany's Mucos Pharma – manufacturer of a supplement containing bromelain combined with the enzymes trypsin and rutin – people with knee osteoarthritis who took the supplement daily for four weeks reported a reduction in pain on a par with study participants who received the pain reliever diclofenac. And when researchers from the University of Reading in the United Kingdom reviewed published and unpublished studies of bromelain's effects on osteoarthritis in 2004, they identified evidence of benefits for knee and hip pain.

Cures of the future Bromelain's ability to ease inflammation is now leading researchers to test its abilities against other health conditions, with promising results. In a 2012 University of Connecticut mouse study, bromelain eased inflammation caused by allergy-induced asthma attacks; researcher Eric R Secor Jr says that in the future bromelain may be an effective add-on therapy for easing these attacks in humans.

Meanwhile, Duke University gastroenterology researcher Jane E Onken has recently inves-tigated bromelain's anti-inflammatory action as a potential therapy for ulcerative colitis and Crohn's disease, two types of inflammatory bowel disease. This test tube study suggests that bromelain discourages the release of inflammatory chemicals called cytokines and chemokines from diseased tissue.

Recommended doses of bromelain extract range from 160 to 1000 mg a day, divided into four doses. However, a cup of fresh or frozen pineapple may be even better than a pill: in one recent study, that much pineapple had 13 times more active bromelain than a supplement. For osteoarthritis, however, combination supplements containing bromelain, trypsin and rutin have been shown to be an effective treatment. If you are allergic to kiwi, papaya or natural rubber latex be careful with bromelain and pineapple; and if you're allergic to pineapple do not take bromelain. Also, bromelain may raise bleeding risk if you're taking aspirin or a blood-thinning drug. And skip it if you're using an antibiotic in the tetracycline family, as bromelain can increase blood levels of these medications.

OTHER NAME Ananas
ORIGIN Central and South America
PARTS USED Fruit, stem, juice

BROCCOLI

Brassica oleracea, Cymosa group

MEDICAL BENEFITS ◆ Protects against cancers of the prostate, lung, colon, cervix, pancreas, breast ◆ May prevent heart inflammation, atherosclerosis

Many people are put off broccoli by its bitter, peppery flavour. But the chemicals that produce that taste are the same ones that protect against several kinds of cancer and make this vegetable something of a wonder food.

When you cut or chew a piece of broccoli, you start a chain reaction: an enzyme called myrosinase breaks down chemicals in the broccoli cells called glucosinolates. One by-product is an organic compound called sulforaphane, which is present in all brassicas or cruciferous vegetables (such as cabbage, cauliflower, Brussels sprouts, kohlrabi, turnip, rutabaga and kale) but particularly rich in broccoli. Sulforaphane contains sulphur and is partly responsible for broccoli's pungent aroma and flavour. About 20 years ago, Professor Paul Talalay and his colleagues at Johns Hopkins School of Medicine discovered that it also has some remarkable effects on cancer cells in animals.

A stimulating substance At the time, the idea of being able to prevent cancer was controversial. But for Talalay it made sense. He knew that every living plant contains chemicals that protect it against a barrage of attacks from predators and infection, and he thought that, by eating fruit and vegetables, humans might also benefit from this disease-fighting mechanism. Focusing on brassicas, the researchers tested more than a dozen vegetables for the presence of beneficial compounds. They discovered that sulforaphane in particular, when added to cultured rat liver cells, stimulated the cell's ability to neutralise cancer-causing chemicals.

When Talalay and colleagues published the structure of sulforaphane in 1992 in the *Proceedings of the National Academy of Sciences,*

As well as sulforaphane, broccoli is rich in phytochemicals, fibre, folate, minerals and vitamins, especially vitamins C, K and A.

in CLOSE-UP

Sulforaphane benefits the body in several ways. It inhibits the activity of an enzyme called HDAC, which can interfere with beneficial gene activity, and it also blocks the formation of fibres that enable cancer cells to divide, thereby preventing those cells from proliferating. And while the formation of cancerous cells usually turns off a process called DNA methylation – which is vital for normal cell development – sulforaphane switches it back on.

Experts suggest eating about 150 g (5 oz) – essentially a large cupful – a day of broccoli to get the full health benefits. If you balk at this bulk, try 2 tablespoonfuls of broccoli sprouts a day instead – they contain up to 50 times the level of protective compounds as the adult plant. Most broccoli supplements are not effective, as they lack the crucial myrosinase enzyme.

it created a sensation. Within months, health food stores were selling powdered broccoli as a new wonder weapon against cancer, and the story even made it to the front page of *The New York Times*.

Cruciferous compounds Since that time, many studies have shown that glucosinolates and their breakdown products, such as sulforaphane, stop cancer cells from proliferating. In cell cultures, sulforaphane especially has been shown to cause the destruction of many types of human cancer cells, including pancreatic, colon, prostate and cervical cancer cells. It inhibits the growth of pancreatic tumours in mice, and early studies also suggest it may protect heart tissue from inflammation and atherosclerosis.

However, much of this early research was done in laboratory animals or in cell cultures, where sulforaphane is added directly to a dish of cancer cells. What's far more complex to unravel is whether eating broccoli will suppress tumour growth in a living person. One of the first studies to provide strong evidence that diet *does* have an effect was a 2008 UK study by the Institute for Food Research. The researchers found that men who consumed more than one portion of cruciferous vegetables each week had a lower incidence of prostate cancer.

Also in 2008, a study at the Roswell Park Cancer Institute found that smokers and former smokers who regularly ate broccoli and its relatives were less likely to develop lung cancer. A smoker may ingest 500 or so chemicals in a single inhalation, and it may be that sulforaphane or another chemical stimulates enzymes to break down carcinogens in smoke.

ORIGIN Asia, but now grown worldwide
PART USED Flower head

In one 2012 study, breast cancer survivors who consumed high levels of cruciferous vegetables had a significantly reduced level of disease recurrence and mortality.

Pioneering researcher Paul Talalay examines some samples of broccoli sprouts.

CHILLI PEPPER

Capsicum spp.

MEDICAL BENEFITS ◆ Treatment for osteoarthritis, rheumatoid arthritis, diabetic neuropathy, postherpetic neuralgia ◆ Potential treatment for nerve pain associated with HIV/AIDS ◆ Traditional remedy for nasal congestion

A sprinkle of chilli pepper gives vegetables, meat and beans a red-hot kick. But applied to human skin, pepper's active ingredient, capsaicin, cools off the fiery agonies of arthritis and nerve pain.

Native to the Americas, the *Capsicum* genus includes numerous species of flowering plants that produce large red, yellow or green fruits. These include bell peppers (also known as capsicums or, simply, peppers) and the spicy, capsaicin-containing varieties known as chilli peppers.

Chilli peppers have long been recognised as much more than a mere spice. Native Americans rubbed chillis on their gums to ease toothaches. And the Incas reportedly burned dried chillis to fend off invading Spaniards – by blinding them (just as today capsaicin-laced self-defence sprays are used by some law enforcement officials to repel attackers). Carried back to Europe from Central and South America in the fifteenth and sixteenth centuries, hot peppers were grown in monastery medicinal gardens in Moravia as early as 1566. By the 1850s, advertisements in Ireland's *Dublin Free Press* were touting a red-pepper extract as a toothache remedy.

Source of the heat Capsaicin, the chemical responsible for the fireworks in your mouth when you bite into a chilli pepper, was first isolated from the fruit in its pure form in 1876, by British chemist John Clough Thresh. Early use of hot peppers as a pain remedy relied on the fact that capsaicin creates a burning sensation on contact. This acts as a 'counterirritant' – a fast, welcome distraction from a nasty toothache, for example.

But it took nearly 130 years for researchers to uncover and harness capsaicin's unique ability to soak into pain-sensing nerve fibres

High-tech pepper patch

Painful and difficult-to-treat nerve pains associated with shingles infections (called postherpetic neuralgia) and with HIV/AIDS are no match for a new patch containing 8 per cent capsaicin. Applied to affected skin and left in place for 60 minutes, the patch eased postherpetic neuralgia pain by 30 per cent or more for 40 per cent of those who tried it during a 2008 study of 402 people at the University of Wisconsin–Madison. High-dose capsaicin seems to stunt pain receptors on nerves; these can grow back, but the treatment can be repeated every three months, up to three times a year. Ask your doctor for information.

Chillis are a good source of vitamin C. However, eating large amounts may cause nausea, stomach pain and diarrhoea.

After harvesting, women in Orissa, India, sort chilli peppers into rows.

and shut them down, turning off aches for weeks or months at a time. In 1979, researcher Tony Yaksh at the Mayo Clinic discovered in laboratory studies that repeated applications of concentrated capsaicin depleted levels of 'substance P', a neuropeptide within nerve fibres that spurs inflammation and irritation. Without substance P on board, nerves can't transmit pain signals to the brain.

This led to the development of ache-easing, over-the-counter capsaicin creams that are now widely used by people with arthritis or diabetic neuropathy – nerve damage that often occurs in feet and fingertips in people with high blood glucose levels. In one 1991 Case Western Reserve University study of 101 people with osteoarthritis or rheumatoid arthritis, those who used capsaicin cream daily said pain dropped by between 33 and 57 per cent after four weeks. When 252 people with diabetic neuropathy used capsaicin cream or a placebo for eight weeks in a 1991 US study, the capsaicin users reported a 58 per cent improvement in pain relief.

OTHER NAMES None, but varieties include cayenne, jalapeño, tabasco
ORIGIN Central and South America
PART USED Vegetable

What You CAN DO

For osteoarthritis, rheumatoid arthritis and diabetic neuropathy, apply an over-the-counter cream containing 0.025 per cent capsaicin to aching joints or feet four times a day for three to four weeks. About 40 per cent of people who try this experience stinging, burning or skin redness at first, but these effects fade as capsaicin desensitises nerves, say experts from London's Whipps Cross University Hospital. If you're experiencing nerve pain called postherpetic neuralgia after a bout of shingles, try a cream containing 0.075 per cent capsaicin. And next time you have a cold, sprinkle chilli (flakes, powder or finely chopped fresh chilli) onto your food – its heat will stimulate drainage from the nasal and sinus passages.

CITRUS FRUITS

Citrus spp.

MEDICAL BENEFITS ◆ Prevention of cholera, peptic ulcers, scurvy, stroke; cancers of the mouth, skin, lungs, breast, stomach, colon

Aboard the great sailing fleets of the sixteenth to eighteenth centuries, scurvy killed more sailors than battles, storms and other illnesses combined, until, in 1753, a British surgeon prescribed a simple preventive measure: a daily dose of citrus.

A condition caused by a deficiency in vitamin C, scurvy took a terrible toll among early mariners. One sailor described how, for example, it 'rotted all my gums … [and made] my thighs and lower legs … black and gangrenous'. The illness really came into the spotlight after the deaths of 1400 sailors during a British expedition in 1740–42. A few years later, British Royal Navy surgeon James Lind undertook an experiment when the disease struck the *HMS Salisbury*, giving sick men oranges and lemons, vinegar, cider, sea water, nutmeg or 'elixir of vitriol' (a mix of alcohol, sulphuric acid and aromatics). After just six days, the citrus-eaters recovered enough to resume work. And within a few decades, citrus juice – often the lime juice that earned British sailors the nickname 'Limeys' – was officially added to sailors' rations.

Scurvy is rare today. But research is revealing new, life-saving properties that make oranges, lemons, limes and other citrus the 'must-eat' – or 'must-sip' – fruits of the twenty-first century.

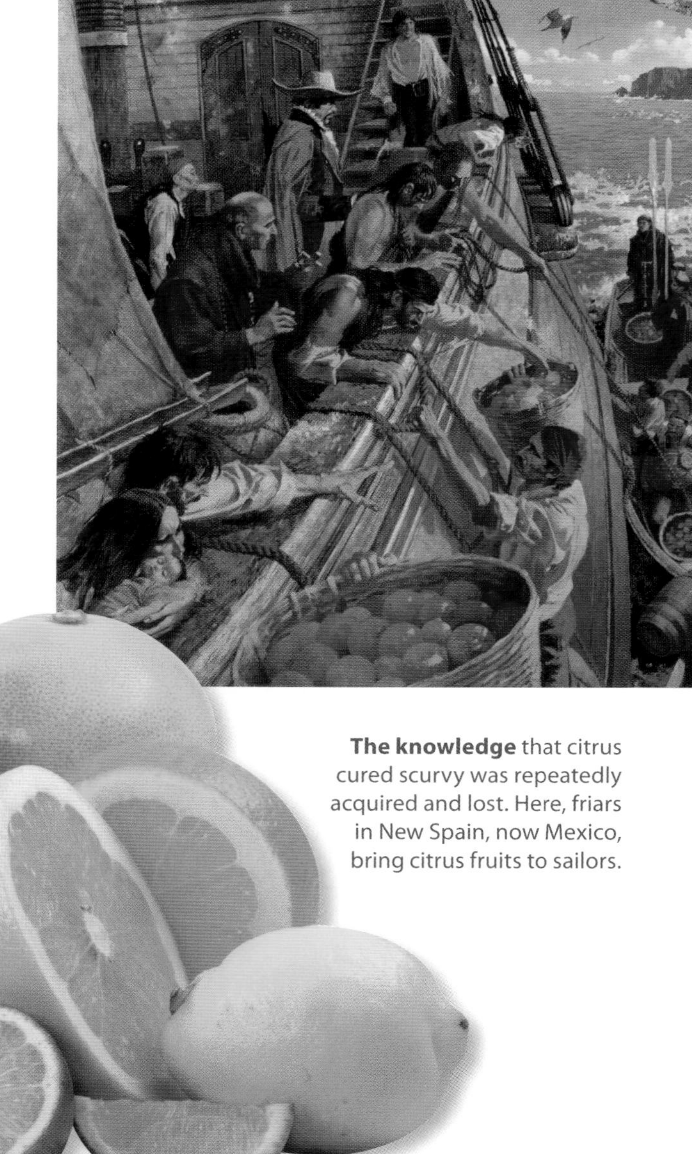

The knowledge that citrus cured scurvy was repeatedly acquired and lost. Here, friars in New Spain, now Mexico, bring citrus fruits to sailors.

Citrus species are diverse but all have a thick skin lined with pith protecting moist segments holding seeds.

To harness the full health benefits of citrus, have a serving or two of fresh fruit or juice daily rather than taking a pill. In fact, you can skip vitamin C pills entirely: a medium-sized orange or a half-cup (4-oz) glass of juice provides more than the 75–90 mg recommended for good health by the US Institute of Medicine. But endurance athletes and people who do physical work outdoors in cold environments – such as marathon runners, skiers and soldiers – may get some protection from the common cold by taking 250–1000 mg of vitamin C daily, says one authoritative 2007 scientific review by the University of Helsinki.

A 2012 UK study found regular citrus consumption could cut stroke risk by almost 20 per cent.

The benefits of fresh Citrus is of course one of the richest food sources of vitamin C. This potent antioxidant disarms rogue molecules called free radicals inside cells before they can damage DNA, boost inflammation and raise cancer risk. One orange delivers all the vitamin C most people need in a day, but, unlike a vitamin C tablet, a juicy grapefruit or glass of orange juice also contains 60 cell-protecting, inflammation-soothing flavonoids that work together to reduce risk for cancer and strokes, something a pill cannot do. One cancer-fighter called limonin sticks around in the body for up to 24 hours, according to a 2005 study conducted for the US Agricultural Research Service. This longevity may help keep cancer cells suppressed, so they cannot reproduce.

After the vitamin C supplement craze of the 1970s, 1980s and 1990s – spurred by publication of two-time Nobel laureate Linus Pauling's books claiming vitamin C cured the common cold (a claim dismissed by later studies) – Italian researcher Serena Guarnieri of the University of Milan decided to test pills against real fruit juice in an ingenious head-to-head study in 2007. Volunteers drank orange juice, plain sugar water or sugar water spiked with 150 mg of vitamin C, then each had their blood tested several times. After sipping orange juice, DNA damage was 18 per cent less after 3 hours and 16 per cent less after 24 hours – but the other groups saw no protective benefits.

ORIGIN Asia
PART USED Fruit

Citrus protection Vitamin C cannot cure cancer. But munching or sipping citrus regularly could lower your risk, say researchers from Milan's Mario Negri Institute. In a 2010 study, they compared the eating habits of 12,956 people with a variety of cancers to those of people who did not have cancer. The verdict? Consuming citrus regularly slashed risk by 53 per cent for oral cancers, 18 per cent for colorectal cancers, 58 per cent for esophageal cancers and 31 per cent for stomach cancer.

Limes in a time of cholera

Lime juice protected British sailors against scurvy in the 1800s – and also saved villagers in the West African country of Guinea-Bissau from cholera during a 1996 outbreak. Scientists from that country and from Scandinavia, aware of earlier Brazilian research finding that the acidity in lime juice could kill cholera bacteria in food, swung into action during the epidemic. In areas where residents were urged to mix as little as a quarter-cup of lime juice into the traditional peanut sauce served over rice, rates of cholera infection fell by two-thirds.

TURMERIC

Curcuma longa

MEDICAL BENEFITS ◆ Potential treatment for Alzheimer's disease, cancer ◆ Traditional treatment for muscle pain, wounds, eczema, arthritis, heartburn, stomach ulcers, gallstones, inflammation, cancer

This golden spice has long been prized for its healing properties in Ayurvedic medicine, and in modern studies shows promise against Alzheimer's disease and cancer.

In 2012, researchers at Sweden's Linköping University announced a major breakthrough: an experimental drug based on curcumin, the active compound in turmeric, extended the lives and improved the behaviour of fruit flies with an insect version of Alzheimer's disease. Dozens of earlier lab and animal studies had pointed the way, outlining curcumin's ability to slow or stop the processes that lead to Alzheimer's disease; in one 2006 test tube study from the University of California Los Angeles, for example, curcumin had spurred macrophages to break up the signature, beta-amyloid plaques of Alzheimer's. And other, more recent research has since suggested that curcumin can protect against this degenerative disease by fending off plaques as well as cooling inflammation.

in CLOSE-UP

In 2009, University of Michigan chemist Ayyalusamy Ramamoorthy used a high-tech imaging technique called solid-state NMR spectroscopy to take a closer look at how turmeric might protect cells. Ramamoorthy discovered that molecules of curcumin insert themselves into cell walls. Once there, they act like traffic police, regulating many of the actions of the cell membrane in ways that he suspects increase resistance to microbes that cause disease. Meanwhile, researchers at Oregon State University found in a 2012 study that curcumin also boosts levels of a protein called CAMP (cathelicidin antimicrobial peptide) that plays an important role in the body's immune system.

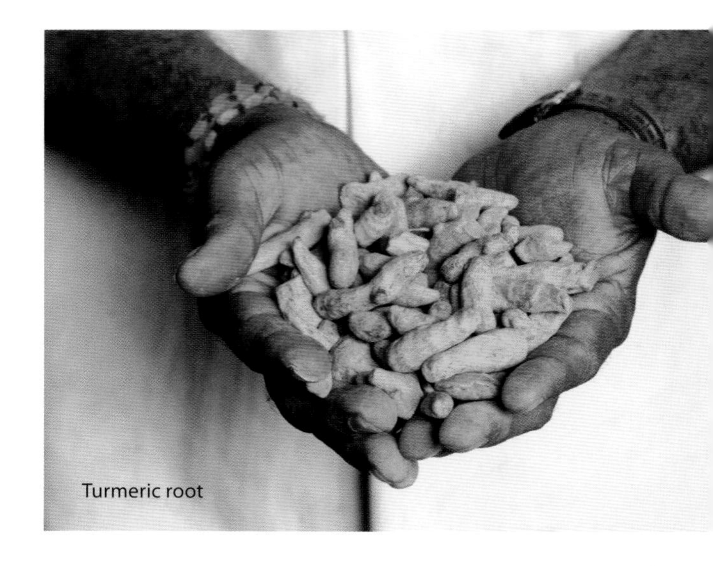
Turmeric root

Protection in your pantry? Curcumin may also have the ability to protect against some forms of cancer and to prevent the growth and spread of existing cancers. Recently, researcher Beatrice Bachmeier at Munich's Ludwig-Maximilians University found that curcumin could inhibit the spread of prostate cancer and breast cancer. In these cases, the compound seems to work by reducing levels of inflammatory cancer-promoting 'cytokine' compounds. This might also mean that curcumin could play a role in making current cancer treatments, such as chemotherapy and radiation, more effective, allowing standard doses to be reduced and limiting side effects. A research centre at the University of Leicester, England, is also pioneering research into curcumin's effects on treatment-resistant prostate cancer.

Delivery solutions One challenge with human studies is getting curcumin past the stomach, where digestive juices diminish this compound, leaving little to be absorbed into the blood. One scientist has come up with a solution, however: a microscopic capsule that survives this acidic

OTHER NAMES Turmeric root, Indian saffron, 'Holy powder'
ORIGIN India
PARTS USED Root, rhizomes

environment. In a 2009 rat study, Koji Wada of Japan's Kagoshima University found that encapsulating curcumin in 'nano-sized' bubbles of fats increased blood levels of this compound fourfold. Another solution, tested in 2010 at the University of South Dakota, involved delivering microscopically tiny doses of curcumin directly into cancer cells. These tiny pellets, called Nano-CUR, were inserted into therapy-resistant ovarian cancer cells in a test-tube study. The result? The cells became more sensitive to chemotherapy with the drug cisplatin and to radiation, so that lower treatment doses effectively suppressed the growth of the cancer cells.

But even the direct route *can* work. In a 2011 study, University of California researcher Marilene Wang asked 21 people with head and neck cancers to give samples of their saliva before and after chewing two curcumin tablets totalling 1000 mg. One hour later, another sample of saliva was taken. Wang measured levels of cancer-enhancing cytokines and found they were reduced.

Further human trials are now underway. One at Australia's Edith Cowan University is looking at whether taking curcumin supplements for a year will stave off early signs of Alzheimer's. And University of Leicester researchers are testing to see if curcumin can improve drug response in people with advanced bowel cancer.

Until more detailed studies from human trials are published, the best option is to use turmeric in cooking. Curcumin supplements are widely available, but there is little agreement on what constitutes a safe dose. Too much curcumin could cause stomach upset, nausea, dizziness or diarrhoea. Turmeric and curcumin supplements are not recommended if you have gall bladder disease (it could worsen symptoms) or are having surgery in the near future (it can thin the blood).

Considered a symbol of purity, turmeric is used in many Indian rituals, such as this one at the Vandimala Temple in Chengannur.

GUAR BEAN

Cyamopsis tetragonoloba

MEDICAL BENEFITS ◆ Potential treatment for irritable bowel syndrome, constipation ◆ Potential add-on treatment for high blood glucose and high cholesterol

Guar gum, made from ground guar bean, is widely used to improve the texture, flavour and shelf life of many processed foods. But scientific research says it also has potential to improve a wide variety of health conditions, too.

The guar bean plant is grown in India and Pakistan as a vegetable and cattle fodder. The bean contains large amounts of galactomannan gum, which turns into a gel when guar bean is ground into a powder then mixed with water.

Relieving digestive discomfort The latest on the health benefits of guar gum comes from the Gastroenterology Unit at Italy's University of Genoa, where, in a series of studies, digestive-disease expert Edoardo Giannini added small amounts of this soluble fibre to the diets of a group of people with irritable bowel syndrome (IBS). Giannini's first study, published in the journal *Nutrition*, attracted worldwide attention because the guar gum appeared to ease both the diarrhoea and constipation that can come with IBS and soothed abdominal pain.

In a second study, Giannini found that adding guar gum to one of the newest IBS therapies – an antibiotic that knocks out overgrowths of bacteria in the small intestine – wiped out 91 per cent of errant bacteria, compared to 86 per cent with drugs alone. The guar gum advantage? It could be the fact that this fibre also reduces intestinal 'transit time', moving stools – and presumably unwanted bacteria – out more swiftly. Other studies show that guar

Guar gum is sold in powdered form as a thickener and binder for baking and cooking and is often used in gluten-free recipes. Add 2 teaspoons for every cup of flour in a recipe. If you'd like to try it as a supplement, the typical dose used in research studies, such as those in people with diabetes conducted at the University of Helsinki, is 5 g (1 teaspoon) mixed into water, juice or milk three times a day. But talk with your doctor first; guar gum can decrease the effectiveness of some birth control pills, antibiotics and diabetes medications.

In a study by the University of Faisalaba Pakistan, levels of LDL ('bad') cholester in rats fed chapatis made with guar gu fell by 30 per cent.

gum can help ease constipation and also promotes release of a natural, bowel-soothing lubricant called mucin, too.

Lowering cholesterol In the 1980s and 1990s, scientists in Finland took a closer look at guar gum powder's effects in people with diabetes and high cholesterol, with intriguing results. University of Kuopio researchers asked 39 people with type 2 diabetes to have a teaspoon of guar gum, stirred into milk, juice or water, three times a day. After 13 months, their total cholesterol levels had fallen by up to 7 per cent. In a pair of similar studies at the University of Helsinki involving 32 people with type 1 and 2 diabetes, guar gum lowered blood glucose after meals and improved long-term blood glucose control – which can lower risk for diabetes-related complications such as vision loss and kidney failure. The take-home lesson? According to lead researcher Helena Vuorinen-Markkola, guar gum should never replace diabetes medications, but could be an adjunct treatment.

OTHER NAMES Cyamopsis gum, jaguar gum
ORIGIN India, Pakistan
PARTS USED Seeds

Feed the good bugs

Bacteria aren't just illness-causing villains. A growing stack of research shows that maintaining a healthy balance of 'good bugs', or probiotics, in your digestive system could help ward off gastrointestinal problems, discourage the development of allergies in children and even influence how much you weigh and how well you feel (see. p. 291). One key to nurturing the beneficial bugs: feed them well with 'prebiotics' such as guar gum. Researchers from Italy's University of Genoa found in a 2006 study that people who took guar gum daily had more of two types of good-bug probiotics, *Lactobacillus* and Bifidobacteria, in their intestinal tract. Findings were similar in a study by the United Kingdom's University of Reading, where 31 volunteers munched biscuits laced with guar gum or a placebo. The guar group's levels of good bugs went up.

An Indian worker checks the quality of the guar bean harvest. The beans are dehusked and ground to powder for making the gum.

India and Pakistan are the main sources of guar beans, though small crops are also grown in places such as Australia and China.

LIQUORICE

Glycyrrhiza glabra

MEDICAL BENEFITS ◆ Potential treatment for indigestion, hepatitis C, memory loss, cancer, skin infection ◆ Traditional treatment for stomach ulcers, heartburn, indigestion, toothache, fever, asthma, bronchitis, coughs

For thousands of years, liquorice has had a well-deserved reputation for soothing irritations such as sore throats and upset tummies and relieving congestion. Now it appears it might also have other, yet more powerful properties.

Unlike the anise-flavoured black liquorice that is sold in confectionery shops and grocery stores, an old-fashioned liquorice stick is actually the dried root of the liquorice plant. Sink your teeth into one and what happens next just might surprise you. Hidden inside is a super-sweet compound called glycyrrhizin. This and dozens more chemicals lend this ancient herb its healing medical potential – and a few notable downsides.

Stomach protection In the middle of the twentieth century, liquorice was for a time considered a natural and effective remedy for stomach ulcers, after Dutch physician FE Revers used it to treat his patients. Intrigued, researchers in the 1950s discovered that liquorice compounds worked by triggering the release of stomach-protecting mucus and by protecting the stomach's lining from the ravages of pepsin, a powerful digestive enzyme.

It has since been shown, however, that long-term exposure to the glycyrrhizin in liquorice can boost blood pressure, cause water and sodium retention and lower levels of potassium in the body, making it unsafe for extended use.

OTHER NAMES Liquorice root, sweet root, sweetwood, Yashtimadhu (Ayurveda), *gan-cao* (Chinese)
ORIGIN Asia, Mediterranean
PART USED Root

Liquorice root

And although researchers in India have experimented successfully with a safer, glycyrrhizin-free liquorice to ease ulcer pain, today most people take antibiotics to wipe out the bacteria that cause stomach ulcers, and most scientists have switched their attention to other exciting healing possibilities in liquorice.

Stalling cancer In a lab study conducted at India's Roland Institute of Pharmaceutical Sciences in 2011, for example, substances in liquorice were shown to stand up to cancer. The compounds licochalcone-A, glabridin and licocoumarone halted the growth of, or killed, breast cancer, prostate cancer and leukaemia cells. Glycyrrhizin and glycyrrhizic acid also put the brakes on the formation of tumours in skin, colon, liver, uterine and breast cancers.

This use of liquorice has not been widely tested in humans, but one herbal prostate-cancer formula that contained liquorice, PC-SPES (no longer available), was shown in human studies to slow the progression of some prostate

A perennial legume, liquorice can grow densely, producing long, oval leaves and purple-tipped pale flowers.

in CLOSE-UP

Glycyrrhiza glabra's **antistress and anti-inflammatory effects may do the brain good. When older men took a liquorice extract containing the compound carbenoxolone during a 2004 study at the University of Edinburgh, verbal memory and fluency (the ability to put thoughts into words), improved. Carbenoxolone seems to help by inhibiting a brain enzyme that helps make stress hormones, which contribute to age-related brain changes. Scientists say more research is needed but that a growing stack of lab research backs liquorice's potential for memory enhancement. In one mouse study, for example, animals that received liquorice extract excelled at learning and memory tests.**

cancers. Certainly, liquorice is no substitute for conventional cancer therapy, but scientists think it has potential – enough for researchers to title a 2009 report in *The Journal of Clinical Investigation* 'Can licorice lick colon cancer?'

Fighting infection In the future, liquorice could also be a mainstay in medicine's arsenal of infection-fighters. A 2010 University of Texas study revealed that glycyrrhizin can help damaged skin create bacteria-fighting proteins called antimicrobial peptides, which are an important defence against infection. This could lead to treatments to counter antibiotic-resistant infections, such as those that sometimes occur in severe burns and can be fatal.

Perhaps most surprisingly, this sweet root could even be a dentist's dream. Two liquorice compounds, licoricidin and licorisoflavan A, have been shown, in lab studies, to kill off two major types of cavity-causing bacteria and three types of bacteria that fuel gum disease.

What You CAN DO

Peeled liquorice root is available in dried and powdered forms and as capsules, tablets and liquid extracts. The safest dose for most adults is 1–5 g of liquorice daily containing 1–10 mg of the active ingredient glycyrrhizin, for four to six weeks. But note that in large amounts and in people with hypertension or heart, kidney or lung disease, liquorice containing glycyrrhizin can cause adverse reactions. Choosing deglycyrrhizinated liquorice (DGL) – liquorice with the glycyrrhizin removed – can lower the risk of serious side effects.

TOMATO

Lycopersicon esculentum

MEDICAL BENEFITS ◆ Helps protect against cancers of the lung, stomach and prostate, heart disease, dementia, bone loss ◆ Possible protection against cancers of the cervix, breast, mouth, pancreas, oesophagus, colon, rectum

A hearty bowl of spaghetti with tomato sauce, a slice of pizza or a refreshing glass of tomato juice provides tasty and satisfying gratification at meal-time or snack-time – and a deeper benefit, especially for men.

Evidence continues to mount that enjoying tomato products several times a week reduces risk for prostate cancer and possibly other cancers. Much of the credit goes to a hard-working carotenoid called lycopene, though it seems it doesn't work its magic alone.

Early indications that tomatoes might douse prostate-cancer risk came in 1989, from California's Loma Linda University, after a six-year study of 14,000 men found that those who munched the most tomatoes had 'significantly decreased prostate cancer risk'. Other studies that tracked men's health and eating habits found a similar trend. When Harvard School of Public Health researcher Edward Giovannucci monitored the diets of 47,000 men for 12 years, he found that those who had tomato products two or more times a week were 25 per cent less likely to develop prostate cancer and 34 per cent less likely to develop aggressive prostate cancer than men with the lowest intakes.

These dramatic results led to a flurry of interest in lycopene, an antioxidant found also in watermelon and pink grapefruit but at especially high levels in tomato. Supplement makers flooded health food stores with lycopene supplements claiming to 'support prostate health'. Yet as so frequently happens, these single-nutrient, high-dose pills fell short of their promise, with few studies finding real benefits.

Instead, a new picture is emerging in which lycopene acts as a 'team player' along with related substances found in crimson-hued fruits and vegetables – known collectively as 'the red family'. According to the American Institute for Cancer Research, compounds in tomatoes,

in CLOSE-UP

Test-tube studies suggest that lycopene works against cancer in many different ways. In one University of California, Los Angeles, study, lycopene restored cell-signalling capabilities that slowed the growth of cancer cells. A 2010 study by researchers from the Catholic University School of Medicine in Rome found that lycopene triggered chemical changes that induced self-destruction in tumour cells. And a 2012 study run by the University of Portsmouth, England, found that lycopene disrupted the ability of cancer cells to link with cells lining blood vessels; without access to a blood supply, cancer cells cannot grow.

Though seen as typically Mediterranean, tomatoes originated in South America, only reaching Europe in the early 1500s.

watermelon, red peppers and other red foods have in lab studies stopped the proliferation of cancers of the breast, lungs and endometrium (lining of the uterus).

Benefits for bones and heart But don't pigeonhole tomatoes as just cancer-fighters. In a surprising 2011 study by St Michael's Hospital in Toronto, Canada, 23 women who followed an experimental tomato- and lycopene-deficient diet for four weeks showed troubling changes in bone tissue. Lead researcher Erin S Mackinnon concluded that a daily dose of lycopene may therefore be 'beneficial in reducing the risk of osteoporosis'. And a 2011 review of 55 lycopene studies by Karin Ried from Australia's University of Adelaide concluded that 25 mg of lycopene a day – the amount in a cup of tomato soup or tomato juice – could reduce heart-threatening LDL cholesterol by as much as 10 per cent.

OTHER NAME Love apple
ORIGIN Western South America
PART USED Fruit

Enjoy cooked tomato products regularly. In one 2002 study at the Harvard School of Public Health, men who ate two servings per week had a 23 per cent lower risk of prostate cancer than those who rarely ate tomato products. Classic, deep-red tomatoes are rich in a form of the beneficial antioxidant lycopene called all-trans lycopene; but in one 2009 study for the US Department of Agriculture, researcher Betty Burri found that orange- and tangerine-hued varieties were a better source of tetra-cis-lycopene, a more readily absorbed form. Cooked tomato products, such as sauce or stewed tomatoes, contain the highest levels of available lycopene; and eating them with a small amount of fat, such as olive oil, enhances absorption according to the American Cancer Society. Skip lycopene supplements: in a rat study conducted in 2003 at the University of Illinois Urbana-Champaign, tomato powder reduced cancer risk while lycopene supplements did not. Researchers suspect vitamins and minerals in tomatoes work with lycopene to shield cells from cancer.

ENGINEERING BENEFITS

While the genetic engineering of food plants has many conservationists and consumers worried about its impact on health and the environment, certain advances in this field could significantly improve the lives of peoples in the developing world.

Genetically modified (GM) foods, also known as genetically engineered (GE) or transgenic foods, contain DNA from other organisms and are normally created to provide a significant advantage in terms of yield or health effects. And the benefits of such foods *are* compelling. Among them, according to the US Human Genome Project, are food products with better taste and quality, higher nutrient levels, faster growing times, better yields and improved resistance to disease, pests and herbicides. This can translate, proponents say, into better health and more secure sources of food to feed the world's burgeoning population – expected to reach 9 billion by 2050.

A price to pay? There are also concerns, however. While humans have, in effect, been genetically altering food plants for thousands of years through selective breeding, taking the process to this next level worries some. In the United States, an estimated 60–70 per cent of processed foods on grocery store shelves contain at least one ingredient from a GM source – most often from soya beans or corn. Could these transgenic edibles trigger new types of allergies or lead to unintended and unforeseen health consequences? Will GM crops threaten the natural genetic diversity of the world's food supply? Could the widespread use of GM seed for crops put economic control of food production into the hands of a few large corporations? While questions such as these linger, the advantages are more clear-cut.

Golden rice One of the most impressive GM success stories is golden rice. Developed by Ingo Potrykus of Switzerland's ETH Zurich University and Peter Beyer from Germany's University of Freiburg, it contains not only the full genetic code of everyday rice (*Oryza sativa*) but also bits of DNA from bacteria and even daffodils. As a result, as this rice grows, it develops a golden hue as it accumulates beta-carotene, an anti-oxidant nutrient that the body converts into vitamin A. Researchers estimate golden rice can save the lives of 1 million children every year by bolstering their disease resistance and save the eyesight of an additional 350,000 by correcting vitamin A deficiencies that damage the eyes and lead to blindness.

Banana bonuses In Uganda, where the plantain, a type of banana, is an important food, with residents eating nearly 1 kg (2 lb) apiece per day, government researchers are using genes from onions, dahlias and other plants to make bananas resistant to fungal infections,

SMART CHOICES

Given widespread concerns about the safety and environmental effects of some GM crops, many consumers are demanding that such foods be clearly labelled. In Australia and the European Union, this is already the law. But in the United States, which grows 53 per cent of the world's transgenic foods, it is not the case. Although some food makers voluntarily label 'non-GM' foods, there's no third-party verification of these claims. Consumers can, however, steer clear of GM foods by choosing certified organic products, which must always be made without GM ingredients. To avoid meat from animals raised on GM feed, look for labels stating '100% grass-fed', and opt for wild over farm-raised fish. Some people also choose to avoid altogether products commonly made from GM crops, such as corn, soya beans, canola and cottonseed.

most notably a devastating disease called black sigatoka. It's a major threat to the Cavendish banana, which is also popular in the United States, Britain and Australia, as well as native bananas and plantains in Asia, Africa and Latin America. And another team in Uganda is working on creating GM bananas that are resistant to nematodes, weevils, bacterial wilt and a mould called Panama disease, as well as looking at genetic changes that will yield higher levels of vitamin A and iron. Taking a different approach, experts from the Bhabha Atomic Research Centre in Mumbai, India, say that bananas could soon be modified to deliver a hepatitis B vaccine to millions of people.

Custom crops University of Naples researchers experimented in 2011 with transgenic, salt-resistant tomatoes that could be grown on some of the 10 million ha (24.7 million acres) of farmland lost globally each year to high saline levels caused by irrigation. If grown commercially, the salt-proof plant would clean the soil while producing a nonsalty tomato for eating.

In 2012, Alan Fogelman of the University of California, Los Angeles, reported at the annual meeting of the American Heart Association that lab mice that ate tomatoes engineered to produce a peptide that acts like 'good' HDL cholesterol experienced a reduction in levels of heart-threatening plaque in their arteries.

Left: In Brazil, the Monsanto company is trialling soya bean crops that have been modified to make them resistant to certain insect pests.

Right: As a major staple food in the developing world, the banana could be a useful delivery vehicle for medical benefits.

Right: A scientist compares a normal rice plant (right) with a GM version that supplies additional vital minerals.

Left: This corn has been modified to make it resistant to weedkillers – a more controversial form of genetic engineering.

Above: Golden rice tissue cultures are grown in laboratories at research facilities for testing.

PEPPERMINT

Mentha x piperita

MEDICAL BENEFITS ◆ Treatment for indigestion, irritable bowel syndrome, coughs, headache ◆ Traditional treatment for digestive problems, nausea, cholera, colds, cramps, bloating

Modern studies are confirming that this age-old herbal remedy – named for the hapless Greek nymph Minthe, who was turned into a plant by a jealous goddess – has potent properties.

A highly versatile herb long used to flavour sweets, toothpaste and mouthwashes among other things, peppermint was also used as a chest rub in the nineteenth century to ease whooping cough. Modern-day research backs up this use, with studies finding that a minty chest rub can reduce mild wheezing and coughing. And while it doesn't really break up nasal congestion, you'll find menthol or mint in cough and cold remedies and teas because it stimulates sensory receptors in the nose that detect cold temperatures – so you at least feel as if you're breathing more freely. A 1996 study by researchers from Christian-Albrechts University in Kiel, Germany, even proved that peppermint can ease tension headaches in just 15 minutes and keep pain at bay for up to an hour.

The essential oils in peppermint, especially menthol and menthone, are stomach-friendly. They were shown in laboratory studies conducted by pharmaceutical company SmithKline Beecham in 1983 and 1991 to relax the smooth muscle that lines your intestinal tract, which in turn eases cramping, and they stimulate the flow of bile, a digestive juice that breaks down fats. In addition, they relax the ring of muscle at the top of your stomach, which can make burping easier – but could also boost odds for heartburn if you lie down soon after a large meal that includes mint!

Peppermint tea

What You CAN DO

Enjoy mint in cooking or as a tea (steep 1 teaspoon of dried peppermint in a cup of boiling water for 10 minutes, strain and sip). For irritable bowel syndrome, take one or two peppermint oil capsules two to three times a day; enteric-coated capsules are recommended because they pass through the stomach without being digested, so that the oil reaches the intestines. Got a tension headache? Rub a few drops of peppermint oil tincture (10 per cent oil, 90 per cent alcohol) on your forehead. Don't give peppermint to babies or toddlers or use oil on their faces, as it can disrupt breathing.

Like other mints, peppermint has elongated leaves with serrated edges. A cluster of purple flowers crowns the stem in summer.

A potent hybrid

Works of ancient Greek literature allude to mint leaves being used to clean surfaces used for serving food. The Romans are known to have used mint to add a pleasing scent to bathwater and toiletries, and these practices were subsequently adopted in many parts of medieval Europe. But the species we know as peppermint, *Mentha* x *piperita*, was not recorded until the early eighteenth century. A natural cross between watermint (*M. aquatica*) and spearmint (*M. spicata*), it was soon cultivated widely in England and carried to North America by colonists, where it became a popular herbal remedy.

Taming IBS Peppermint can ease the pain of irritable bowel syndrome (IBS), too. When Turkish researchers gave 90 people with IBS a peppermint oil capsule or placebo three times a day for eight weeks, the mint group found surprising relief – one in three felt a significant reduction in abdominal pain.

In a 2007 study at the University of Chieti and Pescara, Italy, 57 people with IBS took two peppermint oil capsules twice a day for four weeks and experienced an average of 50 per cent reduction in discomfort. Four years later, Australian scientists discovered that, as well as easing cramping in the intestinal tract, peppermint acts through a pain-sensing channel called TRPM8, reducing signals in nerve pain-sensing fibres in the intestinal walls. These fibres often go on high alert after a bout of stomach flu, which can lead to IBS, the researchers said.

And mint may someday offer even more benefits. Botanical-medicine experts say that in test tubes peppermint tea has demonstrated antibacterial and antiviral activities, too.

OTHER NAMES Peppermint, lamb mint, brandy mint, balm mint, curled mint, amenta, lammint
ORIGIN Unknown, possibly the Mediterranean
PARTS USED Leaves, stems

OLIVE

Olea europaea

MEDICAL BENEFITS ◆ Prevention of heart disease, stroke, dementia, cancers of the breast, respiratory tract, upper digestive tract ◆ Potential to lower risk for osteoporosis, diabetes

Today, the amazing benefits of oil pressed from olives are known far and wide. But prior to 1958, this tasty 'good fat' was a secret little known beyond Mediterranean kitchen tables from Portugal to Greece.

It took pioneering University of Minnesota biologist Ancel Keys to make the connection. Keys embarked on the ground-breaking Seven Countries Study in 1958. It tracked the health and diets of 12,000 men from Italy, the Greek Islands, Yugoslavia, the Netherlands, Finland, Japan and the United States. Once ironically dubbed 'Mr Cholesterol' by the American media, Keys uncovered convincing evidence that diets rich in saturated fats such as fatty meat and butter boosted 'bad' LDL cholesterol and heart-disease risk. The good news? He found that a Mediterranean menu (see p. 260) packed with olive oil and fruit and vegetables protected tickers and arteries. Keys' work changed the way the world eats, leading one expert to call him 'truly a giant of 20th-century work' in the field of diet and heart disease.

in CLOSE-UP

Olive leaf extract, used by ancient Greeks to cool fevers, contains some of the same health-promoting polyphenols found in olive oil. In 2007, researchers from Australia's University of Queensland found that olive leaf extract was better at neutralising cell-damaging free radicals than 55 other herbs they analysed. It also shows promise against high blood pressure and cold symptoms in human studies. If you'd like to try olive leaf extract, take it with food to avoid digestive irritation. Doses range from 500–2000 mg a day; follow package directions.

Health insurance in a bottle But even Keys (who died in 2004 at the age of 100) might be surprised at the range of health benefits now claimed for olive oil. It's uncommonly rich in a monounsaturated fat called oleic acid and in compounds called polyphenols, a combination that has unique abilities to cool off bodywide inflammation, keep artery walls flexible so that blood pressure stays lower, reduce cholesterol, switch on genes that guard against heart disease and a prediabetic condition called metabolic syndrome, and protect cells from damage.

A headline-making 2012 study by the Catalan Institute of Oncology in Barcelona that tracked 40,622 people for 13.4 years found that those who used 2 tablespoons of olive oil a day were 44 per cent less likely to die from heart disease.

Rows of gnarled, twisted olive trees create a typical Mediterranean scene. Some olive trees have been shown to be 2000 years old.

Try to aim for 1–2 tablespoons of olive oil a day; use extra virgin olive oil, as it has higher levels of health-promoting, inflammation-soothing compounds called polyphenols. Drizzle on vegetables or salad or use it as a bread dip. But think twice about cooking with it: heat destroys between 5 and 30 per cent of the polyphenols, according to the American Institute for Cancer Research.

Enjoying one tablespoon a day in food reduced risk 28 per cent. A major review of studies on olive oil and cancer by Milan's Mario Negri Institute for Pharmacological Research concluded that using the oil regularly could reduce breast cancer risk by 38 per cent and could protect against cancers of the respiratory and upper digestive tract and colorectal cancer.

Mediterranean protection A healthy diet that includes olive oil matters for your mind, too. In a dramatic 2011 study at the University of California Davis, magnetic resonance imaging brain scans of 770 people over 65 years of age found that those who followed an olive-oil-rich Mediterranean diet were 36 per cent less likely to have signs of brain damage from silent strokes, lowering their risk for dementia.

Meanwhile, in a 2009 study of 215 people with type 2 diabetes, researchers from the Second University of Naples, in southern Italy, found that 56 per cent of those following a healthy diet with olive oil controlled their diabetes without drugs, compared to just 30 per cent who stuck to a low-fat diet. The reason? Compounds in olive oil help the body process blood glucose in a healthier way.

Other good news about olive oil concerns bone health. A 2012 study of 127 men conducted at Hospital Dr Josep Trueta in Spain found that a healthy diet incorporating olive oil even seems to help preserve bone mass – which could protect against fractures.

ORIGIN Crete and/or Syria
PART USED Oil from pressed fruit

RICE

Oryza sativa

MEDICAL BENEFITS ◆ Prevention of heart disease, diabetes, obesity

A staple food for half of the world's population, rice 'is life' for billions of people, according to the United Nations Food and Agriculture Organization. And proof is mounting that the most nutrient-dense rice types also bring good health.

In China, black rice is widely used to make porridge and sweet snacks such as rice cakes.

Rice cultivation probably first took place in China's Yangtze Valley more than 10,000 years ago.

According to a 2007 report from Cornell University plant geneticists, the earliest records of human consumption of rice are microscopic, fossilised remains found in caves in China's Yangtze River Valley, and rice was farmed in paddies in China as early as 4000 BC. Fast-forward to the present day and rice from China is still on the leading edge of change. One particular type long overlooked by the West, known as black or 'forbidden' rice, was once so revered in China that only the emperor was permitted to eat it. This sweet, sticky variety, which takes on a dark purple hue when cooked, is emerging as a superfood packed with a surprise dose of cell-protecting antioxidants.

Long reach A spoonful of dry black rice contains more anthocyanins (health-promoting antioxidants) than a spoonful of blueberries – plus more fibre and vitamin E, according to Zhimin Xu of Louisiana State University Agricultural Center in Baton Rouge, Louisiana. In a 2010 study, Xu analysed samples of black rice and found that its anthocyanins

What You CAN DO

Choose wholegrain rice – brown, black or red – over milled and polished white rice to enjoy this grain's healthy fibre and nutrients. When buying bread, breakfast cereal, crackers and other baked goods that contain rice, look for the words 'brown rice' or 'whole' or 'wholegrain' before the type of rice.

Harvesting a rice paddy

are water-soluble. That means they may be able to reach body tissues that other nutrients can't get to. In another 2010 study, researchers at South Korea's Ajou University found in a mouse study that black rice anthocyanins have powerful anti-inflammatory effects. Researcher Sun Phil Choi noted that this means black rice could have potential as a therapeutic agent for the treatment and prevention of diseases associated with chronic inflammation, including diabetes, heart disease, arthritis and even some cancers.

Rice in a bottle?

Rice bran oil is made from the inner hulls and nutrient-rich 'germ' of whole-grain rice. Use it in cooking or as a topping for salads and vegetables to glean heart benefits. In a 2005 Louisiana State University study, people who were given 2–3 tablespoons of rice bran oil daily for 10 weeks as part of a controlled diet saw their 'bad' or LDL cholesterol levels fall by 7 per cent.

The benefits of brown But don't give up on brown rice, the fibre-rich grain championed by 1970s counterculture types and modern-day nutritionists. This form of rice has just the hull of the grain removed, leaving the rest of the kernel – and nutrients – intact. Compared to milled and polished white rice, brown rice has 67–90 per cent more vitamin B1, B3 and B6; 50 per cent more manganese and phosphorus; 60 per cent more iron; and 100 per cent more fibre. This superior profile is responsible for a cornucopia of health benefits that make switching from white to brown a worthwhile swap.

In a 2003 Harvard School of Public Health study of 74,000 women, those who got plenty of dietary fibre from brown rice and other whole grains were 49 per cent less likely to gain weight than women who ate mostly refined grains such as white rice. Hearts benefit, too. Switching to all whole grains including brown rice for 10 weeks helped subjects reduce their blood pressure and shed an average of 0.9 kg (2 lb) apiece in a 2006 study run by the US Department of Agriculture.

ORIGIN India, China
PARTS USED Seeds

PEA

Pisum sativum

MEDICAL BENEFITS ◆ Prevention of type 2 diabetes, high blood pressure, stomach cancer ◆ Possible treatment for obesity, high blood pressure

Humans have been enjoying peas as a food for millennia, but only lately have they identified the active ingredients in peas that are responsible for their health benefits.

In 2011, archaeologists from Slovenia's Scientific Research Centre of SASA (Slovenian Academy of Sciences) reported the discovery of fossilised peas in a Neolithic lakeside settlement dating back to 3110 BC. Prehistoric pea-eaters might have been surprised by a 2009 study by Mexico's National Institute of Public Health that found that people who consumed even a small daily dose of a polyphenol antioxidant called coumestrol – the amount you'd get from about a quarter-cup of cooked peas – reduced their risk for stomach cancer by as much as 50 per cent.

Peas for prevention Peas – green or yellow – offer other unique nutritional benefits. Especially notable are four saponins found in peas (and a handful of other vegetables and fruits) that take their names from the pea's Latin name, *Pisum*: pisumsaponins I and II and pisomosides A and B. Researchers from Japan's Kyoto Medical University reported, in a 2001 paper, that these compounds displayed anti-inflammatory properties. Added to the high fibre content and cell-protecting isoflavones in peas, the presence of inflammation-cooling saponins could be yet another reason why eating peas regularly (along with other legumes) lowered diabetes risk 38 per cent in a Vanderbilt University study, reported in 2008, that tracked the health of 64,227 women for four and a half years.

Another surprise: peas pack a heart-pampering omega-3 fatty acid called alpha-linolenic acid (also found in walnuts and purslane). Combined with the ingredients listed above, this may explain why, in a 2001 study at Tulane University, New Orleans, people who ate peas and other legumes at least four times per week were 21 per cent less likely to develop coronary artery disease compared to people who rarely consumed these foods.

Peas are also rich in the mineral molybdenum (one cup of cooked dried peas delivers twice your daily needs) and may therefore help people

Peas are high in nutrients including vitamins A, B6, C and K, as well as fibre, folate, protein and various minerals.

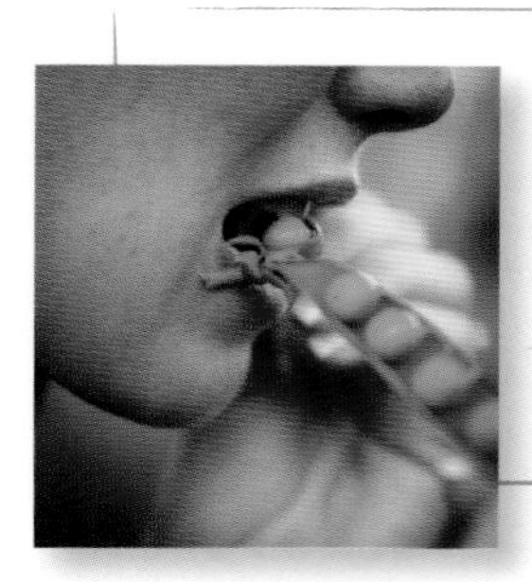

Add peas to your menu regularly – fresh, frozen, dried or canned. Put them into rotation with other legumes (dried beans) several times a week. You can buy pea protein powder online and in health food stores; follow label directions and use as you would other protein powders in beverages and in cooking.

who are sensitive to sulphites (added to many foods as a preservative). Sulphite sensitivity often causes headaches or increased heart rate and may be triggered by low levels of molybdenum, according to a 1998 report from the Princeton Brain Bio Center. Adding peas to your diet could therefore alleviate the problem.

Protein in the spotlight Cutting-edge pea research, meanwhile, is focusing on another pea constituent: protein. In a 2012 University of Ottawa study, researchers found antioxidant and anti-inflammatory properties in a specially prepared hydrolysate of yellow pea protein. A 2009 rat study at the University of Ottawa found that a similar pea protein concentrate lowered high blood pressure.

Pea protein is also being developed as a food additive by companies in Canada and France. Because it takes a long time to digest, it helps satisfy hunger and may therefore have a future application in weight-loss products.

OTHER NAMES Split peas, yellow peas, green peas
ORIGIN Central Asia, Middle East
PART USED Seed

in CLOSE-UP

Cooked dried peas may be an ideal comfort food for people with type 2 diabetes. In a 2003 study by Germany's University of Göttingen, researchers measured the blood glucose and insulin response of diabetics who ate a meal containing potatoes or cooked dried peas. Blood glucose was nearly one-third lower among the pea-eaters than the potato-eaters; insulin levels were about 10 per cent lower – a healthy sign that their bodies needed less insulin to process blood glucose. The scientists concluded that peas – as a side dish or in a soup or stew – are a safe, blood-glucose-friendly substitute for carbohydrate-rich foods like potatoes. They even suggested that diabetics who have to count carbohydrates can disregard two-thirds of the carbs in peas, because the legume's high fibre levels slow the release and absorption of blood glucose.

A woman prepares peas in a Cambodian market. Peas are a vital legume worldwide.

CRANBERRY

Vaccinium macrocarpon

MEDICAL BENEFITS ◆ Prevention of recurrent urinary tract infections ◆ Possible prevention of stomach ulcers

Cranberry's distinctive tang makes delicious juice and a tasty traditional sauce for turkey. What's more, these berries might help fight off urinary tract infections (UTIs) – though the evidence remains inconclusive.

The berries and leaves of the cranberry plant have a long history as folk remedies for urinary problems, diarrhoea, and even diabetes, liver trouble and wounds. In the 1960s, papers began appearing in medical journals noting a possible connection between consumption of cranberry juice and a reduced risk for bladder infections. If this was correct, what was the link?

One early theory was that the juice made urine more acidic, thereby disabling bacteria. But that was proved wrong in 1984 by microbiologist Anthony Sobota of Youngstown State University in Ohio. In test-tube, mouse and human research, he found that, instead, cranberry juice limited bladder infections by preventing 75 per cent of *Escherichia coli* bacteria from adhering to the bladder wall – the most common cause of such infections.

Ideal candidates Today supermarkets, chemists and natural food stores are packed with cranberry juice blends and cranberry-extract supplements. Yet following the headlines about conflicting cranberry and UTI research has been like following a ping-pong match. 'Skip It!', 'Ineffective' and 'No Good' say

Harvesting cranberries often involves flooding the beds and using a machine to dislodge the berries. As they float, they can be easily gathered.

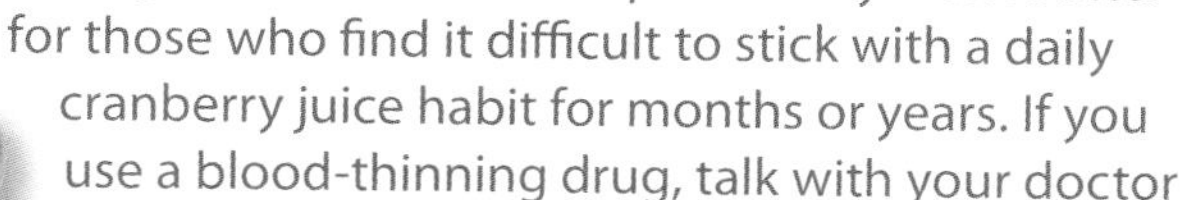

Enjoying two glasses of cranberry juice a day – or taking a 500-mg cranberry extract supplement twice daily – could cut your risk for future bladder infections if you tend to have recurring UTIs. Tablets and capsules may work better for those who find it difficult to stick with a daily cranberry juice habit for months or years. If you use a blood-thinning drug, talk with your doctor before drinking cranberry juice or taking a cranberry supplement on a daily basis. And don't depend on cranberry products to cure an existing bladder infection – that requires antibiotics.

some recent news reports, while others have declared that cranberry 'Beats Infections', 'May Keep Bladder Infection Away' and 'Can Protect Against Urine Infections'.

In October of 2012, a review by researcher Ruth Jepson of Scotland's University of Stirling of 24 large, well-designed studies sorted out the data. Her conclusion? Cranberry juice and pills – which cannot treat existing infections – are unlikely to help most people avoid UTIs. However, in people who suffered recurrent bladder infections, two daily cranberry doses cut their risk by 14 per cent.

What's more, a 2011 study at the Academic Medical Center in Amsterdam, Netherlands, of 221 women who experienced six to seven UTIs per year, suggested another benefit. Those who took a low-dose antibiotic cut their UTIs to two per year, while those who took a 500-mg cranberry extract twice daily reduced their UTIs to four per year. The cranberry advantage? It won't trigger antibiotic resistance.

Berry good ulcer prevention The same nonstick mechanism that keeps bacteria from clinging to the inner lining of the bladder, it turns out, offers some protection from the ulcer-inciting ravages of the *Helicobacter pylori* bacterium. In a 2005 Beijing Institute for Cancer Research study, 189 people who tested positive for *H. pylori* infection sipped a daily glass of cranberry juice or received a placebo. People in the cranberry group were five times more likely to be free of the ulcer-causing bacteria after 90 days as those in the placebo group. The downside? Many people didn't respond at all to cranberry juice.

OTHER NAMES American cranberry, bog cranberry
ORIGIN North America
PART USED Fruit

in CLOSE-UP

The ruby-red colour of a cranberry or glass of cranberry juice comes from proanthocyanidins, protective plant chemicals that halt bacterial invaders in an ingenious way. In 2008, researchers at Worcester Polytechnic Institute in England found that cranberries discourage infection by disabling tiny hair-like projections called fimbriae (singular: fimbria) that some bacteria use as hooks. Fimbriae are present on the *E. coli* bacteria that cause most bladder infections and on *Helicobacter pylori* bacteria that cause most stomach ulcers. Normally, fimbriae are tipped with proteins called adhesins that can dock with cells. Cranberry compounds alter fimbria tips so they're less effective.

BILBERRY

Vaccinium myrtillus

MEDICAL BENEFITS ◆ Potential supplementary treatment for glaucoma, cataracts, retinopathy

British World War II pilots reportedly credited their pinpoint accuracy during night bombing raids to the bilberry jam they'd enjoyed at teatime. Though never confirmed, the story highlights the potential health bonuses of this dainty fruit.

Used in European herbal medicine for over 1000 years, bilberry's fruit and leaves have been called on to treat diarrhoea, mouth and throat irritations, coughs and tuberculosis. Bilberry-leaf tea is a widely used folk medicine for diabetes and for urinary tract infections, too. But today it is this midnight-blue berry's storehouse of powerful anthocyanins – chemical compounds with strong antioxidant and anti-inflammatory actions – that have been the subject of scientific research.

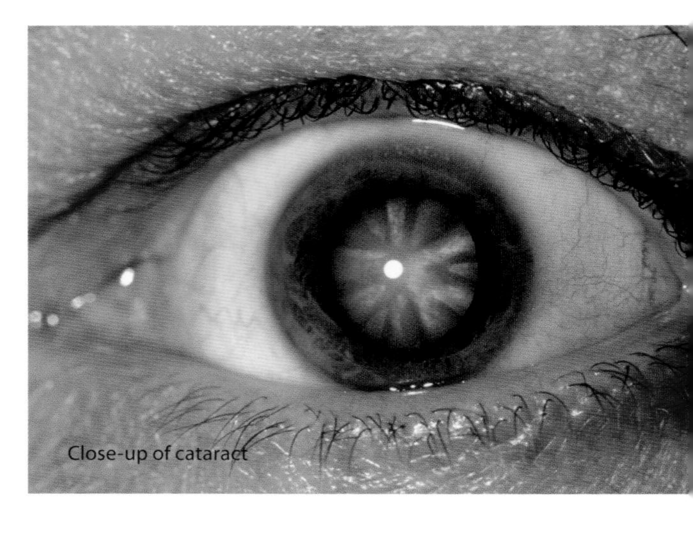
Close-up of cataract

The eyes have it Anthocyanins give bilberries their deep blue-red tint. In the body, these compounds have been shown in numerous studies to improve circulation in the tiny blood vessels that deliver oxygen- and nutrient-rich blood to individual cells. As antioxidants, they also protect cells from damage. In one widely cited Italian study published in 1989, 50 elderly people with early stage cataracts who took a combination of bilberry extract and vitamin E saw cataract progression slow by 97 per cent.

Antioxidant power may explain the results of another Italian study from 1987, of 14 people with damage to their retinas and to tiny blood

Fresh bilberries can be hard to find; frozen ones may be more readily available. Juices and extracts are sold in health food stores.

Seeing in the dark

If bilberry jam boosted the prowess of British bomber pilots in World War II, could it help the US Navy? In 2000, Eric R Muth of the Naval Aerospace Medical Research Laboratory in Pensacola, Florida, set out to answer that question after several European studies suggested that bilberry had night vision-sharpening powers. Fifteen Navy SEAL personnel took 160 mg of a bilberry extract three times a day for three weeks. But tests showed no improvements. And a 2004 review of bilberry studies by the Peninsula Medical School of the Universities of Exeter and Plymouth in England came to the same conclusion; however, researchers noted that further study is needed to find out if bilberry might still improve night vision in people with impaired eyesight due to diseases such as diabetes or glaucoma.

A British bomber crew gathers in front of its plane after a raid on the German city of Hamburg in 1943.

vessels in their eyes, due to diabetes or high blood pressure. They received bilberry extracts containing 115 mg of anthocyanins or a placebo daily. After a month, tests showed their retinas and the blood vessels had improved.

Glaucoma patients also experienced improvements in one small Korean study. Researchers gave anthocyanins from bilberry to 132 study volunteers at a dose of 60 mg twice daily for two years; another 103 received a gingko supplement and 97 others received neither. Eye tests showed that vision improved in those who took the anthocyanins; these volunteers also had fewer 'weak spots' in their field of vision. Lead researcher Seong Hee Shim noted that bilberry anthocyanins may help eyes by improving circulation, which could in turn help control dangerously high fluid pressure in the eye that in glaucoma can damage the optic nerve.

Go with the flow That circulation boost has body-wide benefits. In a 2010 lab study by Slovenia's University of Ljubljana, a bilberry extract increased blood flow and helped stabilise heart rhythm after heart attack in rats. A 1995 lab study at Italy's CNR Institute of Clinical Physiology found that bilberry extract restored blood flow to injured hamster tissue. Several Italian studies from the 1980s found that people with various circulation problems saw blood flow improve upon taking bilberry extract daily.

Meanwhile, bilberry anthocyanins improved symptoms in people with a bowel disease called ulcerative colitis, in a preliminary 2012 study at University Hospital Zurich, Switzerland.

Do not use bilberry in place of medications recommended by your doctor for eye or circulation conditions. If you'd like to try bilberry as an add-on therapy, look for an extract standardised to contain 25 per cent anthocyanins. Follow package directions for dosage. Talk with your doctor before using bilberry if you take medications for diabetes or to discourage clotting.

OTHER NAMES Black whortles, dyeberry, European blueberry, huckleberry, whortleberry, wineberry
ORIGIN Europe, North America
PARTS USED Dried fruit, leaves

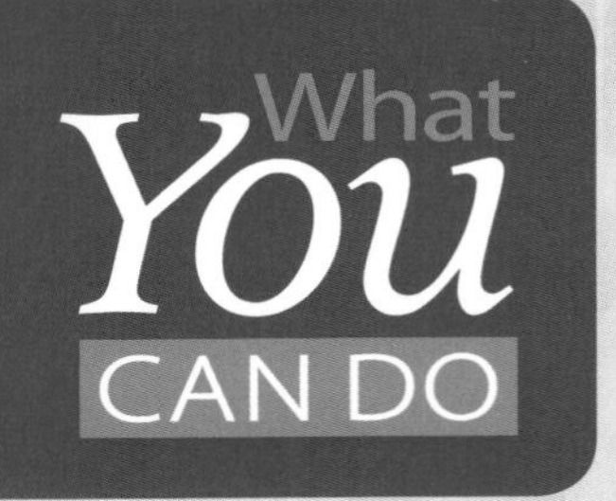

POWER FOODS

What's the best way to harness the disease-fighting power of plant foods? Walk right past the supplements aisle in your grocery store, and head straight to the fresh produce department.

An abundance of research shows that in almost all cases, phytochemical-rich plant foods beat supplements for lowering risk of serious ailments including heart disease, stroke, diabetes, cancers, vision problems and more. Almost every type of fruit and vegetable delivers a unique portfolio of antioxidants, vitamins, minerals and other beneficial compounds.

Eating about 2 cups of fruit and 2½ cups of vegetables a day – and eating a rainbow of colours – is a proven way to maximise the power of fresh produce. In a 2004 Harvard School of Public Health study, this amount reduced heart disease risk by 30 per cent compared to people who ate less than 1 cup a day.

Yet, while all fruits and vegetables are beneficial, some are more beneficial than others. Try to include the following in your diet on a regular basis:

Spinach Packed with carotenoids like beta-carotene, spinach (and other dark leafy greens such as kale) lowered risk for diabetes by 14 per cent in one 2010 study undertaken at Leicester Royal Infirmary in England. The lutein and zeaxanthin in spinach accumulate in the retina, protecting eyes from cell-damaging, vision-stealing free radicals. Spinach has been shown to reduce risk for aggressive prostate cancers, too.

Blueberries Elevated levels of flavonoids in berries may explain why people who dig into these sweet treats on a regular basis were found to have a 40 per cent lower risk for Parkinson's disease in one 2011 Harvard School of Public Health study. Consuming blueberries daily improved memory and sharpened thinking in one study and lowered levels of heart-threatening triglycerides in another.

A healthy kale crop

Pumpkins The brilliant yellow, gold and orange colours of these vegetables indicate that they deliver carotenoids including beta-carotene, which most likely reduce risk for cancers of the mouth, larynx, pharynx, lungs and oesophagus, according to the American Institute for Cancer Research. Their high fibre levels will help protect against prostate cancer, too.

Walnuts The gamma-tocopherol form of vitamin E in this tasty nut lowered risk for heart disease in a 2006 review by Tufts University, Massachusetts. And the combination of omega-3 fatty acids and fibre in nuts may explain why 28 g (1 oz) a day slashed risk for a prediabetic, heart-threatening condition called metabolic syndrome in a 2008 study at the University of Rovira i Virgili in Catalonia, Spain.

BETTER TOGETHER

Like Batman and Robin or Superman and Supergirl, superhero foods are often more powerful when you team them up. Here are four delicious pairings that maximise the phytochemicals in plant-based superfoods:

Apples plus chocolate: Apples are rich in quercetin, an anti-inflammatory flavonoid that cuts risk for allergies, heart attacks and cancers of the lungs and prostate. Chocolate's antioxidant catechins reduce risk for heart disease. Pairing the two helps prevent the formation of heart- and brain-threatening blood clots, says a 2000 study from Rome's Sapienza University.

Orange juice plus oatmeal: Enjoying a vitamin C-rich food or drink with a bowl of old-fashioned oats delivers twice the artery-pampering benefits of oats alone, says a 2004 study from the US Department of Agriculture's Antioxidants Research Laboratory. Together, the phenols in the oats and the vitamin C in the orange juice work to prevent build-up of plaque on artery walls.

Olive oil plus spinach: Eating good fats – like those in olive oil, nuts, canola oil and avocado – with leafy greens boosts absorption of fat-soluble carotenoids such as lutein, lycopene, beta-carotene and zeaxanthin, says a 2012 study from Purdue University, Indiana. These compounds help protect against heart disease, cancer and vision-robbing macular degeneration.

Broccoli plus tomatoes: In a 2007 rat study from the University of Illinois, this duo shrank prostate-cancer tumours dramatically. Researchers aren't sure why, but note that compounds in each (lutein in tomatoes, sulforaphane in broccoli) discourage this cancer – and seem to work even better together.

GRAPE

Vitis vinifera

MEDICAL BENEFITS ◆ Prevention of heart disease ◆ Potential treatment for mobility and balance problems associated with ageing, blood pressure and diabetes associated with obesity ◆ Potential prevention of cancer ◆ Potential anti-ageing treatment

It hardly seemed fair. In the 1980s, researchers began noticing that the French had low rates of fatal heart disease despite a penchant for cigarettes and saturated fat. (The cheese! The pâté! The pastries!) Did red wine explain this French paradox?

Quite possibly, and for more than one reason. Two decades of research into alcohol's effects on the cardiovascular system has revealed that for many people, *moderate* drinking can reduce heart disease risk – by 20–30 per cent, says a 2003 study of 38,077 men conducted at Boston's Beth Israel Deaconess Medical Center. Red wine (and other alcoholic drinks) helps hearts by boosting levels of HDL cholesterol, discouraging the formation of blood clots, reducing inflammation and relaxing arteries.

The magic ingredient But in 2003, Harvard Medical School researcher David Sinclair announced the discovery of a substance in grapes – especially the skins of red grapes – that might explain the purported health magic of wine: resveratrol. Also found in peanuts and some berries, resveratrol captured the public imagination and the minds of scientists when Sinclair and others announced that it extended the lives of yeast cells, fruit flies and the worm species *Caenorhabditis elegans*, all laboratory organisms commonly used in ageing studies.

The reason was tantalisingly simple, it seemed: resveratrol, Sinclair reported in a 2004 study, activated an enzyme called sirtuin that maintained telomeres, the protective 'caps' on the ends of the long strings of DNA in every living cell. Like the plastic ends on a shoelace, telomeres wear out over time, leaving DNA vulnerable to damage that leads to a host of age-related health conditions. The suggestion that resveratrol might slow ageing was enough to kick-start an explosion of supplements that soon packed the shelves of natural food stores

To take advantage of red wine's healthy effects, drink no more than ½–1 glass per day for women, 1–2 for men. Looking for resveratrol without the alcohol? Try red or purple grape juice or red grapes, which pack almost as much resveratrol as red wine. Peanuts and peanut butter supply lower levels. Supplements are available, but the optimal dosage is still unknown and high doses may interfere with medications including statins and antihistamines.

and clogged the internet – even though no-one knew whether this polyphenol affected human health or what an optimal dose might be.

Resveratrol comes of age A decade later, we know much more about what resveratrol can and can't do. For starters, it may work better in overweight people than in those who are already at a healthy weight. In a 2012 Washington University study, 29 healthy women who took resveratrol for 12 weeks saw no benefits, yet in a 2011 study at Maastricht University in the Netherlands obese men who took 150 mg daily for one month saw blood pressure fall by as much as 8 points.

Resveratrol is showing promise against cancer, too, and this potential benefit has been the subject of over 1500 published studies. The compound's antioxidant powers are one reason it has helped reduce the size and growth of tumours in many test-tube and animal trials.

ORIGIN Northern Iran
PART USED Crushed, fermented fruit

Resveratrol is concentrated in the grape skin. As white wine is made without the skin, it has much lower levels of the compound.

in CLOSE-UP

The way resveratrol works and how it may best be harnessed have been re-evaluated lately. Experts believed until recently that it boosted health by, as David Sinclair noted, protecting DNA. But in early 2012, researchers from the US National Institutes of Health announced that resveratrol works by inhibiting enzymes involved in regulating energy inside cells. Nailing down exactly how it functions could pave the way for resveratrol-based drugs. 'Resveratrol has potential as a therapy for diverse diseases such as type 2 diabetes, Alzheimer's disease, and heart disease,' said lead study author Jay H Chung. 'However, before researchers can transform resveratrol into a safe and effective medicine, they need to know exactly what it targets in cells.'

Resveratrol

Now, researchers are recruiting cancer patients for studies of resveratrol's effects in humans. Furthermore, interest in this compound's possible use against Alzheimer's disease is growing, too. A major US study involving 26 medical centres is currently underway. It will test a twice-daily resveratrol supplement on people over 65 years of age with mild to moderate dementia due to Alzheimer's disease.

GINGER

Zingiber officinale

MEDICAL BENEFITS ◆ Treatment for motion sickness, morning sickness, nausea due to chemotherapy ◆ Possible treatment for post-surgery nausea ◆ Traditional treatment for chills, arthritis, migraines

Queasy tummies meet their match in spicy ginger root, a popular cooking herb that's been a home remedy for digestive complaints, colds and flu, achy joints and head pain for thousands of years.

Today, ginger's strongest, research-backed claim to fame is its ability to soothe nausea in many guises – motion sickness, morning sickness and stomach upsets. But some preliminary research also supports its long-time use as an anti-inflammatory ache-easer.

Reducing nausea Imagine trying to hold onto your breakfast as your chair spins on one leg – so it's not just revolving, but also tilting up and down in wobbly circles. And you're blindfolded! That's what 36 stalwart volunteers did for a noteworthy 1982 Pennsylvania State University study that helped establish ginger's beneficial effects against motion sickness. Researcher Daniel B Mowrey found that capsules of dried, powdered ginger worked better than the popular motion-sickness remedy Dramamine (dimenhydrinate).

In 2003, research conducted at the University of Michigan confirmed ginger's benefits – this time courtesy of 13 volunteers who ate cheese-and-bacon sandwiches then sat inside a spinning barrel painted with nausea-inducing black-and-white stripes! In this study, 1000–2000 mg of dried ginger root, in capsules, reduced nausea by about 40 per cent; afterwards, nausea levels fell twice as fast – in five minutes rather than ten – in the ginger group compared with those taking a placebo.

Relief for mothers-to-be Morning sickness affects up to 85 per cent of women during the first three months of pregnancy. Here, too, ginger can help – and herbal medicine experts at Bastyr University, near Seattle in the United States say it's safe to take at recommended doses during pregnancy. In a 2005 review of seven morning-sickness studies, ginger significantly reduced nausea and vomiting in pregnant women.

Six of the studies followed the women until they gave birth and found ginger did not increase risk for birth defects, did not

Fresh ginger root is preferable to dried ginger, as it contains higher levels of the active compound 6-gingerol.

Ginger comes in many forms. You can make a tea by steeping 1 teaspoon of grated fresh ginger in boiling water; strain and sweeten. Or you can take capsules of dried ginger. Follow dosage directions; experts suggest 250 mg four times daily to quell nausea. Another option is to chew candied ginger; a 2.5-cm (1-inch) piece is equivalent to about 500–1000 mg of dried ginger.

shorten pregnancy, or cause any serious side effects for mothers-to-be (though some burped a little more often!).

And that's not all. In a 2011 study at the University of Rochester, 644 cancer patients undergoing chemotherapy took capsules containing ginger or a placebo twice a day for six days – starting three days before chemotherapy treatment. Those who received ginger had significantly less nausea.

> Ginger boosted sluggish digestion by 25 per cent in a 2011 study by Taiwan's Chang Gung University College of Medicine.

A pungent soother So what is responsible for this root's digestive-system-soothing powers? When researchers at the University of Exeter in the United Kingdom reviewed the evidence in 2000, they concluded that an active compound called 6-gingerol plays a starring role by relaxing muscles along the gastrointestinal tract. In 2011, in a laboratory study at the Pharmacy Institute at the Free University of Berlin, in Germany, scientists found that gingerols and shogaols from ginger bind to receptors on cells in the small intestine – blocking the action of nausea-inducing chemicals produced by the body, such as serotonin.

Some of ginger's time-honoured uses also have real science behind them. In India, the root is considered a useful anti-inflammatory against arthritis. In several case studies, including a 1992 report on 56 people with arthritis or muscle aches from Denmark's Odense University, those who took ginger supplements regularly for three months or more reported a significant easing of pain.

Ginger also has a reputation in Asia as a drying, warming herb that can chase the chills of a cold or flu. In one 1991 lab study reported by Japan's Hokkaido Institute of Pharmaceutical Sciences, an extract containing gingerols boosted body temperature in animals by 0.5°C within half an hour.

OTHER NAMES Black ginger, Jamaican ginger
ORIGIN India
PART USED Rhizome (rootstock)

Traditional Wisdom

Ginger turns up in a surprising range of healing traditions that date back thousands of years. In Malaysia and Indonesia, new mothers sip ginger soup during the first month after childbirth; it is thought to increase body temperature and aid in sweating away impurities. Ginger was employed for illnesses linked to cold and damp weather in traditional Chinese medicine, and the ancient Greeks ate ginger wrapped in bread as a digestive aid. And in India's Ayurvedic medicine tradition, this pungent herb was thought to soothe headaches and joint aches. Ginger was popular around the world by the Middle Ages, when a pound of ginger cost as much as a sheep in England.

Blue sea star and corals

PART TWO

ANIMAL MAGIC

CHAPTER FIVE

DOMESTIC ANIMALS AND PETS

CHAPTER SIX

LAND MAMMALS

CHAPTER SEVEN

REPTILES AND AMPHIBIANS

CHAPTER EIGHT

INSECTS, SPIDERS AND WORMS

CHAPTER NINE

AQUATIC ANIMALS

American alligator

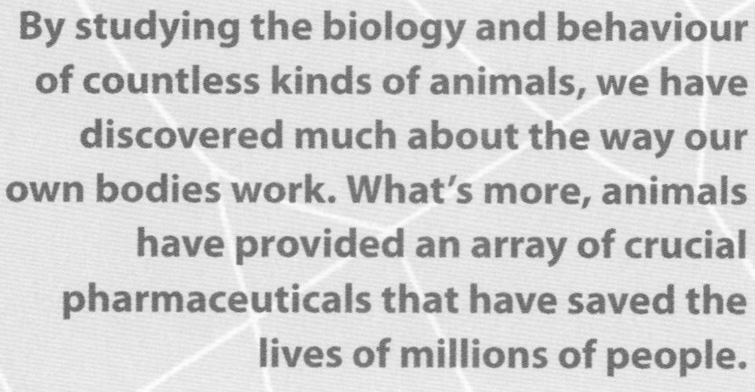

By studying the biology and behaviour of countless kinds of animals, we have discovered much about the way our own bodies work. What's more, animals have provided an array of crucial pharmaceuticals that have saved the lives of millions of people.

Animals might not have delivered as many pharmaceutical successes as plants, but when it comes to drug development potential they offer an advantage that plants don't have. From an evolutionary perspective, almost all animals share with us the same fundamental physiology. And that makes them particularly valuable as a resource for human health.

Common patterns

Shared biology with animals is the reason why we have been able to take a hormone from a fish – calcitonin from coho salmon – and use it to our advantage as a safe and highly effective treatment and preventative for the debilitating bone condition known as osteoporosis. It is also why the lives of countless type 1 diabetes sufferers have been improved and saved by administering insulin extracted from the pancreases of pigs and cows.

Even more distant relatives in the animal kingdom, such as lowly invertebrates including insects and molluscs, have made contributions to human health because they share evolutionary origins and basic body systems with us. We have, for example, learned much from slugs and snails about nerve cells and this, in turn, has helped us better understand our own nervous system and how it functions.

Poisonous possibilities

Our similarities with other animals have been a source of inspiration for drug development for almost a century. But in recent decades, with advances in biochemistry and molecular biology, some of the most promising pharmaceutical prospects from animals have been linked to capabilities we don't share – venom and toxin production.

Because poisonous compounds in the animal kingdom are at the core of a relentless battle between predator and prey, they're

Red deer

subjected to the constant pressures of natural selection. As a result, they're often highly complex and contain multiple components. They're also designed to act directly, at the molecular level, on the main life support systems of animals, their purpose usually being to debilitate, immobilise or kill by targeting, for example, cardiac, nervous or other vital systems. With biochemical tweaking, these actions can be diluted or slightly shifted to create huge pharmacological benefits.

Already, animal toxins have provided a range of life-saving drugs and therapies, including painkillers, anticoagulants and medicines that lower blood pressure. So far, reptile venoms have provided the most pharmacological breakthroughs and promise. But over the past 30 years or so there's been growing interest in a wider array of animals with venomous bites and stings or toxic flesh, including spiders, shellfish and many other marine invertebrates.

Pigs

COW

Bos taurus

MEDICAL BENEFITS ◆ Potential treatment for Alzheimer's disease ◆ Potential use against anthrax outbreaks ◆ Food supplement that may aid recovery after strenuous exercise

Constituents of cow's milk could help humans in various ways, from ameliorating the effects of Alzheimer's disease to the containment of an outbreak of anthrax.

Like all mammals, cows feed their newborns on milk. The first milk, known as colostrum, is not only a food but serves to pass on the mother's immunity to her young – the yellowish protein-rich liquid is packed with antibodies, growth factors and antimicrobial agents. Bovine colostrum has long been used as a food supplement and in ancient healing systems such as Ayurveda, and it is often touted by traditional health practitioners as a 'miracle food' that can boost strength and immunity.

Australian researchers have shown that both athletic performance and recovery after exercise improve with regular consumption of powdered colostrum supplement. And British researchers have been investigating the effects of colostrum in preventing a syndrome known as 'leaky gut', which can occur with heavy exercise. It results in discomfort and diarrhoea and can impair performance. The colostrum helped to reduce this. Colostrum may also have a use in calming the immune response in autoimmune diseases such as asthma and allergies.

Several studies have indicated that a substance in colostrum, marketed as Colostrinin, may help limit the effects of Alzheimer's disease. In one Polish study, 40 per cent of Alzheimer's patients given regular doses of Colostrinin stabilised or improved after 15 weeks. With Alzheimer's, deposits (or plaques) build up and inhibit neurone function; colostrinin is thought to protect neurones from being killed by plaques.

Spore containment An Australia-based biotech company, Anadis, is looking at using colostrum as a key ingredient in a gel for neutralising anthrax spores. Cows are given anthrax vaccinations and their bodies develop antibodies, which pass into the colostrum. As well as neutralising the anthrax, the gel would make the spores clump so that become too large to remain airborne.

ORIGIN Eurasia
PART USED Colostrum (milk)

Bovine colostrum is available as a food supplement from health food stores in many countries, and sold under various brand names as a powder or as capsules. Anecdotal evidence says it improves strength and stamina, but many of the health claims have not been scientifically proven. A colostrum-based drug to help Alzheimer's is still some way off.

DOG

Canis lupus familiaris

MEDICAL BENEFITS ◆ Trained dogs can detect certain cancers ◆ Medical alert dogs assist people who have diabetes, asthma, epilepsy and other conditions

Dogs have such a strong sense of smell that they can detect cancers in humans. Scientists hope this may lead to the creation of more accurate, noninvasive screening tests.

There have been many anecdotal reports over the years about dogs sensing their owners' cancers. Many tell of dogs behaving strangely around their owners or nuzzling at the site where a tumour was later discovered. Some sufferers swear that their dogs 'knew' about their cancer all along. Of course, such testimonials do not serve as scientific evidence.

In 2004, however, real proof of the cancer-scenting abilities of dogs emerged, when a team of researchers in Oxford, England, published a study in the *British Medical Journal* that

A trained search-and-rescue dog is able to locate the scent of a person under more than 5 m (16 ft) of snow.

showed trained dogs were capable of picking up an 'odour signature' of bladder cancer at an early stage of the disease.

Signature smell Though people are well aware of the acuteness of the canine sense of smell, and sniffer dogs are used for all sorts of tasks, the idea that they could pick up a cancer had largely been discounted because scientists thought early-stage cancers did not have a discernible smell. But it turns out they do.

The British researchers found that dogs could identify urine samples from people with bladder cancer. The researchers believe the dogs recognise a mixture of volatile organic compounds released by malignant cancer cells as a tumour grows – a complex array of scents that together create the 'signature smell' of bladder cancer. So sensitive are the dogs' noses that they can detect this specific smell every time.

A third of a dog's brain is devoted to the sense of smell.

Training such smart and sociable animals is easy: a correct identification brings a reward of food, encouraging the dog to find more of the same smell. Any breed of dog can be trained, but dog handlers look for individual dogs that like people, are naturally inquisitive and are good-natured.

A screening tool Soon after that first experiment, the British researchers set up a charity called Medical Detection Dogs, with the aim of training more dogs and funding more research. They hope that by working with the dogs they will be able to identify which chemicals are markers for cancer and develop a machine that can pick up the signature odours. This would make routine cancer screening quick, easy and noninvasive. The researchers are now focusing on the detection of prostate cancer, a major killer. They hope a scent test will be more accurate than the current screening test, which looks for a prostate-specific antigen (PSA) in the blood and is highly unreliable.

Similar research elsewhere is focusing on other types of cancer. In California, dogs are being trained to identify ovarian cancer in urine samples; in Germany, scientists have trained dogs to detect lung cancer from the breath of patients with 99 per cent accuracy.

in CLOSE-UP

When a dog sniffs the ground or a sample in a lab, air is sucked up into its nasal cavity, carrying airborne chemicals, or odours. Each smell may be made up of hundreds of chemicals in varying concentrations. The odour-laden air is forced through scrolls of cartilage and bony tissue called the turbinate bones and these are lined with sensory cells coated in mucus. The chemicals dissolve in the mucus and trigger the sensory cells, which send messages to the olfactory region of the brain, as they do in a human. The cells work together to create a scent 'picture', just as a digital photograph is assembled from millions of pixels. But a dog's nose has about 225 million sensory cells, whereas a human's has just 5 million, so its picture is far sharper and far more detailed.

ORIGIN Eurasia
PART USED Sense of smell

One day this research may lead to screening tools that will save thousands of lives by detecting cancers early. In the meantime you can support the Medical Detection Dogs charity through donations or by sponsoring a puppy – you can even name a puppy if you wish. Details are on the website, www.medicaldetectiondogs.org.uk

Dog detectives

The charity that was set up to help train dogs to detect cancers has another strand to its work that is already improving the quality of life for people with difficult-to-control diseases such as type 1 diabetes, asthma, epilepsy and Addison's disease, a debilitating hormonal disorder. Dogs are trained to recognise minute changes in body odour that occur when their owner is becoming unwell. In the case of diabetes, for example, a person may not be aware that their blood is becoming low in glucose, which can cause fainting or even be life-threatening. But a medical detection dog will pick up a change in body odour as the blood glucose starts to fall, and by licking its owner's hands will remind them to eat some extra sugar. Dogs can also be trained to bring an emergency medical kit to their owner, open doors and even raise the alarm if their owner is not responding.

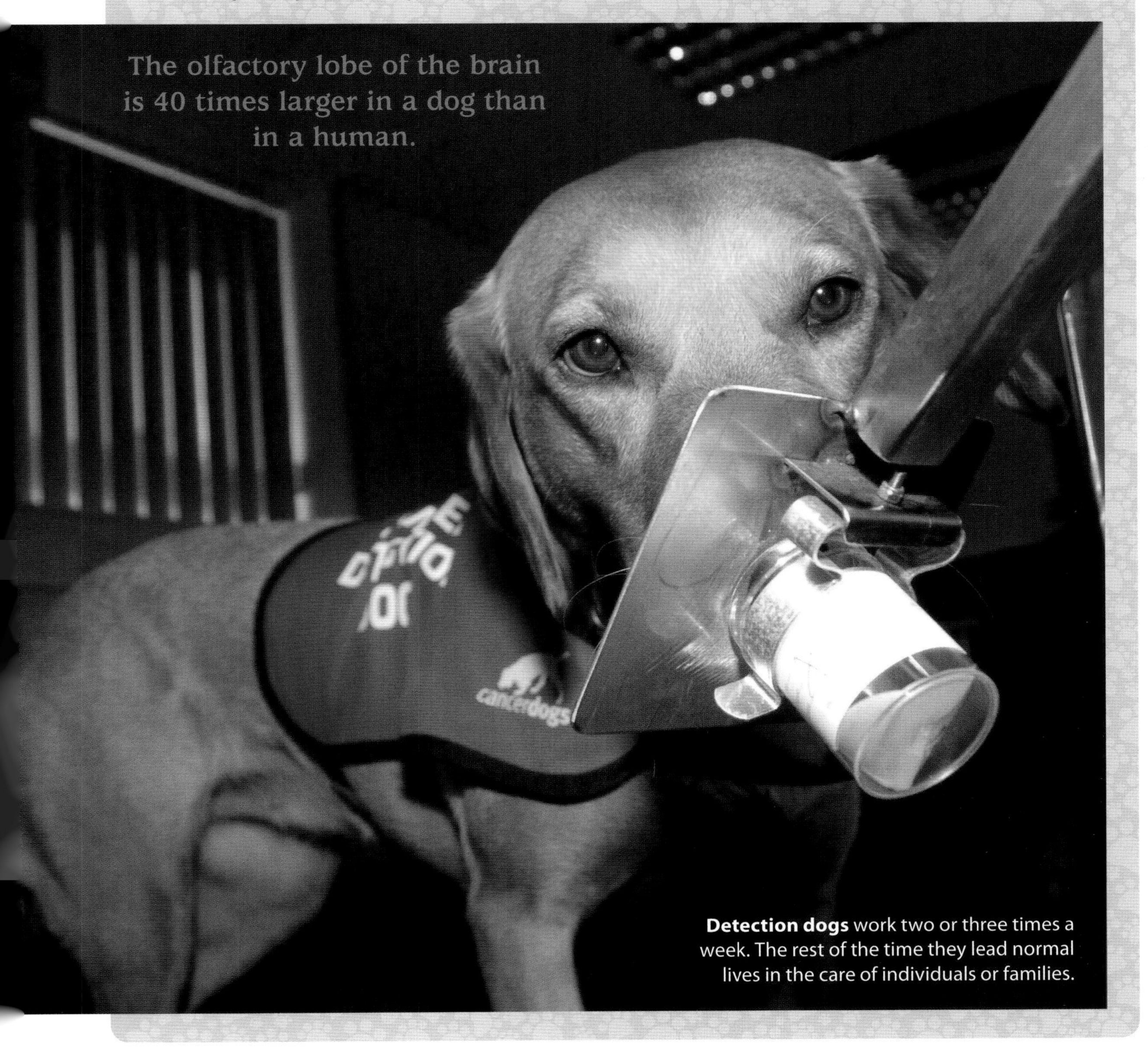

The olfactory lobe of the brain is 40 times larger in a dog than in a human.

Detection dogs work two or three times a week. The rest of the time they lead normal lives in the care of individuals or families.

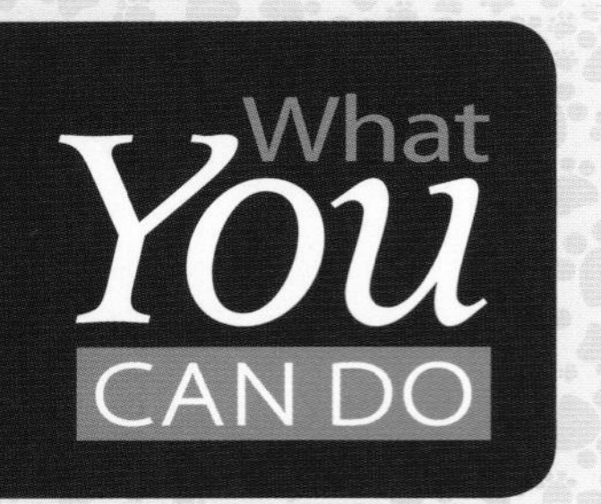

PET POWER

Research is showing that household pets may give us more than just affection and faithful companionship – they may be improving our health in a number of tangible ways.

ADDED PROTECTION

There is evidence that children who have grown up in a household where there is a cat or a dog are less likely to develop asthma. Scientists think this is related to improving a child's immune system and making it more robust and stable. In 2002, researchers at Warwick University in England showed that children who lived with a pet had strong immune systems and were less likely to take days off school due to sickness. This is a similar scenario to that described by the 'hygiene hypothesis' (see p. 204), which claims that people who have been exposed to infectious agents in their childhood are less likely to develop asthma. In contrast, people who grow up in ultra-sterile environments may have less robust immune systems and so may be more likely to develop autoimmune diseases.

There have been numerous studies of the relationships between humans and their pets. Early research in the 1980s found that people who had suffered heart attacks lived longer if they owned a pet compared to those who didn't. A large Australian study in 1992 took this further, discovering that people who owned pets had lower blood pressure and lower cholesterol and thus a lower risk of having a heart attack. Indeed, it seems that simply stroking a dog or cat lowers a person's blood pressure, while psychological studies have shown that pet owners generally suffer less depression than people without pets.

A chemical reaction More recent studies have been trying to find out why pets have these beneficial effects. Scientists have discovered that pets increase their owners' levels of oxytocin, a chemical that acts on the brain and is known as the 'happy hormone'. Not only does this have a beneficial effect on a person's mood but, also, raised levels of the hormone are associated with a number of positive effects in the body, such as enhancing the readiness to heal and grow new cells. There are also studies that show that being with a pet lowers the levels of cortisol in the blood – a hormone that is associated with stress.

Any pet will do Though most of the studies have focused on cats and dogs, it seems that any pet can have a positive effect. Even goldfish. In 2002, researchers at Purdue University, Indiana, in the United States, discovered that simply placing bowls of goldfish in the communal dining rooms of a nursing home encouraged

YOU DON'T HAVE TO OWN A PET

If owning a pet is not an option for you, there are other ways to interact with animals and gain the benefits.

- Volunteer at a local animal refuge
- Offer to walk a neighbour's dog, or set up a dog-walking service
- Take up horse riding
- Visit farms
- Keep chickens
- Feed the birds in your garden

Need exercise and want to meet people?
Choose a dog or horse

Housebound and feeling lonely?
Get a cat, bird, rabbit or fish

Want a pet for a child?
Try gerbils, hamsters, guinea pigs, rabbits or birds

people with Alzheimer's to eat (a loss of appetite is a common side effect of the disease). The nursing facility had already tried treating residents to classic movies and altering the lighting to be more like natural daylight, but there had been no improvement.

The bowls of goldfish had a significant effect: patients began eating more, with subsequent weight gain. It was unclear why this occurred, but it could have been simply the relaxing effect of watching the goldfish swim round and round.

Which is best? Your choice of pet depends on your lifestyle and what you want from your pet. If you are out all day, it isn't fair to keep a dog cooped up alone in your house; a cat would be better. On the other hand if you aim to get out more and do more exercise, you'd be better off with a dog.

If you have heart disease or heart problems run in your family, you might want to get a cat. A large US study that ran for more than 10 years found that people who owned a cat were 40 per cent less likely to die from heart attacks than people without a cat. Owning a dog didn't provide the same protection. Researchers can't fully explain the results, but think they might be to do with the way cats purr: the sound seems to have a calming effect on humans.

HORSE

Equus ferus caballus

MEDICAL BENEFITS ◆ Treatment to relieve symptoms of menopause

When scientists discovered that the pregnancy hormones in mares' urine were similar to those of humans, the way was paved for a new type of medicine called hormone replacement therapy.

In the 1920s, scientists began searching for a way to help prevent some of the unpleasant symptoms associated with menopause, including hot flushes, night sweats and mood swings. These symptoms occur because when women enter menopause their bodies stop producing the female hormones oestrogen and progesterone. Scientists had the idea of making a drug that contained these hormones, so that women could take it to boost their own diminishing supplies.

The first product, Emmenin, was developed in 1930 by researchers from Canada's McGill University, using urine from women in late pregnancy, which is rich in oestrogen. But it was costly to produce, and had problems with its unpleasant taste and odour. Four years later, however, Canadian pharmaceutical company Ayerst Labs developed another drug from the urine of pregnant mares, which had been found to contain two and a half times as much hormone as human urine. This medication was named Premarin (pregnant mare's urine), and it soon became the mainstay of the treatment known as hormone replacement therapy (HRT).

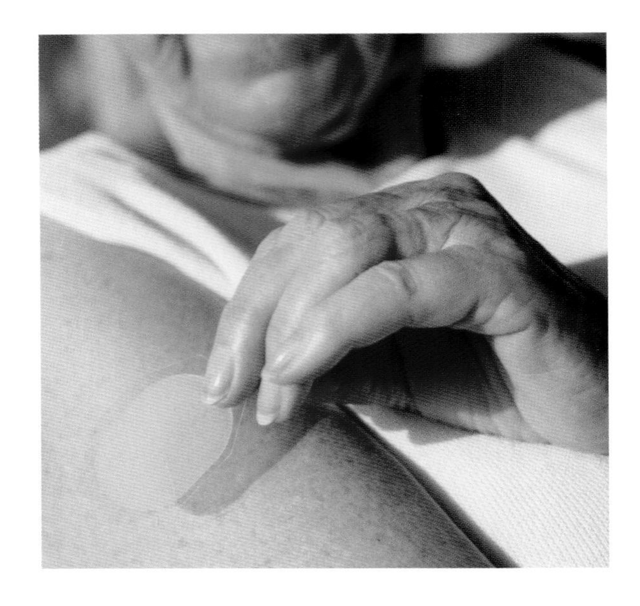

A hormone replacement patch slowly releases oestrogen into the bloodstream to help relieve menopausal symptoms.

Downsides revealed By the 1960s, HRT was being regularly prescribed to millions of women around the world. However, its routine use was called into question in the early 2000s, when a major study revealed that the therapy could increase the risk for breast cancer, heart disease, stroke and blood clots. (Animal welfare activists also campaigned against the drug on the basis that the collection of the urine caused distress to the mares and that the routine destruction of newborn foals was cruel.) As a result, HRT is much less widely used today, though it remains a useful treatment for women with severe menopausal symptoms. Although Premarin is still produced, most oestrogen drugs are now made from synthetic oestrogens.

ORIGIN Eurasia
PART USED Urine

If you feel you need help to alleviate the symptoms of menopause, you should discuss possible treatments with your doctor. HRT may be one of those options, and synthetic oestrogen treatments are widely available.

CHICKEN

Gallus gallus domesticus

MEDICAL BENEFITS ◆ May protect against macular degeneration

The pigments that make egg yolks yellow have been shown to protect against macular degeneration, a condition of the retina that leads to blurred vision and can cause blindness.

Whether you have them fried or boiled, eggs are not just a satisfying breakfast – they may also help to protect your sight. That's because the pigments that make eggs yellow are the same pigments that protect your eyes from the harmful rays of the sun. The retina at the back of the eye is made up of a layer of light-sensitive cells that enable us to see. In the middle there is a region called the macula where the cells are more densely packed; this region is concerned with central, highly focused vision. Particularly in people over 65, these cells may start to die off, due in part to the damaging effects of UV rays in sunlight. The condition is called macular degeneration and it makes reading, driving or recognising faces difficult or even impossible.

Protective pigments There is evidence to show that increasing the amount of antioxidants in your diet can have a protective effect, however, and the two antioxidants that seem to have the most benefits are lutein and zeaxanthin – the pigments that make egg yolks yellow. These pigments are made in the leaves of plants, and you can obtain them from plant sources such as spinach, corn and peppers (capsicums). But scientists have discovered that the body takes up the lutein and zeaxanthin in egg yolks more readily, probably because they are contained in a fat-based matrix along with other micronutrients such as vitamins A, D and E.

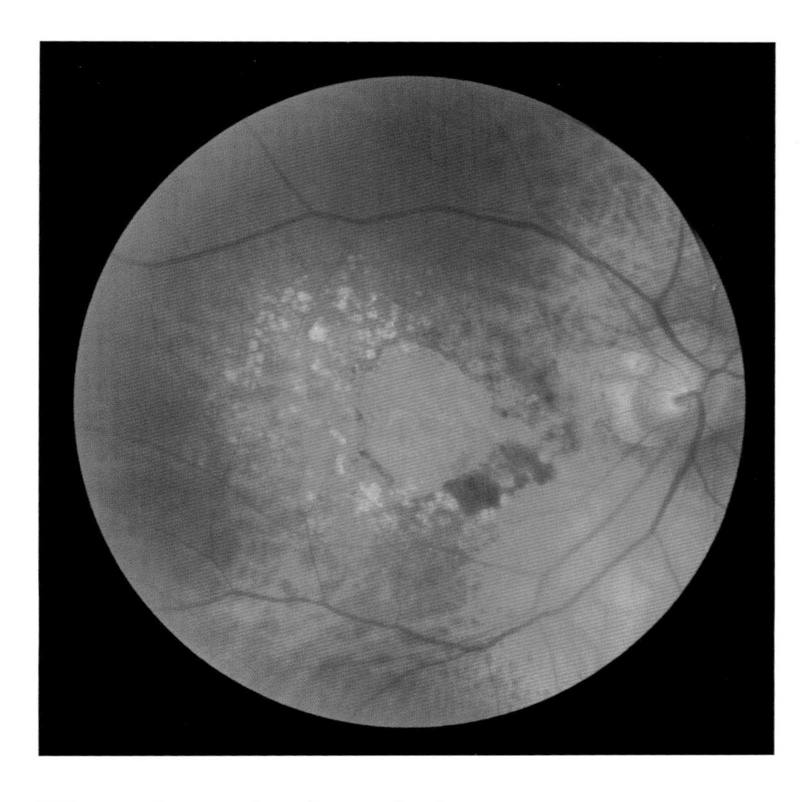

This scan of an eye shows haemorrhaging associated with macular degeneration.

In a study conducted in 2006 at the University of Massachusetts, when patients were given one egg a day for five weeks, the levels of lutein and zeaxanthin in their blood rose significantly. The researchers also measured cholesterol in the participants' blood and found that this was not affected. This is important, as eggs contain relatively high amounts of cholesterol, which once led nutritionists to recommend limiting intake to a maximum of three eggs per week. It seems that the way cholesterol is processed and taken up by the body may be more complicated than previously thought.

ORIGIN India and Southeast Asia
PART USED Egg yolk

You may want to include more eggs in your diet to protect against macular degeneration. However, you should talk to your doctor about how many you should eat, as it will depend on your lifestyle and general health. To maintain eye health, have your eyes checked regularly, protect them from the sun, and eat plenty of nuts, seeds and vegetables.

Canaries are native to the Azores, Madeira and the Canary Islands of the Atlantic Ocean. In the wild they have patterned yellow-and-brown plumage.

CANARY

Serinus canaria domestica

MEDICAL BENEFITS ◆ Could point the way to treatments for Parkinson's disease, Alzheimer's disease, Huntington's disease and depression ◆ May lead to a treatment for brain and spinal injuries

The discovery that adult male canaries can grow regions of their brains opened up a new field of research: neurogenesis. It may one day lead to a cure for common brain disorders.

Up until the 1980s, the scientific community largely believed that adult brain cells (neurones) could not regenerate themselves. Though other cells in the body could be replaced, it was thought that you had your full complement of neurones at birth and throughout your life the number gradually diminished as the neurones died. So, when neuroscientist Fernando Nottebohm, working at New York's Rockefeller University, discovered that certain regions of male canary brains could increase in size, the scientific community was shocked and his research was met with derision. Yet his experiments stood up to scrutiny, so scientists began to wonder: if brain cells could grow in a bird's brain, could this also occur in other animals? Could it be the same for humans?

Other researchers subsequently provided evidence of neurone renewal in the brains of animals and humans, arousing intense interest. Yet, even today, the field of neurogenesis remains controversial, with some scientists maintaining that neurone renewal in the human brain is still unproven and others arguing that the number of neurones generated is so small as to be of negligible value.

Learning to sing Fernando Nottebohm was not looking to overturn scientific doctrine when he made his great discovery; he was simply trying to understand how canaries and other birds learn and communicate through their songs. It turns out that the way the birds learn how to sing is very similar to the way that human babies learn how to talk – through listening, imitating and practising.

For the first month, canaries and other songbirds simply cry to their parents when they need feeding. Then in the second month they begin to babble, rather like a prevocal baby, producing a quiet warbling known as 'subsong'. By its third month, a songbird sings a more structured but still variable type of song called 'plastic song'. By eight months, the young bird is producing what's called 'stable song', which it will sing loudly for the duration of the mating season.

Bird brains At the end of the mating season, however, canaries, and a few other songbird species, appear to lose their mastery of song and re-enter a stage of plastic song, during which they may forget certain syllables and learn new ones. Then, at the start of the next mating season they produce a new stable song, different from that of the previous year. Nottebohm discovered that canary songs were

ORIGIN Canary Islands, Azores and Madeira
PART USED Data from studies of brain

Neuroscientist Fernando Nottebohm enjoys some interaction with the birds that have served his research so well.

associated with nerve cells in the birds' brains, which he called 'song nuclei'. These song nuclei were situated in the forebrains of the birds, the region that controls complex behaviours.

Nottebohm noted that female canaries (which hardly sing) had smaller nuclei than males. He also found that the male nuclei grew bigger in size during the 'plastic song' phase, when males were learning more songs – in other words, it seemed that the birds were able to 'grow' parts of their brains as other regions shrank. At first, Nottebohm thought that the growth of the song nuclei must be due to the brain cells changing size, but he soon ruled that out, coming to the conclusion that the canaries grew new neurones so that they could learn new songs.

Neurone renewal By studying the tiny brains of songbirds as Nottebohm did, scientists can make associations with the human brain and understand more about the way we learn and how the language and auditory centres of our brains work. But by far the most significant aspect of Nottebohm's work was his discovery that the birds were growing *new* neurones. For it implied that if the brain is able to produce new cells, it could possibly repair itself in the event of brain disease or trauma.

Important evidence supporting Nottebohm's claims emerged in 1998, when psychologist and neuroscientist Elizabeth Gould, of Princeton University, documented neurone renewal in the brains of marmoset and rhesus monkeys. This was exciting news as rhesus monkeys are close to humans in their biology. Later the same year, Swedish neurologist Peter Eriksson and US geneticist Fred H Gage published a study that rocked the world of bioscience. They demonstrated that new neurones could be generated in the human brain from so-called stem cells – blank 'starter' cells that can develop into many different types of cells. This raised the possibility of transplanting new stem cells into a damaged brain in order to repair it.

in CLOSE-UP

Like all songbirds, canaries use their vocalisations to establish territory and to tell potential mates that they are around. Their songs are organised into a series of phrases, made up of several syllables; the syllables are composed of a collection of single notes. An individual bird will have its own unique repertoire of different versions of a song. It is not known what advantage male canaries gain from learning new songs each year. Perhaps it is a signal to the females that the bird is healthy, or perhaps it is a reflection of changes in the environment. It may even reflect the need to attract a certain type of mate.

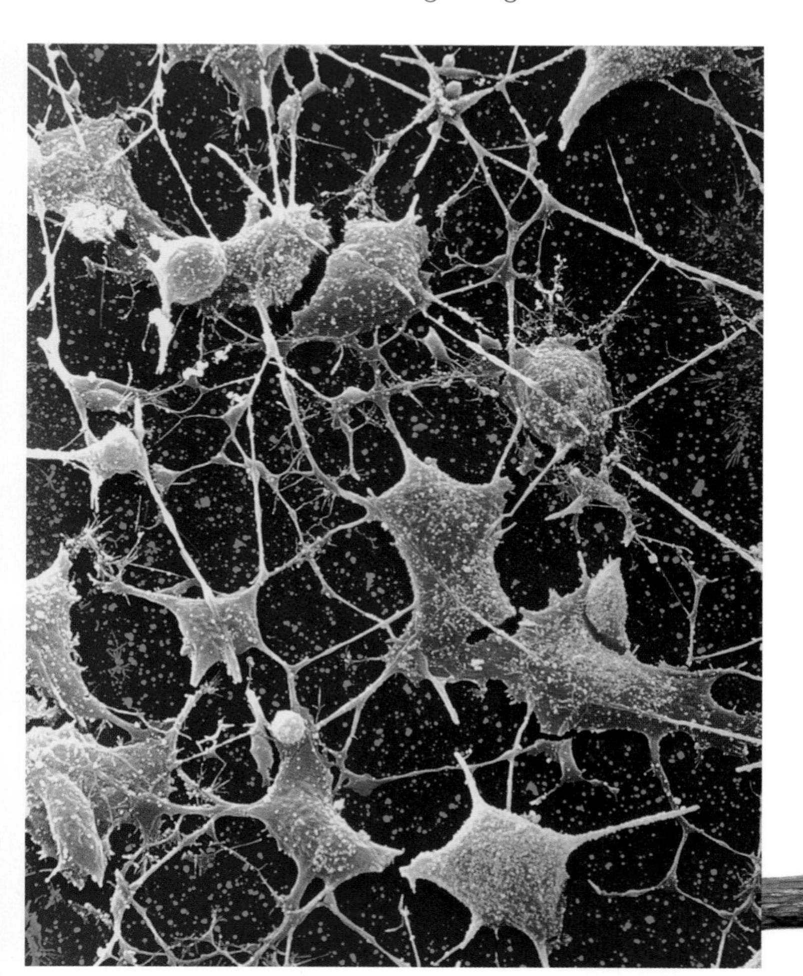

Left: Brain cells, or neurones, as shown in this scanning electron micrograph image, are linked by narrow filaments or dendrites.

Divide and disperse More recently, scientists have made further progress in understanding how neurogenesis occurs. It is now thought that the human brain produces new neurones in two particular areas (but possibly others, too): the olfactory bulb (which processes scents) and a region of the hippocampus (associated with memory, spatial awareness and emotions). Both of these regions are rich in stem cells, which can divide to produce either more stem cells or cells that are destined to become neurones (pre-neurones).

Guided by chemical signals, the pre-neurones migrate along fibres of cells called radial glia, which extend through different layers of the brain. Once in position, the pre-neurones mature to become fully functional neurones. The next part of the process is the least understood: each neurone then 'decides' what its ultimate function will be – for example, it might become a motor neurone or a sensory neurone. Then it grows like the other neurones around it, making connections with them.

Curing the brain Conditions or diseases of the brain that cause neurone death or damage are most likely to benefit from neurogenesis research. These include Parkinson's disease and Huntington's disease, which cause neurones to die off in the basal ganglia, an area of the brain that controls body movements, and Alzheimer's disease, which causes plaques to build up around neurones in parts of the brain that control memory. As scientists learn more about the way the brain works and how neurones form and die, they might be able to develop treatments or even cures for these conditions, and might also be able to repair damage caused by strokes, head traumas and spinal injuries.

Drugs could be developed that stimulate the brain to produce new neurones, or stem cells could be transplanted into the appropriate regions of the brain. Scientists have already discovered that Prozac, a widely used antidepressant, increases the ability of brain stem cells to divide and encourages them to become neurones. Now scientists are trying to find out how much of a role neurogenesis, or lack of it, plays in triggering depression.

Domestic canaries are bred for their strong colours, most often yellow.

A cure or therapy for Alzheimer's and similar brain disorders based on neurogenesis is some way off. However, we can copy canaries by making sure that we learn new things as we get older. There is much evidence to show that we can keep our brain healthy with regular 'workouts' – from tackling a daily crossword puzzle to learning a new language. Regular physical exercise also helps, as does a balanced diet rich in omega-3 fatty acids (see p. 258).

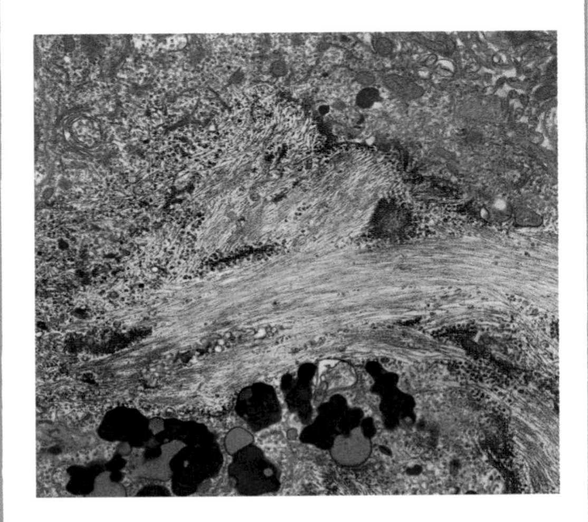

In this scan of a brain cell, the yellow area is a significant build-up of the deposits, or plaques, associated with Alzheimer's disease.

PIG

Sus scrofa domesticus

MEDICAL BENEFITS ◆ Potential new treatment for type 1 diabetes ◆ Possible source of replacement organs

People with type 1 diabetes may soon be able to control their blood glucose with transplanted pancreas cells from pigs.

People with type 1 diabetes are unable to produce insulin, the hormone that helps the body use sugar for energy. To control the disease, diabetics have to keep their blood glucose within a narrow limit by injecting synthetic insulin to lower their blood glucose or eating sugary foods if their blood glucose falls too low. But if current clinical trials are successful, they may one day have another option: an implant of insulin-producing cells from pigs.

The insulin-producing cells, known as beta cells, are found in the pancreas. A pig's pancreas is similar to a human's and the insulin it produces is almost identical, but, as with most animal-to-human transplants, rejection can be a major problem: transplanted cells may work initially but are soon recognised as foreign and destroyed by the body's immune system.

In 1996, New Zealand-based biotech company Living Cell Technologies (LCT) began an experiment using beta cells from newborn pigs, based on the theory that because the cells were so new they might be less 'visible' to the human

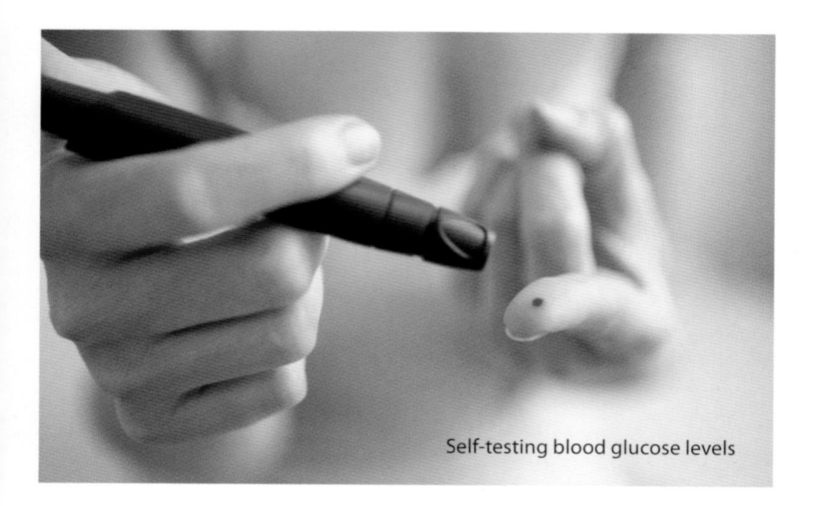

Self-testing blood glucose levels

in CLOSE-UP

Pigs have always been useful to researchers because their physiology and anatomy are very similar to those of humans. Pigs are omnivores and so their digestive system is similar to ours; there are also similarities in the way their kidneys work, how they breathe, the way their glands work and their circulatory system. And a pig's pancreas is similar in size to a human's and produces insulin that is almost identical to human insulin. In fact, pig insulin was used to treat type 1 diabetes for most of the twentieth century, along with cattle insulin. Initially, in the 1920s, the use of animal insulin was based on guesswork. It was only in the 1980s, when scientists finally unravelled the structure of insulin, that they could see that it was virtually identical in humans, pigs, cattle and many other animals. And at that point they were able to make synthetic insulin.

Pig organs could become widely used in transplants if scientists can find a way to prevent organ rejection.

recipient's immune system. The cells were transplanted into the peritoneal cavity (which contains the stomach, intestines, liver and pancreas) of six diabetic volunteers. In four of the patients the cells disappeared, but in two the cells survived, and researchers noticed that the patients' bodies had sealed off the cells in a jelly-like substance.

Chance discovery One of the successful patients was Michael Helyer. At first, the implanted cells reduced his need for insulin by 30 per cent, but after a year he had reverted to his usual intake. The researchers thought the experiment had failed, even though Helyer reported feeling generally better, insisting it must be due to the implant. In 2007, the researchers decided to check on the state of his implant and to their surprise found the encapsulated cells embedded in tissue and still producing small amounts of insulin. It was a breakthrough, and it encouraged LCT to conduct further clinical trials in Russia, New Zealand and Argentina. This time LCT transplanted the cells in a seaweed-based capsule whose coating allows small molecules, such as insulin, to escape while keeping out larger molecules, such as the recipient's antibodies, which might destroy the cells. The trials began in 2009 and so far results have been promising. More trials will be needed, however, before transplanting pig beta cells becomes a widespread treatment.

ORIGIN Asia
PART USED Pancreatic beta cells

Organ transplants

Scientists are looking at the possibility of growing organs in pigs for transplantation into humans. And to prevent the human recipient's body rejecting the organs, they plan to spike the pig's DNA with human genes. Clinical trials using pig-grown corneas could begin within the next two or three years.

DEER

Cervidae

MEDICAL BENEFITS ◆ Treatment for osteoarthritis ◆ Possible treatment for rheumatoid arthritis ◆ May enhance understanding of wound healing and organ regeneration ◆ Traditional treatment for boosting immune system, anaemia, fertility, bone and joint health, improving strength

Imagine being able to regrow a finger. Scientists believe that by studying the way deer regenerate their antlers we may come closer to being able to do just that.

Only a mature stag can produce a set of antlers. They grow bigger every year, and can eventually weigh up to 30 kg (65 lb).

All male members of the deer family, including elk, moose and reindeer (caribou), grow a new set of antlers each year – from scratch, in just a matter of months – then shed them at the end of the annual mating season. The ability to regenerate such large appendages each year is unique to this family among mammals and rare in the animal kingdom as a whole (horns, in contrast to antlers, are permanent and cannot be regrown). Understanding how it happens could have significant implications for human medicine, particularly in the fields of wound healing and organ regeneration.

Velvet cure Deer antler, or more specifically 'velvet antler' – which refers to the soft, newly grown antler, not just the velvet skin – has been used in Chinese medicine for 2000 years. Often

in CLOSE-UP

Antlers demonstrate a stag's fitness for mating. They start to sprout in spring and the rate of growth accelerates through summer. Initially, they are composed of soft cartilage, well supplied with blood vessels and nerves and covered in a downy skin known as velvet, but come autumn, as the mating season begins and the stag's testosterone levels soar, they harden into bone. The outer velvet then dies and is rubbed off against vegetation. Stags have been seen gnawing at old antlers, probably to recoup some of the lost minerals.

Red deer antlers grow at a rate of up to 2 cm (¾ in) per day.

prescribed as a tonic, it is reputed to boost the immune system, improve stamina and reduce swelling. It is also prescribed to promote wound healing and strengthen bones, and said to be an aphrodisiac and to enhance fertility.

Today, clinical evidence is amassing to back the use of velvet antler as a treatment for osteoarthritis and as a supplement to enhance strength and endurance in athletic performance. Some studies indicate it may also prevent tumour growth, enhance mood and improve circulation. People with osteoarthritis take chondroitin sulphate as an anti-inflammatory, and velvet antler contains a high concentration of this compound, as well as significant amounts of glucosamine sulphate. Both appear to inhibit the depletion of bone and cartilage. The use of velvet antler in treating rheumatoid arthritis is being studied at the University of Calgary and the University of Alberta in Canada.

Healing substances When antlers fall off, they leave wounds that heal quickly, without forming a scar. Researchers have found that velvet antler contains substances that encourage healing, and could be of use to humans. Of particular interest are three hormones known to promote growth of skin tissue: insulin-like growth factor (IGF-1), epidermal growth factor (EGF) and transforming growth factor-β1 (TGF-β1). In a recent study, an ointment made from velvet antler, containing these compounds, enhanced healing when applied to the skin of rats.

Even more intriguing is how the stags manage to regrow their antlers. Scientists have found stem cells at the bases of antlers – essentially 'blank' cells that can develop into many different types of cell, such as a skin cell or a cartilage cell. If they could find out what triggers the stem cells and controls their development into antlers, the knowledge could be applied to the regeneration of human limbs and organs. Scientists know that the shedding is initiated by a fall in the hormone testosterone, a change linked to an increase in day length, and they think oestrogen may be a key cellular regulator. However, much more research on a molecular level is required to unravel what is clearly an intricate process.

In China, velvet antler is seen as second only to ginseng in its restorative powers. This man is preparing sliced antler for use in a soup.

ORIGIN Europe, Asia, northwest Africa
PART USED Young antler before it hardens

Powdered velvet antler is available in capsule form from health shops. As a general tonic and to fight fatigue, the recommended dosage is usually one or two 250–350 mg capsules per day. Higher doses may be used, under supervision of a health practitioner, for conditions such as osteoarthritis. The effects of velvet antler gradually accumulate and are typically seen after eight to twelve weeks.

AFRICAN GIANT POUCHED RAT

Cricetomys gambianus

MEDICAL BENEFITS ◆ Detection of tuberculosis ◆ Saving lives through the detection of landmines ◆ Could be used to detect pollutants in soil and carry cameras into hazardous locations to help with rescue missions

So sensitive are rats' noses that Belgian health workers in Africa have been able to train members of one native species to detect tuberculosis and another major human hazard, landmines.

Over the years, rats have gained a terrible reputation: always the first off a sinking ship, spreading plague and pestilence. But now the African giant pouched rat is set to redeem this rodent family by helping health workers screen for tuberculosis (TB). Rats of this species trained by a Belgian organisation, APOPO, based in Tanzania in Africa, can detect specific volatile compounds of *Mycobacterium tuberculosis* (Mtb), the bacterial species that causes TB. When presented with a row of sputum samples, a rat moves along the line sniffing carefully. If it detects the target Mtb compounds, it scratches at the sample – and receives its reward.

Employing trained rats in this way is much faster than smear microscopy, the traditional method of screening. Whereas a microscopist can process 40 slides a day, a rat can get through the same number of samples in seven minutes. Rat screening is also more effective. Experiments comparing rat screening with microscopy found that the detection rate increased on average by 30 per cent using rats. This is important with a disease as contagious as TB because every infected person who is missed can subsequently infect up to another 15 healthy people per year. Using rats is especially useful when there are large numbers of people to screen in regions of the world where medical and laboratory resources are limited, such as Africa. They are cost-effective, too: the rats work for peanuts – literally.

in CLOSE-UP

Rats have an exceptional sense of smell – one of the most sensitive of any mammal – and they smell in stereo, with each nostril functioning independently. This means that not only can they discern between many types of smell but they can also map them in their minds – in fact, this is how they navigate their territories in the wild (their eyesight is poor). Experiments have shown that rats can even discern between TB and other microorganisms of the respiratory tract, correctly identifying the TB.

At an APOPO testing centre, an African giant pouched rat sniffs its way along a line of samples, under the eye of a handler.

Landmines are usually triggered by any load of more than 5 kg (11 lb). Weighing in at under 1.5 kg (3.3 lb), the African giant pouched rat is unlikely to set one off.

Founder of APOPO Bart Weetjens keeps a close eye on his protégés. It takes about nine months to train a rat for landmine or TB detection.

Using rats, clinics in Tanzania have screened 20,000 people – and identified 2500 cases that had been missed by conventional screening.

Heroes in the making Before being trained to sniff out TB, African giant pouched rats were already saving lives by detecting landmines. APOPO (a Belgian acronym meaning 'Anti-Personnel Landmines Detection Product Development') has been training them since 1998 and now has an 'army' of 300. The Belgians justifiably call their rats 'HeroRATS'.

Bart Weetjens, a product engineer from Belgium, founded APOPO in response to the unexploded landmine problem in sub-Saharan Africa. He knew that in poor areas of Africa a cheap and cost-effective solution was needed for the dangerous task of detecting landmines. Thinking back to a childhood pet rat, he recalled its great sense of smell and trainability. The African giant pouched rat was chosen for the project because it is native to the region, has a long lifespan and is resilient to many tropical diseases. Though large, growing up to 90 cm (3 ft) long, it is still light enough that it won't trigger a mine if it walks across one. Like all rats, the species learns quickly, making it easy to train with a simple reward system.

Rats are now helping to clear landmines in Mozambique and Thailand, too. And as well as TB and landmine detection, there are other potential applications: sniffing out pollutants in soils, illegal drugs and so on. Another avenue of research is focusing on training rats to carry cameras on their backs so that they can crawl under mounds of rubble after an earthquake to look for survivors.

OTHER NAME Gambian pouched rat
ORIGIN Africa **PART USED** Acute sense of smell

What You CAN DO

If you want to support the work of APOPO, visit the website www.apopo.org. For a small subscription, you can adopt your very own HeroRAT and receive updates about its vital work saving lives in Africa.

COMMON VAMPIRE BAT

Desmodus rotundus

MEDICAL BENEFITS ◆ Potential anticoagulant for treating strokes

A compound in vampire bat saliva that keeps blood flowing has been harnessed to develop a new anticoagulant drug for dissolving dangerous blood clots.

The vampire bat faces the same problem as any bloodsucker – how to overcome its prey's natural defences of constricting blood flow and sealing the wound with a clot? Unlike mythical vampires that sink a large pair of fangs into their victims and suck the blood out, vampire bats make a small cut with their razor-sharp incisors then lap at the wound with their tongues. By licking at the wound the bat mixes the blood with its saliva – and potent anti-clotting agents. In this way, it can feed for as long as it likes and the blood keeps on running.

Doctors already use anticlotting agents to treat people who have had an ischaemic stroke (a stroke in which a blood clot has travelled up the blood vessels and into the brain); the agents break down the clot and thin the blood. But the compound in vampire bat saliva promises to be more effective and less dangerous than the existing drugs. Not only that, it may well extend the window in which stroke sufferers can be successfully treated by several hours.

Finding the trigger The anticoagulant properties of vampire bat saliva have been known about since the 1930s. But it was not until the 1990s, following improvements in biotechnology, that scientists were able to start unravelling the compounds involved. One of the enzymes responsible was identified as *Desmodus rotundus* salivary plasminogen activator (DSPA) and given the nickname 'draculin' – who says haematologists don't

ORIGIN Central and South America
PART USED Saliva

During a 20-minute feed, a vampire bat can consume 20 g (0.7 oz) of blood – the equivalent of half its body weight.

In 2009, phase III clinical trials of desmoteplase, the compound based on vampire bat saliva, began and are in progress in hospitals and clinics around the world. Developed by Lundbeck, it is hoped that if all goes well in these trials, the product could be brought to market in 2014. Check then with your doctor for further information.

have a sense of humour? The next step was to genetically engineer a copy of the enzyme for use in clinical trials. This was achieved in 2003; the engineered compound is called desmoteplase and is owned by the Danish pharmaceutical company Lundbeck.

> Strokes caused by a blood clot travelling to the brain account for 85 per cent of all strokes.

So far, clinical trials have shown desmoteplase to be highly effective at clearing clots. And although trials are continuing, initial results suggest the compound could be administered up to nine hours after a stroke. This would be an important breakthrough, with the potential to save thousands of lives, since existing stroke medications can be given only within the first three hours after a stroke without running the risk of internal bleeding in the brain.

in CLOSE-UP

Blood carries its own anti-clotting agent, but it is in an unreactive form called plasminogen. This means the blood only breaks down clots as it needs to – otherwise we would suffer regular internal bleeding. When required, the body releases a trigger chemical to turn the plasminogen into plasmin, which then breaks down the clot. In humans, this trigger chemical is called tissue-type plasminogen activator (tPA). Scientists have bioengineered a copy, called alteplase, and this is what they give stroke patients to break down blood clots. Alteplase is, however, indiscriminate and acts not just on fibrin but also on other tissues, which can lead to catastrophic internal bleeding if the drug is given more than three hours after a stroke. Desmoteplase, in contrast, is 200 times more fibrin specific, targeting only the clot. As a result, it can be given at any time during the first nine hours.

Vampire bats hunt at night. By day they roost in dark places such as caves and disused buildings, often in huge colonies.

WATCH AND LEARN

We may not be able to talk to the animals – but we can learn a lot by simply watching what they do. A new field of science known as zoopharmacognosy involves studying how some animals cure themselves of disease, in the hope of uncovering natural medicines that might also be used to treat human ailments.

The term 'zoopharmacognosy' comes from the Greek roots *zoo* (animal), *pharma* (medicine) and *cognosy* (knowing) and refers to the way animals self-medicate by using particular plants, soils and insects to treat and prevent diseases. For many years this 'animal wisdom' was the stuff of old wives' tales, reflected in folklore and the common names of plants. But since the 1990s, thanks to the work of a few researchers, the subject has gained serious recognition.

Bitter medicine A pioneer in the field is Michael Huffmann, a primatologist at Kyoto University, Japan. In 1987, while studying a group of chimpanzees in Mahale, Tanzania, along with his guide, Mohamedi Seif Kalunde, he noticed some interesting behaviour among the chimps. One of them, Chausiku, looked under the weather: she was resting for long periods and seemed generally lethargic. Huffmann watched as the chimp went up to a particular plant, pulled off several young branches, stripped the bark and began chewing the pith and spitting out the fibrous remains.

Unusual feeding habits may be the first sign that an animal is self-medicating.

Mohamedi, a park ranger and elder traditional healer of the local Tongwe tribe, identified the plant by its native name, Mjonso (better known as bitter leaf, *Vernonia amygdalina*), saying that the Tongwe used it as a medicine for malarial fever, stomachaches and intestinal parasites. Huffmann was intrigued. It was the rainy season and peak time for infection by *Oesophagostomum stephanostomum*, a nematode worm that lives in the guts of chimps. The next day Chausiku appeared much better. Huffmann knew he was on to something.

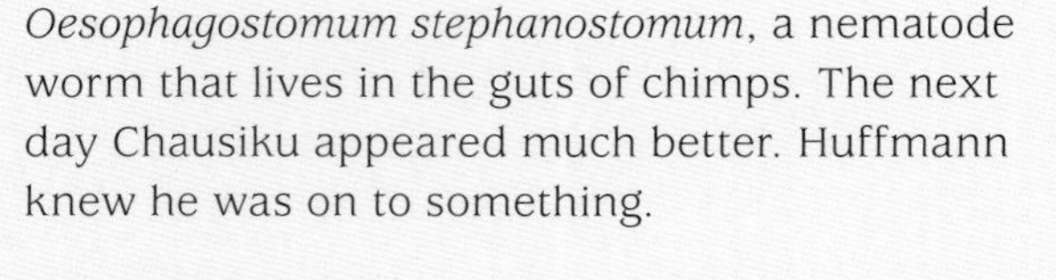

Active ingredient It turned out that the behaviour was not limited to one chimp – many others would munch on the bitter-tasting herb, but only occasionally. Huffmann began looking at dung samples of chimps before and after they were seen chewing on the herb. He found that the worm load was considerably decreased after the chimps had chewed the plant.

The next step was to identify the chemical in the plant that was killing the worms. Through international collaboration with laboratories in France, Japan and the United Kingdom, 13 new compounds were discovered, the most relevant and active being vernonioside B1. The substance was shown to have antiparasitic, antitumour and antibacterial properties. The plant also contains toxic chemicals, which explains why the chimps eat it in small amounts and only when sick. Huffmann's work became the first to scientifically demonstrate self-medication by an animal.

A natural instinct Many similar cases have since been observed. In the 1990s, researchers in Kenya were intrigued when they witnessed a heavily pregnant elephant search for a particular plant, a member of the borage family, which she then consumed in large quantities. Days later she gave birth. When the plant was analysed, it turned out that the leaves and bark of this tree contain chemicals that induce uterine contractions. Local tribeswomen know about the drug, too, taking the leaves themselves in preparation for birth or to induce an abortion.

It seems likely that much of traditional medicine would have developed in this way, by observing nature. And today the study of animal self-medication could provide the key to a whole pharmacopoeia of useful medicines.

ANIMAL CURES

Documented examples of animal self-medication include the following:

Chimpanzees eat bitter leaf pith (*Vernonia amygdalina*) and *Aspilia* leaves to eliminate intestinal parasites, as well as *Trichilia rubescens* leaves, which have antimalarial properties.

Capuchin monkeys rub mashed leaves of the jungle shrub *Piper marginatum* into their skin to deter parasites.

Birds of many species rub ants onto or encourage ants into their feathers; the ants release chemicals that combat parasites and infections.

Sifaka lemurs eat the bark of fig and tamarind trees when they are pregnant to stimulate milk production and kill intestinal parasites.

Honeybees are prone to attack from the fungus *Ascosphaera apis*, which causes a disease that kills bee larvae. For protection, the bees line their hive with propolis, a sticky resin from plants that has been shown to have antimicrobial properties.

Tiger moth caterpillars consume hemlock to control tachinid fly parasitic larvae.

Left: Orangutans chew leaves of the *Commelina* plant and then apply the chewed leaves as a balm for sore muscles, joints and skin.

Right: Female elephants will roam far afield in search of the borage tree, which induces labour.

Left: Like many other animals, macaws eat clay soils to calm the digestive system and neutralise toxic substances.

Above: Elk eat the bark of the aspen tree for pain relief. The bark contains a chemical similar to one in aspirin.

Right: European starlings line their nests with bay leaves to keep them free of fleas.

HIPPOPOTAMUS

Hippopotamus amphibius

MEDICAL BENEFITS ◆ Potential more effective form of sunblock ◆ Possible new type of antiseptic

Hippos spend a lot of time in the sun, yet never get sunburned. Their secret is a red, oily secretion, similar to sweat, that acts as a sunblock – and might also work for people, too.

It looks like blood and smells pretty rank, but scientists believe that hippo 'sweat' (it's not actually sweat, since it is produced by glands under the skin, not in it) may one day lead to a new and especially effective type of sunscreen for humans. For the red, oily secretion contains chemical components that absorb and scatter ultraviolet light; in addition, at least one component also acts as an antiseptic, protecting against infection.

What You CAN DO

The researchers acknowledge it may be some time before hippo sweat is made into sunscreen. The ultimate goal is a combined sunscreen, antiseptic and insect repellent – which could be worth the wait.

Absorbent pigments Hippos live in Africa and avoid the heat by spending most of the day wallowing in water, only moving onto land at night to feed. Although the water helps to keep them cool, it doesn't do much to protect their skin from the strong sun. What's more, scientists noted some time ago that even albino hippos, which lack the darker, protective pigment in the skin of regular hippos, suffered no ill effects from the strong and almost constant African sunshine. Clearly something other than skin pigment was protecting them, and it turned out to be their 'sweat'.

The true nature of hippo sweat was revealed in 2004 by a team from Kyoto Pharmaceutical University, Japan. The researchers used cotton swabs to take samples from the backs of two hippos living in Ueno Zoological Gardens in

Hippos often lie under water but must resurface every four minutes or so to breathe. They can even do this in their sleep.

One in three of every cancers diagnosed in the United States is a skin cancer.

Tokyo – a brave act considering the size and well-documented aggressive nature of hippos. Analysing the sweat, they discovered two pigments: one red and one orange. They named the red pigment hipposudoric acid and the orange pigment norhipposudoric acid. Both compounds were shown to absorb light in the ultraviolet and visible range (200–600 nm) of the spectrum, making them effective sunscreens; the red pigment was also shown to have antibacterial properties.

Like sweat, the secretion also helps to cool the skin through evaporation, while its water-resistant properties protect the skin from long hours under water. Being oily, the substance also clings to the skin, so the protection lasts for several hours and does not easily wash off.

Scattering light In 2009, a team of researchers from the School of Engineering at the University of California, Merced, took another look at hippo sweat and found that it contained two types of crystalline structures: banded and nonbanded. The banded structures had concentric dark circles that were spaced so that they interfered with the wavelength of incoming light. The result was that the light was scattered – effectively, it was blocked. The nonbanded structures help the secretion to spread over the surface of the hippo's skin and slow the rate at which it dries out.

So not only does hippo sweat act as a sunscreen, it is also a sunblock, spreads well, is water resistant and has antiseptic properties, too – all of which is inspiring further research. Marketing moguls may need to come up with a more appealing name, and would definitely need to make sure it smelled better, but if the properties of hippo sweat turn out to be as promising as they look we could soon be slathering it on as we head for the beach.

ORIGIN Africa
PART USED Skin secretion

The ancient Greeks noted the red secretion on the skin of the hippopotamus – and assumed the animal was sweating blood.

in CLOSE-UP

The red pigment in hippo sweat is highly acidic (approximately 100 times more acidic than vinegar), making it extremely effective at killing off bacteria. This is especially helpful for an aggressive animal that regularly gets wounded in battle and spends most of its time submerged in murky river water. The secretion's antiseptic properties help to explain why the gaping flesh wounds often seen on hippos never seem to get infected.

AMERICAN BLACK BEAR

Ursus americanus

MEDICAL BENEFITS ◆ Potential treatment for trauma victims, kidney failure ◆ Possible application in long-term stasis, such as space travel ◆ Traditional treatment for gallstones

The processes used by bears to lower their metabolic rate during hibernation could one day help save the lives of victims of heart attack and stroke, and may even help us explore outer space.

It makes sense for black bears to hibernate – they live in regions where there are long months of winter when food is scarce. By slowing their metabolism they can sleep through the worst of the snow and emerge when food is abundant again. Although several types of animal wait out the winter in this way, scientists have discovered that black bears hibernate differently from most, and the way they do it could have applications in human medicine.

In 2011, a team of researchers from the Institute of Arctic Biology at the University of Alaska Fairbanks became the first to monitor hibernating bears continuously for five months. What they discovered was intriguing and not what they expected. When most animals go into hibernation they slow their metabolism by about half of the normal rate for every 10°C (18°F) drop in body temperature. But the black bears in the study managed to slow their metabolic rate to just 25 per cent of the normal rate with only a 6°C (10°F) drop in body temperature. Since the bears' temperature dropped only slightly, the scientists reckon that they must use some kind of biochemical mechanism, perhaps through hormone-like substances in the blood, to lower their metabolism. Identifying this mechanism could have implications for trauma victims who need emergency treatment.

Improving outcomes When someone suffers a heart attack or stroke, time is of the essence and the sooner they receive expert treatment the better the outcome. If doctors knew a way

Traditional Wisdom

Since they live off their body fat, hibernating bears have high cholesterol levels. Yet they never develop gallstones. This is because their bile is rich in ursodeoxycholic acid (UDCA), a chemical that dissolves gallstones. Bear bile has long been used in Chinese medicine to treat gallstones and today there are many chemically synthesised versions of UDCA available, offering people with cholesterol gallstones an alternative to having their gallbladder removed.

A black bear usually enters its den in October or November, having put on an extra 14 kg (30 lb) or so of body fat.

A bear den may be in a cave or tree cavity or in a hollow beneath a rock or log. Females give birth, usually to two cubs, in early February.

of putting them into 'suspended animation', similar to the way in which bears hibernate, then there would be more time to get them to the expert care they need. The same is true of organ transplants: if doctors could find a drug that would put the organs into stasis, there would be more time to make them available to a suitable recipient.

Learning how to put people into hibernation also has implications for space exploration. The greatest obstacle in reaching other inhabitable planets is the vast distances involved. To reach, say, another solar system, we would need to be able to travel for much longer than an average human lifespan. Putting people into hibernation might just make this possible.

ORIGIN North America
PART USED Ability to hibernate/ lower metabolic rate

Hold the water!

Studying how bears put their body systems on hold might also have other, more down-to-earth benefits. When black bears hibernate, they last months without eating or drinking, yet their bodies maintain a perfect water balance with no muscle wastage. They do not urinate or defecate either; instead their bodies become recycling units. Kilojoules and water come from the breakdown of fat tissue, while muscle tissue and organs supply protein. Such tissue breakdown yields urea, which would be toxic if it accumulated. Normally it is excreted in urine, but during hibernation the bears use the components of urea to build new proteins. As a result the amount of urine entering the kidneys drops by 95 per cent. Doctors are keen to find out exactly how bears manage this, as it could be of benefit to people with kidney failure.

SOUTHERN COPPERHEAD

Agkistrodon contortrix

MEDICAL BENEFITS ◆ Potential treatment for cancer of the breast, skin, ovary, prostate and brain

The painful bite of a venomous viper, known for stalking its prey through the swamps and woodlands of the southern United States, may harbour a new treatment for a range of deadly cancers.

When a copperhead bites its victim, it releases a compound called contortrostatin, which keeps the blood fluid so the venom can disperse. While investigating potentially useful products derived from reptile venom, Professor Frank Markland, Associate Dean for Scientific Affairs at the University of Southern California's Keck School of Medicine, observed that contortrostatin was similar in structure to human proteins called disintegrins. These proteins prevent cells, including cancerous cells, from moving into neighbouring tissues, by inhibiting blood clotting and cell adhesion (cell adhesion is essential for cells to communicate with each other and respond to changes in the local environment, such as a need for blood to start clotting).

Double effect Markland wondered if contortrostatin might similarly interfere with the ability of cancer cells to spread. In a 2005 experiment, he made mice immunodeficient by removing their thymus (the organ that programs white blood cells to repel infections). Then mice were injected with brain cancer cells and given a dose of contortrostatin. Not only did the snake protein slow the growth of the tumour, it also stopped the tumour generating the blood supply it needed to spread.

But contortrostatin isn't just lethal to brain cancer: it also fights prostate cancer. A 2010 study by Markland's team showed contortrostatin, combined with the drug docetaxel (see p. 45), slowed the spread of prostate cancer more effectively than docetaxel alone.

Southern copperhead

OTHER NAMES Copperhead, highland moccasin, chunkhead, death adder
ORIGIN Southern and eastern United States, Mexico
PART USED Venom

It looks like contortrostatin treatments could be available fairly soon. Frank Markland recently cofounded a new company, Applied Integrin Sciences, to fund safety studies. If the drug is given the all-clear and US Food and Drug Administration approval, clinical trials should follow. The chances of this happening were boosted recently when Markland succeeded in mass-producing a form of contortrostatin called vicrostatin and developed a method for introducing it into the body – sheathed in fatty molecules to hide it from the immune system.

AMERICAN ALLIGATOR

Alligator mississippiensis

MEDICAL BENEFITS ◆ Possible source of antiviral, antibacterial and antifungal drugs ◆ Potential use in topical ointments to reduce infection in diabetic ulcers and infected burns

One of the most primitive vertebrates in the world could be the source of new medicines to treat a huge range of serious infections while avoiding the problem of antibiotic resistance.

It's a tough life being an alligator. You live in a filthy swamp filled with bacteria, viruses and rotting plants. You're constantly at war with the neighbours, especially during the mating season, and as a result can find yourself missing an eye, leg or even an entire tail.

Somehow though, despite their dirty domestic scene and the potential for infection, alligators show a remarkable capacity to recover from these terrible wounds – injuries that would kill many other species. It's no surprise then that scientists have been trying to fathom the secret of the alligator's amazing ability to heal. And their discoveries could have exciting implications for treating a range of human ailments.

After being declared endangered in the 1960s, the American alligator has recovered and is now widespread in the US southeast.

in CLOSE-UP

Alligators and their close relative, the saltwater crocodile, can survive massive injuries that would kill many other species. The late Steve Irwin, also known as the 'Crocodile Hunter', discovered just how much one crocodile had endured when he was called to remove it from an Australian waterhole. The 4.2-m (13½-ft) croc, christened Nobby, had been shot with a high-powered rifle some years before and half his bottom jaw had been blown off. Despite this, he had recovered and continued to hunt and eat. His relocation was deemed necessary after he ate a dog.

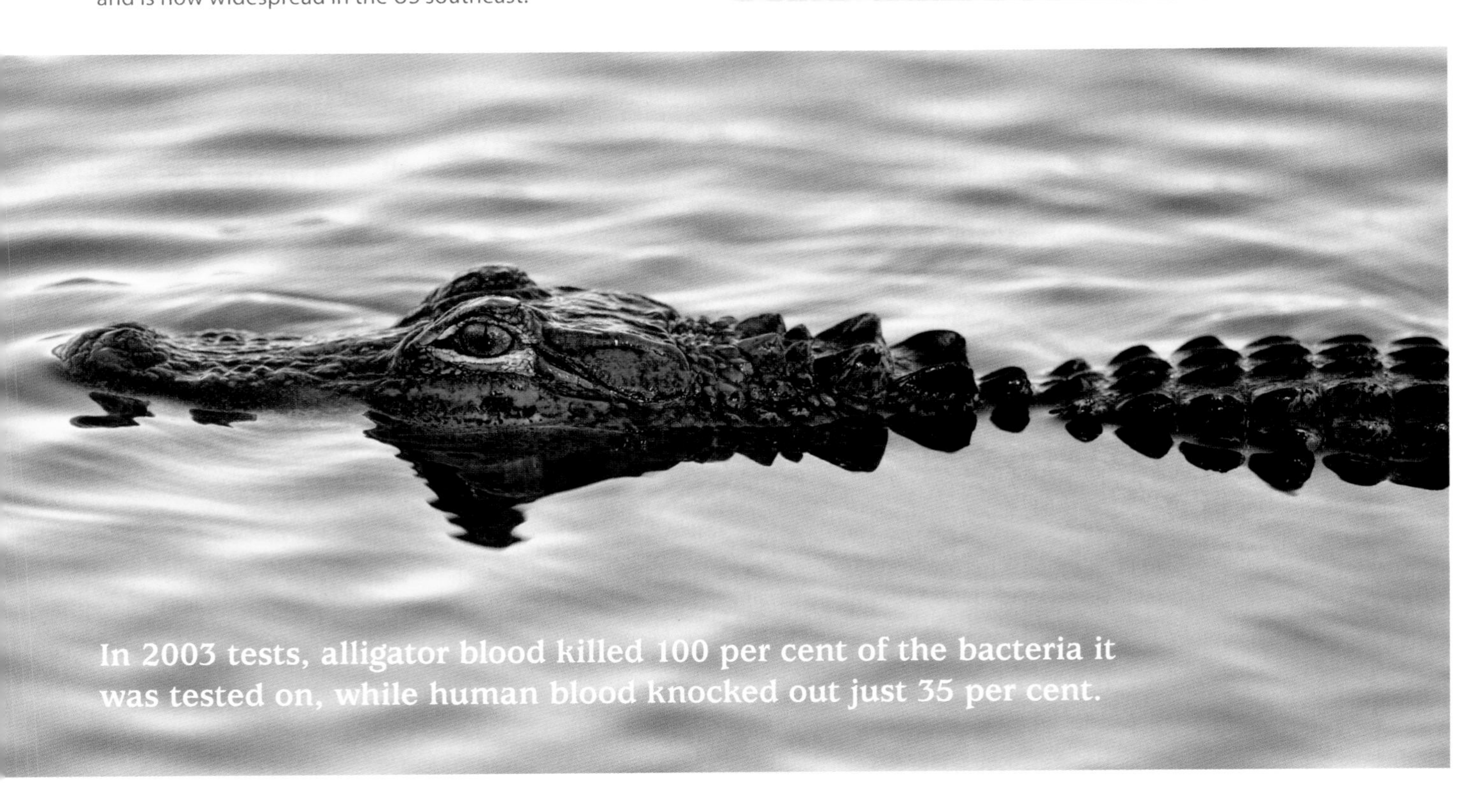

In 2003 tests, alligator blood killed 100 per cent of the bacteria it was tested on, while human blood knocked out just 35 per cent.

Knockout effect Biochemist Mark Merchant from McNeese State University in Louisiana is one of those leading the charge to unravel the mysteries of alligator blood. In 2003, his team showed that an extract of alligator serum (white blood cells with the platelets removed) killed 10 times as many bacteria as did extracts of human blood – and all in just a few minutes. In 2006, Merchant and colleagues went a step further when they found that alligator blood serum killed the yeast *Candida albicans*, one of the main microorganisms responsible for infections in diabetics, HIV patients and organ transplant recipients. Not only that, but alligator blood also killed the HIV virus itself – the virus that causes AIDS. Other research has shown that alligator blood destroys methicillin-resistant *Staphylococcus aureus* (MRSA), one of the many bacteria now resistant to antibiotic treatment.

ORIGIN Southeastern United States, from Texas to North Carolina
PART USED Blood

Patrolling proteins The full extent of the potency of alligator blood came to light in 2008 when Merchant and colleagues showed that the serum kills a staggering 23 different strains of bacteria. Work then began in earnest to identify how alligator blood lays waste to such a range of pathogenic organisms. Researchers suspected that a particular peptide or peptides (fragments of proteins) must be lurking in the white blood cells of alligator blood. Merchant facetiously dubbed the mystery molecules 'alligacin'.

Merchant and others have since isolated these proteins and identified their structure. The proteins are believed to belong to a group called antimicrobial peptides (AMPs). These are present in every kind of animal, but alligators seem to be especially well endowed with them. AMPs patrol the bloodstream and mount a rapid response to invading bacteria, fungi and viruses, buying time for the immune system to tailor-make specific antibodies to the germs. The most promising application for humans looks like being a topical cream for external wounds.

Obtaining alligator blood requires extremely careful handling of the donor.

With the active ingredient in alligator blood yet to be confirmed, and no clinical trials planned in the near future, a commercially available treatment is still years away. Meanwhile, some Asian companies sell alligator blood in capsule form, claiming it improves libido, rejuvenates the skin, increases platelet numbers, relieves menstrual cramps, treats colds, allergies and AIDS, and stimulates insulin production. But Mark Merchant warns such products do not have US Food and Drug Administration approval and cautions that injecting or ingesting raw alligator blood can make you sick or even cause anaphylactic shock – tests have also shown that alligator serum in high concentrations can be toxic. For similar reasons, home remedies based on blood collected from alligators are not recommended.

AXOLOTL

Ambystoma mexicanum

MEDICAL BENEFITS ◆ Potential treatments for severe burns, spinal cord damage, stroke, traumatic brain injury

You can cut the same leg off an axolotl dozens of times, and it will always regrow perfectly. By understanding how this happens, scientists hope to teach the human body how to self-heal.

For thousands of years people have been fascinated by the ability of some animals to regenerate body parts. The hydra, a tiny freshwater relative of the jellyfish, for example, will happily regrow two complete bodies if you chop it in half. While regeneration in such a simple creature is impressive enough, what the axolotl, or Mexican salamander, can pull off is truly amazing. University of Florida geneticist Professor Edward Scott calls the axolotl 'the champion of vertebrate regeneration' and with good reason. Cut off almost any part of the axolotl and it will regrow: limbs, heart, eyes, spinal cord – even its brain can regenerate.

A growth industry Today, scientists are abuzz about the potential of the axolotl to provide clues as to how humans, too, could regenerate damaged or lost tissue. Professor David Gardiner of the University of California, Irvine, points out that humans must have a genetic program for limb regeneration within our genome because this program was used to make our arms and legs when we were embryos. The challenge for regenerative medicine, he says, is to learn how to reactivate it.

Green blood Edward Scott from the University of Florida's Adult Stem Cell Program has been conducting some fascinating experiments to identify which axolotl cells rebuild limbs. Scott

OTHER NAMES Mexican salamander, tiger salamander, Mexican 'walking fish'
ORIGIN Lakes around Mexico City
PARTS USED All tissues

Having lost an arm, this axolotl has grown a blastema, a cluster of stem cells, that will slowly develop to form a new limb.

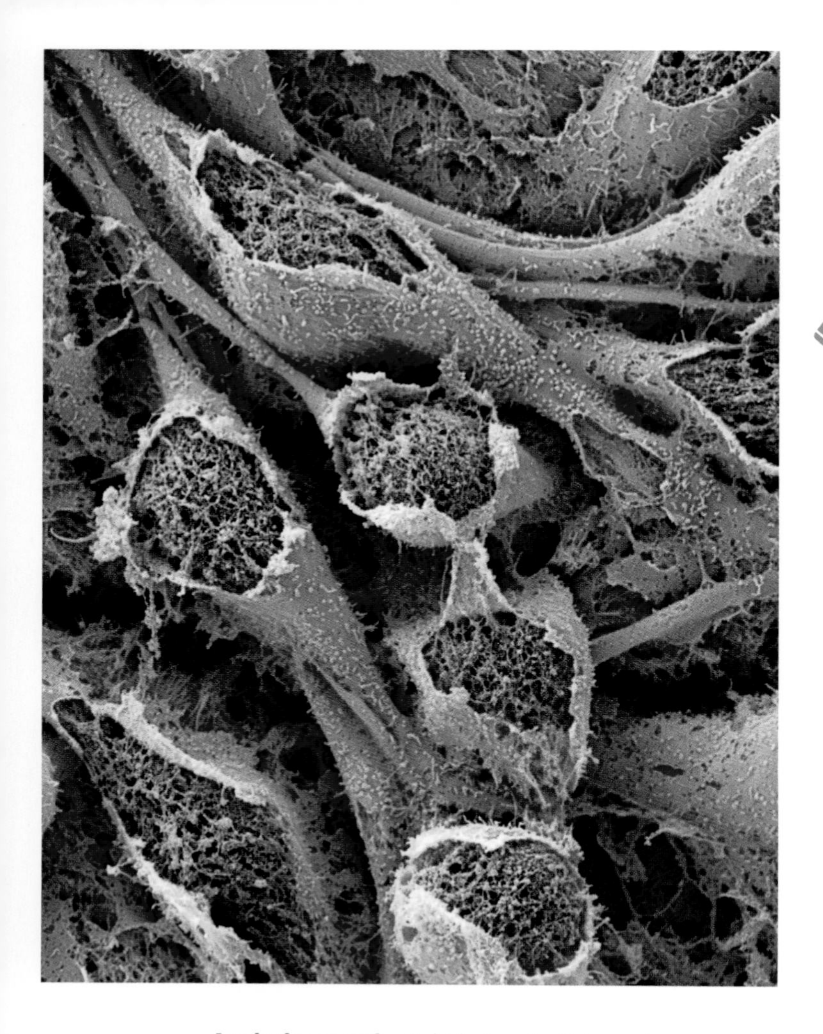

in CLOSE-UP

When a mammal loses a limb, scar tissue is formed by cells called fibroblasts. But in salamanders and some frogs, these same cells sometimes appear to control the regeneration of other kinds of cells and, consequently, the reconstruction of tissue. German-based US researchers Karen Echeverri and Elly Tanaka reported in 2002 that body cells around an amputated axolotl limb behave like stem cells – that is, they revert back to a basic cell type that can potentially develop into any kind of tissue. This 'dedifferentiation' may be controlled by so-called homeobox genes, which are better known for guiding the way embryos form their body parts. Humans also possess homeobox genes, so it may be that they could be coaxed back into action in order to regenerate tissues or organs.

Axolotl research might help scientists work out how human stem cells like these could be engineered to trigger tissue regeneration.

dyed axolotl stem cells with a green fluorescent protein (see p. 230) and transplanted them into a white axolotl. The stem cells developed into green-coloured blood cells, which could be tracked in the circulatory system to see how they helped repair and regenerate lost limbs.

Meanwhile, researchers at the University of Florida are comparing the regenerative abilities of the axolotl with the way mice recover from spinal cord injury and stroke. One approach is to disrupt the axolotl's regenerative ability, and then see if it can be restored with transplanted stem cells. By comparing how a mammal and an axolotl respond to injuries, the researchers hope to identify genes or proteins that could be added back into the mammalian system to kick-start tissue regeneration.

In these ways, scientists are slowly building up a picture of how the axolotl works its miracles, and how we might make use of this knowledge. If humans also have a regenerative talent, albeit a dormant one, this could potentially be revived; then new drugs might be developed that would, for example, trigger self-healing of burned skin or regeneration of damaged organs.

Research on how axolotls regenerate their limbs and organs is still at a very early stage, and no therapies or medications based on these studies are yet available. But scientists hope that in the future such treatments might help repair damage caused by burns, trauma, heart disease, strokes and even Alzheimer's disease.

BRAZILIAN ARROWHEAD VIPER

Bothrops jararaca

MEDICAL BENEFITS ◆ Treatment for high blood pressure (hypertension) ◆ Treatment for heart disease, heart attack, stroke ◆ Reduces diabetes and kidney problems related to high blood pressure

For 20 years now, thousands of people have benefited from ACE inhibitors, a class of blood-pressure-lowering drugs first derived from the venom of a Brazilian viper.

A man picking bananas in a plantation in western Brazil reaches up to cut off a bunch of ripe fruit. Suddenly he feels a sharp pain surge through his leg. Looking down, he sees that the culprit is a slender tan-coloured snake measuring about 1.5 m (5 ft) and bearing brown triangular markings – a Brazilian arrowhead viper. But the plantation worker doesn't get to see his attacker for long. Within seconds, he collapses to the ground in a dead faint, the victim of a catastrophic fall in blood pressure.

Staying low This type of response to a snakebite is quite unusual: most snake venoms affect either the nervous system, causing asphyxiation, or the blood system, causing haemorrhaging. But the poison of the Brazilian arrowhead viper instead renders its victims helpless by reducing their blood pressure. Curious about this unusual effect, physician and pharmacologist Mauricio Rocha e Silva, working at the Biological Institute in São Paulo, Brazil, in the 1950s, took a closer look at exactly what the venom was doing in the body. He discovered that if extracts were given to dogs and guinea pigs, they would make an enzyme he later named bradykinin. It was then found that when animals produce bradykinin, their blood pressure goes down.

This was a major discovery, but it took on even greater significance when one of Rocha e Silva's postdoctoral students, Sérgio Henrique Ferreira,

OTHER NAMES Brazilian lancehead snake, jararaca
ORIGIN Brazil, Argentina, Paraguay
PART USED Venom

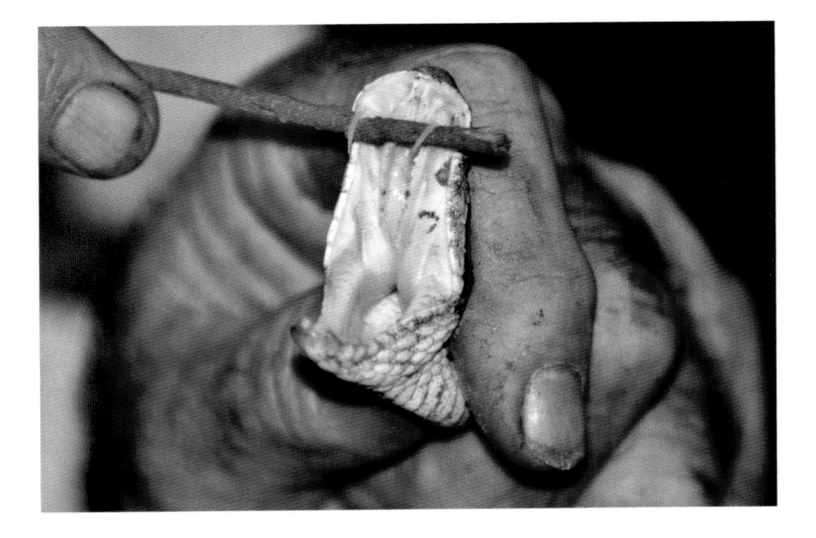

In the first half of the twentieth century, the Brazilian pit viper was responsible for half of all snakebites in southeastern Brazil.

Cause and effect

The link between high blood pressure and heart disease was not understood prior to a major study launched in 1948. The Framingham Heart Study followed 5000 people from the town of Framingham, Massachusetts, for several decades, monitoring their heart health and ultimately revealing the link with blood pressure. This inspired intense research, resulting in many new drugs, including ACE inhibitors.

The Brazilian pit viper's markings make it difficult to spot in undergrowth or even against tree trunks and broad branches.

discovered a protein in the viper venom that inhibits an enzyme that breaks down bradykinin, with the result that more bradykinin circulates in the system, keeping blood pressure low for longer. Ferreira named this protein bradykinin potentiating factor (BPF). In his research, published in 1970, he noted that the discovery might 'prove to be therapeutically useful in pathological conditions such as inflammation and hypertension [high blood pressure]'.

Saving lives High blood pressure affects up to one in five adults and can have a devastating effect on general health. It occurs when small blood vessels in the body narrow. This causes the blood to exert too much pressure against the vessel walls, making the heart work harder. Over time, high blood pressure can enlarge and damage the heart and increase the risk of stroke, kidney disease and diabetes.

in CLOSE-UP

ACE stands for angiotensin-converting enzyme. This crucial body enzyme kick-starts a rise in blood pressure by converting another enzyme, Angiotensin I, into yet another, Angiotensin II. Angiotensin II has a powerful effect on blood vessels, causing them to tighten, and it also impacts on the kidneys, triggering them to reabsorb water rather than releasing it from the body in urine; the combined effect of these actions is to increase blood pressure. So when someone takes an ACE inhibitor, the drug *prevents* the conversion of Angiotensin I into Angiotensin II and, as a consequence, the blood vessels relax and blood pressure is reduced.

UK statistics indicate that high blood pressure affects one in five adults and shortens lifespan by an average of five years.

On the basis of Ferreira's discoveries, US scientists developed a new generation of highly effective antihypertensive drugs called ACE inhibitors, the best known of which is probably captopril (Capoten). Since their launch onto the market two decades ago, ACE inhibitors have had an enormous impact on public health.

Randomised control trials have shown that they can improve heart-failure patients' symptoms, slow the disease and cut hospital admissions by about 30 per cent. A 2012 Dutch review of many ACE inhibitor studies showed that the drugs significantly reduced the number of hypertensive patients who died over the four-year period of the study. And another recent study, from France, showed that if all suitable hypertension sufferers took ACE inhibitors, it would save an extra 12 lives per 1000 patients over four years. For all this we have to thank the ingenuity of several generations of scientists, and the fangs of a secretive Brazilian viper.

If you have high blood pressure, heart failure or have had a heart attack, or if you suffer from diabetes, you may wish to ask your doctor about taking ACE inhibitors. They are only available on prescription and usually come as tablets, which you take once a day (some break down quickly and may need to be taken more frequently than this). Many people with high blood pressure or heart problems need to take more than one medicine, so ACE inhibitors may be prescribed in combination with other drugs, such as a diuretic or a calcium-channel blocker. The most common side effects of ACE inhibitors are excessively low blood pressure and a reduction in kidney function.

FROM POISON TO MEDICINE

The vast range of toxins found in animal venoms is a rich source of medicines that can be used in the fight against ailments ranging from diabetes and cardiovascular disease to cancer.

There are more than 150,000 species of venomous animals across the entire animal kingdom. They include snakes, fishes, lizards, scorpions, spiders, insects and marine invertebrates such as anemones, corals, jellyfish, cone snails and sea urchins. Some animals use poison to paralyse prey, some employ it to defend themselves while others use it to help digest food. Snakes and spiders inject venom via fangs, while fish deliver their toxin through spines, and scorpions and insects use stings; the toxin in jellyfish is packaged in specialised cells on their tentacles called nematocysts.

Smart toxins Not only are venoms varied in type, use and method of delivery, but also in chemical make-up. Most are highly complex substances, often containing up to 1000 bioactive peptides – short chains of amino acids which, when joined together, become proteins. Medical researchers are particularly intrigued by the speed and precision with which toxins act. Often they attach themselves to blood, muscle or nerve cells and alter the way those cells function. Many compounds even target a specific area on a cell, and as a result, they can quickly produce a specific effect on a particular body system without any side effects – for example, almost instantly reducing heart rate or turning off the signalling of one type of nerve, such as pain receptors. Other common effects of poisons include paralysis, rupture of blood vessels and disruption of blood clotting. All of these effects could potentially be harnessed to benefit human health.

Handle with care Getting hold of venoms is a tricky business, and scientists have developed a range of strategies for doing this safely. Sometimes it requires familiarity with, and skill in handling, the animal in question. For instance, at the Australian Reptile Park north of Sydney, a trained handler uses unerring judgment and great dexterity to catch a snake by the tail then quickly grab it behind the head. The head is then held down on a table and the snake is encouraged to bite into a latex-covered beaker. The venom dribbles from the fangs into the beaker, and is quickly vacuum- or freeze-dried, mainly for use in antivenoms.

Similarly, in the United States at Clarkson University, New York, biochemist Jon-Paul Bingham milks cone shells for research on their toxins by enticing them to harpoon a condom-covered test tube opening; the venom then dribbles inside and is collected.

The right ingredients Most snake antivenoms are made by injecting minute doses of the venom into a horse (horses are used because they have a high tolerance of snake venom). The doses are gradually increased as the animal builds up resistance and produces antibodies against the foreign substance. Blood is then taken from the horse and the antibodies are separated out and purified. The horse is unharmed by the process.

When screening venoms for potential beneficial effects, the first step is to give lab animals very low doses of the toxin and see how they react. If the animal has a specific

FIRST AID

What may be the earliest known medicinal use of poison dates from the first century BC. Mithridates, King of Pontus, in the Black Sea region of what is now Turkey, had asked his doctors to find a universal antidote to all poisons. When he was slashed with a sword in battle, his profusely bleeding wound was staunched with a few drops of the venom of the steppe viper, which had been found to act as a coagulant.

King cobra venom has been investigated as a source of anticoagulant drugs and of an ointment to treat arthritis.

Left: Venom is extracted from a gaboon viper to make antivenom. This viper's bite yields the largest amount of venom of any snake.

Below: Keeping a tight grip, a researcher at the University of California, Riverside, collects venom exuded by the fangs of a desert tarantula.

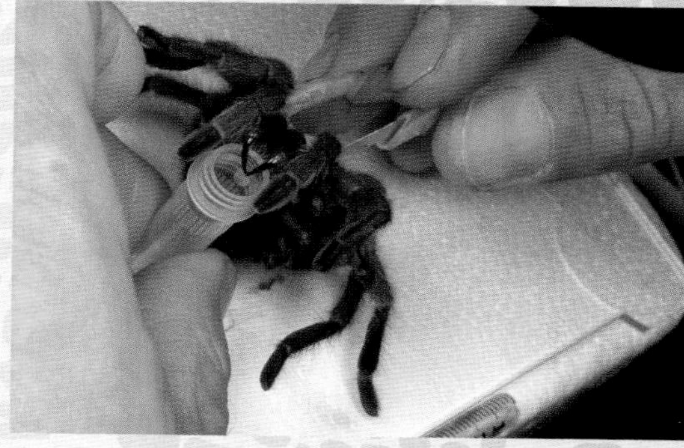

Below: Sea anemone toxins, used by the animal to stun prey, could yield drugs to treat autoimmune diseases such as multiple sclerosis.

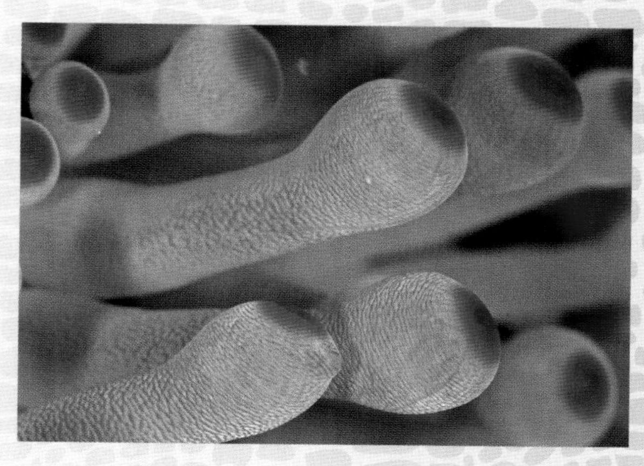

response – for example, pain relief – this gives researchers a clue as to how the compound might be useful in the body.

Once the effect has been identified, researchers work out the chemical structure of the compound, using a range of high-tech methods. This in turn can allow them to create a synthetic version of the substance. Once this was painstaking work, but now scientists can identify thousands of different compounds simultaneously, using computerised, large-scale analyses linked to enormous databases.

Banking on poisons One of the latest initiatives in the field of developing drugs from poisons is the VENOMICS project. A collaboration between European academic laboratories and various biotechnology companies, it aims to use the latest technology, including DNA analysis, to assemble a biobank of 10,000 venom peptides with potential medical applications.

A harpoonlike dart delivers the poison of the cone snail to its prey. The stings of the larger species can be fatal to humans.

MALAYAN PIT VIPER

Calloselasma rhodostoma

MEDICAL BENEFITS ◆ Potential treatment for sudden hearing loss

A drug derived from snake venom that initially held promise for helping people to recover from strokes may now have a new application.

Farmers working in the rubber plantations and rainforests of Southeast Asia know to look out for one particularly unwelcome visitor: the Malayan pit viper. It's responsible for about 700 incidents of snakebite annually and its bite is so toxic it can cause limbs to atrophy. But pit viper venom may have its benefits, too.

A new application Initially, researchers were excited to discover that the snake's venom reduced the body's levels of fibrinogen, a substance vital for helping the blood to clot. So they began looking at whether it had potential to help stroke victims. A drug called ancrod developed from the venom showed promise, with a 1999 study reporting that 42 per cent of stroke patients given ancrod recovered, compared to 34 per cent given a placebo. However, more of the ancrod group suffered bleeding in the brain than the placebo group; and other studies showed no difference in stroke recovery between ancrod and a placebo.

What You CAN DO

If you are affected by SSHL, you might want to find out more about the clinical trials of ancrod, which are due to finish in 2014, with results expected after that. Check the latest at http://clinicaltrials.gov/ct2/show/NCT01621256 or ask your doctor for further information.

Malayan pit viper

But just because a drug doesn't work for one disease doesn't mean it might not have potential to treat another. In 2012, German researchers announced new clinical trials to test ancrod for a totally different condition: sudden sensoneural hearing loss (SSHL).

In many sufferers, SSHL seems to occur overnight, while others notice a loud 'pop' just before their hearing disappears. Researchers now believe the condition occurs when key parts of the inner ear do not get enough oxygen, perhaps as a result of a virus or a blood vessel defect in the ear. In the trials, doctors at the University of Göttingen will give 100 male and 100 female SSHL sufferers injections of ancrod over the course of three days, within a week of their hearing loss. It's hoped that ancrod's blood-thinning properties could help increase circulation and provide more oxygen to deprived areas, at least partially restoring hearing.

OTHER NAME Malaysian pit viper
ORIGIN Thailand, Laos, Cambodia, Java, Sumatra, Malaysia, Vietnam, Burma, China
PART USED Venom

SAW-SCALED VIPER

Echis carinatus

MEDICAL BENEFITS ◆ Source of standard blood-clotting test ◆ Source of anticoagulant medicine used before and after heart surgery ◆ Treatment for heart attack and stroke

This bad-tempered viper rates as one of the four most lethal snakes in India. Yet, paradoxically, it has saved many people from death due to heart attack and stroke.

Saw-scaled vipers waiting to be milked for their venom

The saw-scaled viper, native to Pakistan and India, is so poisonous that a single bite may deliver double the amount of venom required to kill a human victim. Massive haemorrhaging ensues, followed by vomiting, coughing up blood and uncontrollable nosebleeds. In the hands of brilliant medical researchers, however, this deadly venom has been turned into gold.

A substance derived from saw-scaled viper venom, ecarin, is now widely used to test for clotting in heart patients. In the ecarin clotting time (ECT) test, ecarin is added to a drop of the patient's blood. It triggers production of thrombin, which causes the blood to clot. Based on the time this takes to happen, pathologists can tell whether anticlotting medications – such as hirudin, a medication derived from leech saliva (see p. 214) – are doing their job properly. If the blood clots too quickly or takes too long to clot, the physician can adjust the dose accordingly.

Clot buster The venom of the saw-scaled viper has also been used to make several anticoagulant medications, including tirofiban (marketed as Aggrastat). Tirofiban is used to treat blood clots during the onset of strokes and thrombotic disorders, and also during surgery. It belongs to a relatively new group of anti-clotting medications called glycoprotein IIb/IIIa inhibitors, which prevent platelets from sticking together. Another, eptifibatide (Integrilin), is derived from the southeastern pygmy rattlesnake (see p. 201).

OTHER NAMES Indian saw-scaled viper, little Indian viper
ORIGIN India, Pakistan, Sri Lanka, Afghanistan
PART USED Venom

Tirofiban is usually administered by a specialist in a clinic or hospital. Most often, it is injected into a vein and given continuously for at least two days. It is used in combination with heparin, to prevent blood clots, and with aspirin, to prevent a heart attack in people who have unstable angina. Because tirofiban stops blood coagulating, it can cause you to bleed more – seek emergency medical attention if you have bleeding that will not stop. Normally, patients on tirofiban are closely monitored to ensure that blood chemistry and all blood counts are within safe levels.

PHANTASMAL POISON FROG

Epipedobates tricolor

MEDICAL BENEFITS ◆ Potential treatment for ADHD

A substance secreted by a small but highly poisonous Amazonian frog, first gathered by a pioneering US scientist in the 1970s, is still inspiring research into its potential benefits more than 40 years later.

In 1963, a biochemist from Oregon with a love of the outdoors was seduced into taking a closer look at the extensive tropical forests and mysterious indigenous practices of South America. John W Daly was just settling down to a conventional research career after securing a postdoctoral position at the National Institutes of Health (NIH), when his boss, Bernhard Witkop, asked him to run an unusual errand: to travel to Colombia and collect the chemical secretions of the frogs the Indians there had long used to poison their darts.

A fully grown phantasmal poison frog measures just 1–4 cm (0.4–1.6 in) in length.

What began for Daly as an exotic diversion from daily life in the lab led to a lifelong fascination for investigating natural products from amphibians. Several collecting trips later, in 1974, Daly was in Ecuador with herpetologist Charles W Myers, collecting skin secretions from a tiny red-, orange- and white-striped frog, *Epipedobates tricolor*, the phantasmal poison frog. Once back at the NIH lab in Bethesda, Maryland, Daly found that a tiny amount of the frog's secretion injected into mice blocked pain signals. Daly returned to Ecuador and collected enough of the poison to isolate the active painkilling compound, which he called epibatidine, after the scientific name of the frog.

Blocking pain signals Further progress on epibatidine had to wait almost 20 years until a sophisticated technique called nuclear magnetic resonance spectroscopy enabled researchers to identify its exact structure. To their surprise, it turned out to closely resemble nicotine – also known for its painkilling properties. This told them that epibatidine must bind to nicotinic receptors, sites at the junctions between nerve cells that enable nerve signals (including the sensation of pain) to travel to and register in the brain. This binding in turn blocks a neurotransmitter called acetylcholine from sending pain messages along the nerve pathway.

Researchers were also excited to discover that epibatidine worked in a totally different way from the most commonly used painkiller, morphine – while morphine reduces pain, it has many side effects, is addictive and becomes less effective the more it is used. What's more, early tests showed epibatidine was 200 times more potent than morphine.

in CLOSE-UP

When researchers first began studying the phantasmal poison frog, they thought its secretions were produced within its body. But they found that frogs kept in captivity were no longer poisonous. Researchers now believe that the frog gains its poison from its diet – possibly from one of the rainforest insects it gobbles up. Intriguingly, frogs that have been forced out of their native jungle habitat and into nearby banana plantations no longer secrete the poison either.

OTHER NAMES Poison dart frog, poison arrow frog, arrow poison frog
ORIGIN Ecuador
PART USED Skin secretion

Known to survive at only a small number of sites in central Ecuador, the phantasmal poison frog is considered an endangered species.

On the downside Based on these promising discoveries, pharmaceutical company Abbott in North Chicago synthesised a derivative of epibatidine and called it ABT-594. Initial tests in animals were promising and in a clinical trial, reported in 2009, patients with chronic diabetes-related pain experienced relief after taking ABT-594. But unfortunately they also suffered side effects including nausea, dizziness, vomiting, abnormal dreams and weakness. Another setback followed in 2012, when the results of a clinical trial of a different epibatidine derivative, ABT-894, were published. Although this study, carried out at the California Pacific Medical Center Research Institute in San Francisco, found ABT-894 had no significant side effects, it also indicated that ABT-894 did not relieve pain any more effectively than a placebo.

What You CAN DO

Given the setbacks in the most recent studies, it's uncertain whether any painkilling treatments or medications will now be developed from epibatidine. However, Abbott now plans to conduct further research into the use of ABT-894 for ADHD and is looking at conducting clinical trials with children.

A different direction But while the future of epibatidine as a painkiller is uncertain, Abbott, along with European company NeuroSearch, is investigating the use of ABT-894 for treating ADHD (Attention Deficit Hyperactivity Disorder). A 2012 study by Abbott looked at the effect of ABT-894 at different doses on 243 adults with ADHD. It found that symptoms improved in those taking ABT-894 at a dose of 4 mg twice daily, and the drug was well tolerated. The improvements were like those seen in patients taking atomoxetine, an existing ADHD drug.

PROTECTIVE SKIN

Frogs and toads may appear to be small, vulnerable creatures. But over millennia, they have evolved an extraordinary arsenal of defences – most notably in their skin – that not only protects them from predators and disease but might also offer a multitude of medical benefits for humans.

The belief that frogs' skins possess medicinal properties – providing aphrodisiacs, infertility treatments, contraceptives and general cure-alls – is common worldwide. The traditional Chinese medicine *chan su*, for example, contains dried skin secretions from the Chinese toad *Bufo gargarizans* and is traditionally used to treat heart disease, toothache, sinusitis, haemorrhaging of the gums and other systemic illnesses. In recent years, some of these beliefs have been studied and confirmed as true by scientific researchers.

Bolstering immunity Several extracts from frog skin have been shown to aid the immune system. In 1998, researchers in Kolkata (Calcutta), India, found that when cancer patients undergoing chemotherapy received *chan su*, they developed significantly fewer infections. And in a 2004 study, Japanese researchers gave mice *chan su* and found it increased numbers of lymphocytes, one of the body's first lines of defence against infection.

Many frog and toad skins have been shown to contain proteins that appear to influence cells that control insulin release. Experiments at the University of Ulster in Northern Ireland in 2004 and 2005 showed that peptides from the skin secretions of the Pickerel frog (*Rana palustris*), Trinidad monkey frog (*Phyllomedusa trinitatis*) and splendid leaf frog (*Agalychnis calcarifer*) stimulate cells in the pancreas to increase production of insulin, offering potential new therapies for diabetics.

Antimicrobial proteins The immune systems of all creatures include powerful antimicrobial peptides, or AMPs. But amphibian skin is particularly rich in these proteins, because frogs and toads inhabit damp places full of bacteria

FROGS ON FILE

Researchers at the United Arab Emirates University have amassed a collection of 6000 frog skins from around the world. So far, they have purified and identified the structure of the secretions from just 200 of the skins. Meanwhile, sitting in cold storage at the National Institutes of Health in Bethesda, Maryland, in the United States, is a vast repository of frog skins collected over 40 years by pharmacologist John W Daly (see p. 194) during dozens of field trips in South America. Skins from this collection have been the source of potential pain-relief medications, such as epibatidine, while others have become tools for molecular biologists. The structures and value of many remain unknown and await further investigation.

In South America, several species of frogs have skins that contain protective poisons. A dart coated in the toxins of the golden poison dart frog (right) will kill large animals and remain effective for up to two years.

and viruses, and some are particularly potent. AMPs isolated from the skin of the endangered foothill yellow-legged frog (*Rana boylii*), native to California and Oregon, kills methicillin-resistant *Staphylococcus aureus* (MRSA). Other AMPs from the mink frog (*Rana septentrionalis*) destroy the multi-drug-resistant bacteria *Acinetobacter baumannii*, the 'Iraqibacter' bug that infected injured soldiers returning from Afghanistan.

In 2010, Italian scientists at Rome's Sapienza University showed in laboratory tests that living worms infected with multiresistant bacteria and then treated with AMPs had improved survival rates, and researchers at Queen's University, Belfast, discovered in 2011 that frog AMPs can suppress the growth of blood vessels from tumours. The research is at an early stage, but the long-term implication is that it could lead to a treatment for cancer.

Other studies, too, have shown that frog skin proteins kill cancer cells. Researchers reported at the 240th National Meeting of the American Chemical Society in 2010 that AMPs from the yellow-bellied toad *Bombina variegata*, for example, inhibited human leukaemia cells in the laboratory, while another frog skin protein, bufalin, boosted the effectiveness of anticancer drugs.

Highly versatile In just one of many studies of the effects of frog skin compounds on viruses, researchers at the UCLA School of Medicine, Los Angeles showed in 2000 that a different kind of frog skin protein called brevenin-1 inhibited herpes simplex virus types 1 and 2. And a peptide, maximin 3, isolated from the large-webbed bell toad *Bombina maxima* showed anti-HIV activity in laboratory experiments.

In another intriguing experiment carried out in 1995, Indian researchers showed that wounded rats healed faster following the application of a dressing of Indian frog skin rather than regular cotton gauze. And a 1996 study at what is now Mumbai's National Institute for Research in Reproductive Health showed that frog skin proteins have potent antispermicidal activity. Not only did they stop pregnancy but they also killed the pathogens that cause some sexually transmitted diseases. No commercial product has yet been developed, however.

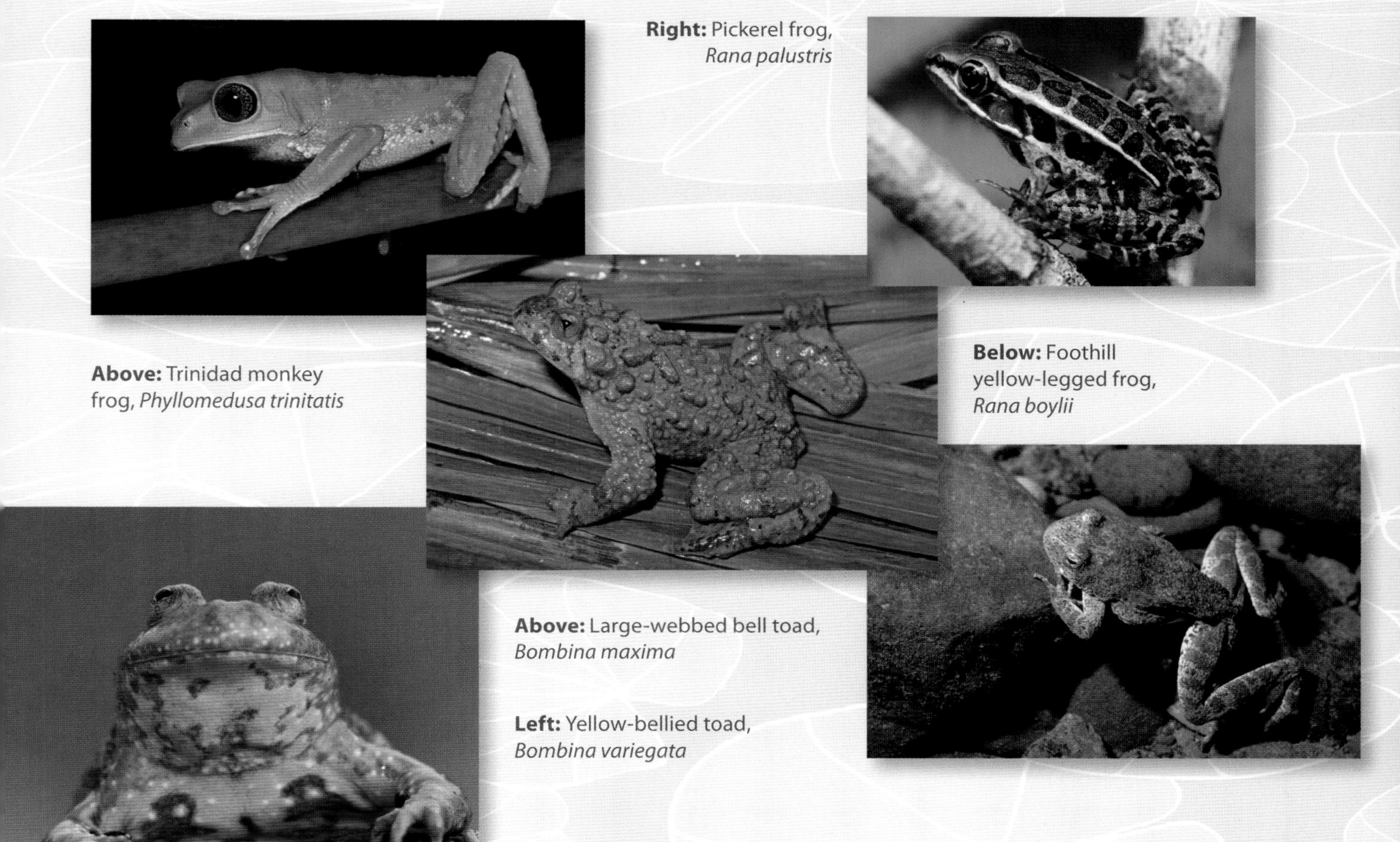

Right: Pickerel frog, *Rana palustris*

Above: Trinidad monkey frog, *Phyllomedusa trinitatis*

Below: Foothill yellow-legged frog, *Rana boylii*

Above: Large-webbed bell toad, *Bombina maxima*

Left: Yellow-bellied toad, *Bombina variegata*

The carrot-and-liquorice colouration of the United States' largest and only venomous lizard is a warning to other creatures to stay well clear.

Traditional Wisdom

In Navajo culture, healers often use a technique called 'hand trembling' to divine an illness. This involves the healer holding their arm over the patient; when the arm starts shaking, the healer enters an elevated consciousness and becomes aware of the nature of the ailment. Because the Gila monster has a habit of shaking a limb in a similar way, the Navajo believed it had healing powers and sometimes called upon its spirit to help with diagnoses.

GILA MONSTER

Heloderma suspectum

MEDICAL BENEFITS ◆ Treatment for controlling blood glucose levels in diabetics ◆ Potential source of weight-loss drug

The early Navajo people of what is now the southwestern United States believed that this large lizard had special healing powers. Centuries on, it turns out they were right.

The Gila monster's poisonous saliva has yielded an almost magical ingredient that has helped save thousands of lives in the past 20 years. Known as exenatide, it is widely used to treat the debilitating symptoms of diabetes and may have other benefits, too.

Mining proteins Dr John Eng was a young research fellow when he was lucky enough to land a job in the laboratory of Dr Rosalyn Yalow, at the Bronx Veterans Administration Medical Center in New York. Yalow had jointly won the 1977 Nobel Prize in Physiology or Medicine for inventing a way to identify novel hormones in animals. Inspired by Yalow, Eng began designing more tests to identify animal proteins that might help fight human diseases. While investigating hormones from chinchillas and guinea pigs, he became excited when he read about studies carried out at the US National Institutes of Health in the early 1980s. These reported that the venom from certain snakes and lizards – including the Gila monster – caused inflammation in the pancreas, the organ that produces insulin. If the venom could stimulate the pancreas, Eng wondered, could it also help diabetics control their blood glucose levels?

Eng ordered some dried and preserved Gila monster saliva from a reptile house in Utah and used a sensitive test he had developed to probe

---

OTHER NAME Giant Gila monster
ORIGIN Western and southern Arizona south to Mexico; rarer in California, Nevada, southwestern New Mexico
PART USED Saliva

the poison for its secrets. In 1992, he described two interesting compounds from the venom, one of which he named exendin. This compound was remarkably similar to GLP-1, a human hormone that stimulates insulin secretion from the pancreas when blood glucose levels are too high. GLP-1 had seemed to hold promise as a source of a drug for diabetics, but unfortunately it degrades quickly in the body – so quickly in fact that, to be of any use in maintaining blood glucose levels, diabetics would need to inject it almost hourly. By contrast, Eng's studies of exendin showed that it stayed in the system up to 24 hours before degrading, making it a much better candidate for a drug.

Going it alone However, when Eng presented his findings to his bosses at the Bronx Veterans Administration Medical Center, they weren't willing to go through the process of patenting his discovery, as they felt it did not specifically help veterans' ailments, such as spinal cord damage and combat injuries. So Eng went out on a limb and began the expensive, uncertain and nerve-wracking process of patenting the drug himself. He contacted pharmaceutical companies and told anyone at medical conferences who would listen about his research.

Finally, the fledgling Arizona-based company Amylin Pharmaceuticals learned about Eng's work in 1996, at the American Diabetes Association Annual Meeting. The company was immediately convinced of the compound's potential and Eng licensed the patent to Amylin later the same year. After nine years in development, all the hard work finally paid off. In 2005, the US Food and Drug Administration approved a synthetic derivative of exendin, called exenatide (also known by the trade name Byetta), for the treatment of type 2 diabetes. A three-year study demonstrating that the drug helped diabetics sustain healthy glucose levels clinched the approval.

Diabetes now affects a massive 8.3 per cent of the US population and in 2007 contributed to 231,404 deaths in the United States alone. With cases of the disease continuing to rise, health authorities hope that exenatide and other drugs can control the symptoms of diabetes and improve the overall health of sufferers.

Appetite suppressant More recently, exenatide has been found to have another significant benefit. One of the effects of the medication on the body is to cause the stomach to empty more slowly. This in turn seems to diminish appetite and result in weight loss. Initial tests on animals and humans have confirmed the effects, and clinical trials are now underway to assess exenatide as a weight-loss drug for nondiabetics.

in CLOSE-UP

The results of a 2009 analysis of the venom of the Gila monster along with that of its close relative, the beaded lizard, have important implications for improving diabetic drugs based on the venom. The studies revealed that there are four different forms of exendin (the salival compound on which exenatide is based), and that the most recently evolved, exendin-1 and exendin-2, are the most toxic. This discovery will help researchers identify which parts of the molecules are most active and therefore most effective as a drug treatment.

If you have type 2 diabetes mellitus, exenatide (Byetta) may improve your blood glucose control when used together with a diet-and-exercise program. Note that exenatide is not insulin and it should not be taken instead of insulin; it can, however, be used with Lantus (insulin glargine), a long-acting insulin – but not with any short- and/or rapid-acting insulin. Until a drug is approved, exenatide should not be taken to aid weight loss.

SOUTHEASTERN PYGMY RATTLESNAKE

Sistrurus miliarius

MEDICAL BENEFITS ◆ Reduces risk of heart attack in patients with unstable angina ◆ May help manage some forms of pneumonia

Among the arsenal of modern drugs that heart specialists and surgeons have at their disposal is one derived from a common but deadly US snake.

You'd be hard pressed to hear the warning sounds of the southeastern pygmy rattlesnake. As its name suggests, it possesses one of the smallest 'rattles' among rattlers. Its bite, however, is a lethal cocktail of chemicals, including a powerful anticoagulant called barbourin that prevents platelets from clotting the blood. It's a dead clever strategy: making the blood 'runny' so that it more rapidly circulates the venom around the body.

Making a difference Robert Scarborough, a brilliant US chemist working at California Biotechnology Inc. during the early 1990s, reasoned that barbourin might also help patients at risk of blood clots. Scarborough developed barbourin into a chemical he called eptifibatide, which mimicked barbourin's effects.

A major clinical study published in 1998 proved that eptifibatide saved lives. Nearly 11,000 patients with acute coronary problems were given either a placebo or eptifibatide. After 30 days, 14.2 per cent of patients taking eptifibatide had suffered a heart attack or died, compared with 15.7 per cent of those given a placebo – a small but significant difference. As a result of the study, eptifibatide received approval for licensing, and today thousands of patients receive Integrilin (the commercial name for eptifibatide) to prevent blood clots before and after heart surgery.

Recently, clinical trials have begun in Denmark to test whether eptifibatide, in combination with Ilomedin (which protects blood vessels from damage) could help hypertensive patients who are critically ill with pneumonia. Researchers hope the addition of eptifibatide will prevent platelets clotting and keep them circulating in the blood to boost the body's immune response.

What You CAN DO

If you have had severe chest pain, or require surgery to open blocked arteries, you may be given eptifibatide to prevent blood clots or heart attack. The drug is only administered in a clinic or hospital, usually intravenously. Let your doctor know if you have recently been on similar medications, such as abciximab (ReoPro) or tirofiban (Aggrastat).

OTHER NAMES Pygmy rattlesnake, dusky pygmy rattlesnake, Florida ground rattlesnake, southeastern ground rattlesnake, hog-nosed rattler, small rattlesnake
ORIGIN Southeastern United States
PART USED Venom

Southeastern pygmy rattlesnake

HOOKWORM

Ancylostoma duodenale, Necator americanus

MEDICAL BENEFITS ◆ Promising treatment for inflammatory bowel disorders (coeliac disease, Crohn's disease, ulcerative colitis) ◆ Possible treatment for other autoimmune disorders such as asthma, type 1 diabetes, multiple sclerosis and allergies

Would you swallow a worm if it cured you of an illness? This is a question sufferers of some debilitating disorders may soon have to consider, given recent promising research into the therapeutic use of parasitic worms.

There are two species of hookworm that invade the human gut, *Ancylostoma duodenale* and *Necator americanus*. While a large infestation of the worms causes anaemia, pain and even death, some scientists believe that in small numbers the worms may be beneficial. Researchers in Australia have been introducing small numbers of *N. americanus* (up to 20) into the guts of people with coeliac disease to see if the presence of the parasites can lessen the symptoms of the disease.

in CLOSE-UP

Like most parasites, hookworms have a complicated, yet effective method of moving from host to host. The eggs leave one infected person in their faeces and a new host can pick up the parasite by walking barefoot on contaminated soil, such as at a riverbank or beach. It takes a day or two for the eggs in the faeces to hatch into larvae and up to 10 days for the larvae to reach the infectious stage, where they can burrow into the skin of a new host. After tunnelling beneath the skin, the larvae reach the bloodstream, which carries them into the heart and lungs. They are then coughed up the windpipe and swallowed, thus making it into the intestines. Once in the small intestine, the larvae mature into adults, where they attach themselves to the intestinal wall, feeding on blood. They can live there for several years, where they will lay hundreds of thousands of eggs. When the eggs pass out of the gut with the stools, the cycle is ready to begin again.

Reining in the immune system Coeliac disease is an autoimmune disorder, a condition that causes the body's immune system to start attacking healthy tissues. In the case of coeliac disease, this happens in response to the plant protein gluten. If someone with coeliac disease eats foods containing gluten (such as pasta or breads made from wheat, barley or rye), their immune system attacks the lining of the small intestine, causing painful abdominal bloating, diarrhoea and constipation, as well as impeding the proper absorption of nutrients. At present there is no cure except to exclude gluten from the diet – and anyone who has tried to do this will know how difficult it can be. But if the Australian scientists are right, help may be available if you are prepared to tolerate a few 'passengers' in your gut.

So far the results from the trials have been encouraging. Though no obvious reduction in symptoms has been recorded, there *is* evidence that the presence of hookworms dampens the body's immune response to gluten. Few participants reported discomfort from the hookworms, while several said they felt more energetic and refused the offer of an anthelmintic (a drug that removes worms) at the end of the study.

The mouthparts of the adult hookworm are prominently displayed in this colour scanning electron micrograph image.

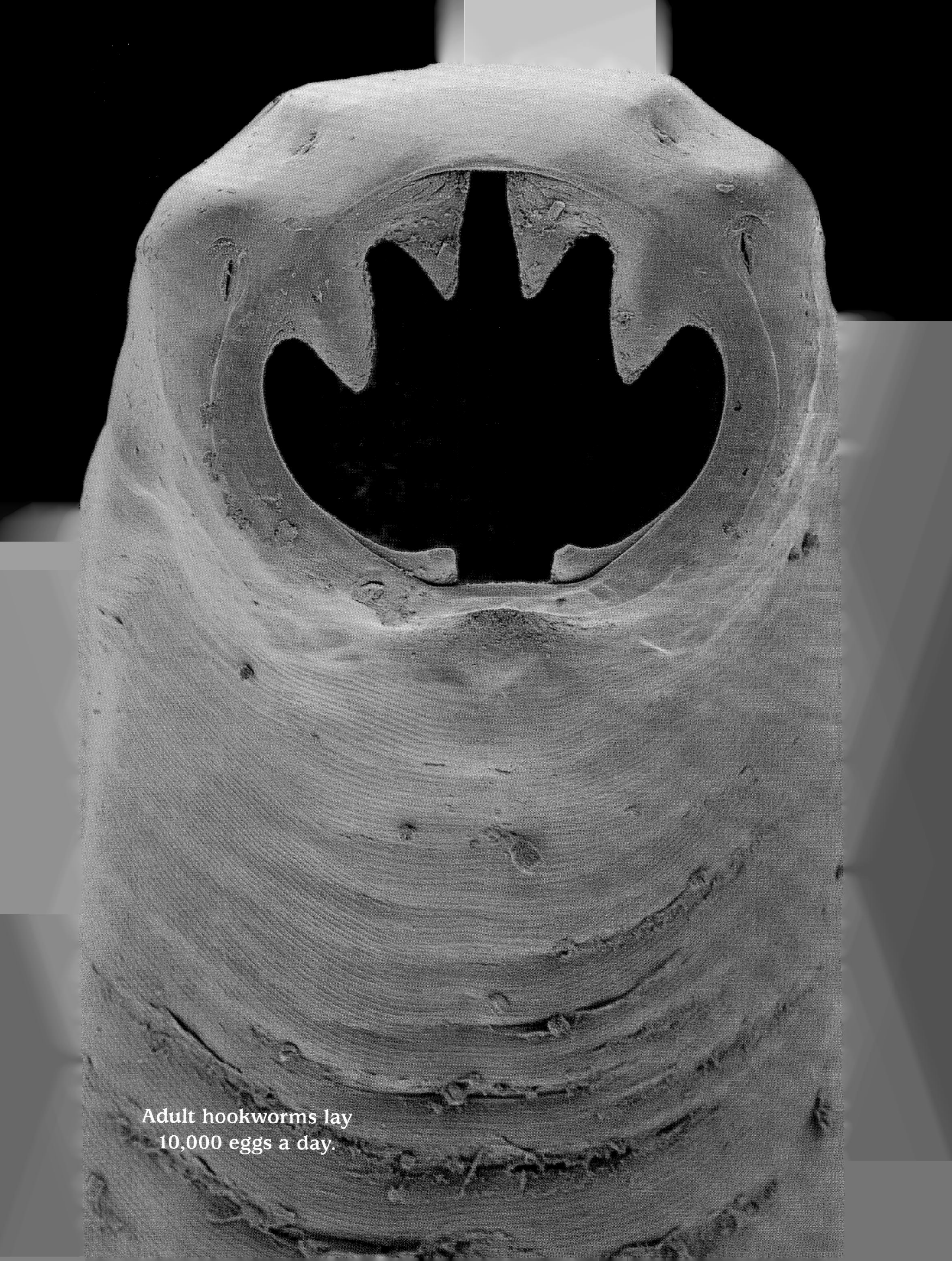

Adult hookworms lay 10,000 eggs a day.

Helminth therapy Using hookworms to treat coeliac disease is part of a broader range of treatments called helminth therapy, where parasitic worms are introduced to the body with the aim of 'dampening' the body's immune response. Studies have involved several different types of parasitic worm and a whole range of diseases, including allergies, asthma and inflammatory bowel disorders (Crohn's disease, ulcerative colitis and coeliac disease).

When a parasite enters its host, its survival relies on its ability to stay put. Parasites do this through subtle interactions with the host's immune response. Introducing parasites, in controlled numbers, appears to help disorders where the body's immune system has gone into overdrive and is attacking itself. If scientists could find out exactly how the parasites interact with the immune system, it could lead to new drugs or treatments.

Coeliac disease affects approximately 1 per cent of the population in developed countries, but often goes undiagnosed.

Alternative worms While studying the effects of helminth therapies, researchers are keen to find relatively safe parasites that can ameliorate the symptoms of disease without causing harm themselves. One such parasite is pig whipworm (*Trichuris suis*). Several studies involving the ingestion of pig whipworm eggs have been shown to alleviate the symptoms of Crohn's disease and ulcerative colitis. The whipworm eggs are thought to be a good choice since they remain in the gastrointestinal tract and are spontaneously eliminated by the body after a few weeks.

In 2012, Delaware-based Coronado Biosciences commenced phase 2 clinical trials in Europe to monitor the effects of pig whipworm on Crohn's disease. And researchers in the United Kingdom are currently investigating whether hookworms may be helpful for people with type 1 diabetes and multiple sclerosis, both of which are autoimmune disorders.

The hygiene hypothesis

In the 1980s, scientists noticed that in developing countries people who were infected with parasitic worms rarely suffered from allergies such as hay fever and asthma. Meanwhile in developed countries, where good hygiene practices and improved sanitation had virtually eradicated gut parasites, allergies such as asthma and other autoimmune disorders were on the increase. In response a theory emerged, now known as the hygiene hypothesis, that the high standards of hygiene in developed countries result in a person's immune system being underexercised, with the result that it starts to attack the body's own tissues. So not only will a little bit of dirt not do you any harm – it might do some good!

ORIGIN Tropics
PART USED Whole

Helminth therapy remains controversial since it involves deliberately introducing a parasite into the body. However, researchers maintain that in controlled conditions the treatment is safe. For the moment the therapy is not available and the only way to receive it would be to take part in an approved clinical trial. Currently, the main centres for research are the University of Nottingham in the United Kingdom; the Princess Alexandra Hospital, Brisbane, Australia; and the University of Iowa in the United States.

HONEYBEE

Apis spp.

MEDICAL BENEFITS ◆ Antibacterial agent ◆ Effective wound dressing ◆ Potential use in cancer treatment ◆ Traditional remedy for sore throat, tickly cough, dry skin (in a face mask)

Only in recent years have scientists discovered the science behind the healing effects of honey, long put to good use in treating wounds, soothing sore throats and nourishing skin. In turn, this has led to a range of new treatments.

Though researchers have known about the antibacterial qualities of honey for some time, it is only recently that they have been able to suggest what might be the source of these qualities. Dutch researchers at the Center for Infection and Immunity Amsterdam put it down to a protein that bees add to honey called defensin-1. In 2010, they examined the effects of medical grade honey on a range of bacteria in the laboratory and then divided the honey up into different chemical components. The most potent antimicrobial action was shown by defensin-1. The discovery could lead to new antibiotics and honey-based medical treatments. However, research at Cardiff Metropolitan University suggests that honey works by inhibiting the formation of biofilms, slimy sheets formed by microorganisms hooking up together, which conventional antibiotics have trouble penetrating. Both may be correct: it is likely that honey's effectiveness is due to a number of mechanisms that work together.

There are seven species of honeybee, but more than 20,000 species of other bees worldwide.

Honeybees play a critical role in pollination. By repositioning hives, beekeepers can increase pollination of selected crops.

Manuka is the best Since honey is made by bees from the nectar of plants, its composition varies depending on where it comes from and which plants the bees have been foraging on. Manuka honey is made by bees foraging on the manuka tree (*Leptospermum scoparium*), which is native to New Zealand and parts of Australia.

Large randomised controlled studies have shown that manuka honey is superior to other types of honey in terms of its antimicrobial properties. It has been formulated as 'Medihoney', which is used in special impregnated bandages, dressings and gels to aid the healing of wounds, especially pressure sores and leg ulcers. As well as being antimicrobial, Manuka honey aids the removal of dead tissue from wounds and moistens the affected area, making it more comfortable and easier to remove and reapply dressings.

More recently, researchers at the Washington University School of Medicine in St Louis, Missouri, have been looking at melittin, a component of bee venom. This peptide is known to have an ability to target renal, lung, liver, prostate, bladder and mammary cancer cells, as well as leukaemia cells. The researchers have been modifying melittin so that they can attach compounds to it and use it as a 'transporter agent'. The melittin could then, for example, carry therapeutic compounds or indicator dyes straight into the heart of tumours.

ORIGIN Europe
PARTS USED Honey, venom

Honey is a great home remedy and has several different uses. The best choice is honey that is 'raw', meaning that it has not been pasteurised, as pasteurisation denatures some of its enzymes and makes it less effective. For this reason you should not allow children under 12 months to ingest raw honey because there is a small chance that it contains bacteria that could be harmful to an underdeveloped immune system. Recommended uses for honey include:

- Grazes, minor burns and cuts: Slather on some honey then cover the wound with clean gauze. Change the dressing two or three times a day.
- Sore throats: Honey is known as a demulcent, which means it coats the throat as it is swallowed and so eases irritation. The sweetness of the honey also encourages salivation, so easing a dry throat and encouraging expulsion of phlegm. Try the following remedy for a sore throat or tickly cough. Steep 2 tablespoons of grated ginger root in a cup of boiling water for 10 minutes. Add 2 teaspoons of honey and one of lemon juice. Drink before bed.
- Dry skin and acne: Bathe the face in warm water to open the pores, then apply a layer of honey to the skin and wash off after 20 minutes. You can then apply a face mask made with mashed avocado and olive oil; the oil will provide moisturising oils (alternatively, whisk in some milk – its lactic acid helps soften dry skin). Adding oatmeal will create a 'scrub' that will help remove dead skin cells.

Alternatively, you can purchase ready-made honey products, which are available from several pharmaceutical and natural health companies; these include wound dressings and gels. Ask your pharmacist for further information.

COCKROACHES

Blattaria

MEDICAL BENEFITS ◆ Potential source of new antibiotics

Cockroaches are better known for spreading diseases rather than curing them, but a recent discovery of antibacterial compounds in the insects' brains could change that perception.

On the whole cockroaches are pretty much despised. They live in dirty places, scavenging on leftover food, and carry harmful bacteria on their feet and bodies. When you find one in your hotel room, it is generally not a good sign – and these tough little creatures can be difficult to eradicate and cost the hotel industry a fortune in pest-control measures. But a recent discovery may soon put cockroaches in the lauded company of penicillin – because of some novel antibacterial chemicals in their brains.

Researchers at Nottingham University in the United Kingdom identified nine separate antibacterial chemicals in the brains and nervous systems of cockroaches. Each chemical appears to be specialised to target a different type of bacteria. The finding will be music to the ears of doctors facing the ongoing challenge of antibiotic resistance. Antibiotics based on these cockroach compounds would be particularly welcome since they have been found to be effective against Methicillin-resistant *Staphylococcus aureus* (MRSA), a notoriously difficult-to-combat and deadly strain of bacteria. The roach antibacterials also made short work of *Escherichia coli*, a commonly occurring bacterium that can cause food poisoning.

ORIGIN Worldwide
PARTS USED Compounds from brain

Chemical defences It makes sense that creatures such as cockroaches would carry their own supply of bacteria-killing chemicals. These chemical defences would allow them to live in dirty places without becoming infected themselves. It is no coincidence either that the antibacterial substances are found only in the brain and nervous systems of the insects. This is the most essential part for survival. Cockroaches could live with the loss of a leg, for example, but brain infection would most likely cause death.

The researchers also looked in the brains of locusts and found similar antibacterials there, leading to the thought that maybe the insect world offers a whole new avenue for antibiotic-hunters to explore.

It could be several years before scientists are able to formulate the antibacterial compounds into drugs fit for use on humans. In the meantime you can help reduce the build-up of antibiotic resistance by using antibiotics only when absolutely essential.

American cockroach

INSPIRED BY INSECTS

We can learn a lot from the way insects interact with their world. In particular, studying the way they move and see has led to significant technological advances, ranging from the invention of rescue robots to X-ray machine enhancements.

Cockroaches, for example, are tough – and fast. They clamber over any terrain, scaling obstacles many times their height with ease. This has fascinated robotics scientists for two decades. By studying the way cockroaches move, researchers have been able to build six-legged robots that are relatively stable on rough terrain.

Until recently, research focused on observing the way the insects moved and on making machines that emulated it. But now an Israeli researcher is planning to take this further by finding out how the cockroach brain is involved (or not) in the movements. Amir Ayali from Tel Aviv University reckons that his approach will lead to lighter, more efficient robots. This is because the cockroach does not 'think' about its leg movements; they happen instinctively. If roboticists could copy this instinctive behaviour where the legs respond to their environment without the roach having to think about it, less computing power would be needed for movement, and so the robot would be lighter and faster on its six little legs.

Remote control In another strand of research, scientists at North Carolina State University tried merging insect with machine, creating a cyborg cockroach. After implanting electrodes into the insect's antennae and rear-end sensory appendages called cerci, the researchers could send

FOLLOW THE LEADERS

Scientists have long been fascinated by some insects' so-called hive consciousness – their ability to work together under the guidance of a collective intelligence. In the Leurre Project (*leurre* means 'lure' in French), researchers from France, Belgium and Switzerland made tiny cockroach-like robots and sprayed them with the pheromones that would make cockroaches accept them as real. The robots were programmed to seek out real roaches and then move towards a light, to see if the other roaches would follow them. Results from research such as this may inspire new ideas in artificial intelligence and have applications in robotics, where groups of tiny robots are programmed to work together to achieve a task.

Honeybees

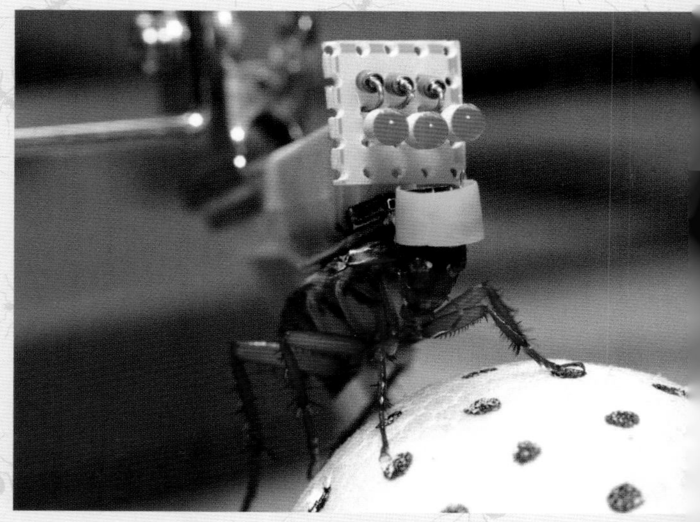

Above: By sending pulses via electrodes, scientists have been able to control cockroach movements.

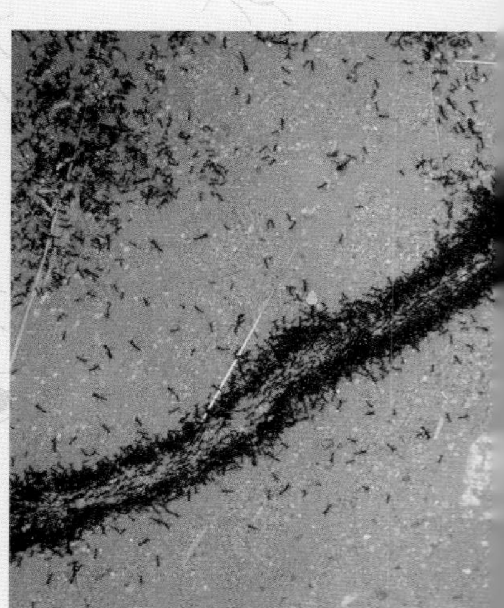

Right: Certain species of ant use polarised sunlight to guide them. Scientists are working on navigation systems based on this principle.

electrical impulses to simulate an obstacle in front of the insect or the sensation of something creeping up behind it, and thereby control its movements. In California, researchers at the University of California, Irvine, attached a cockroach to transmitters and sat it on a free-moving ping-pong ball atop a small, wheeled buggy. Using electrical signals, the researchers could cause the cockroach to respond and move its legs in particular ways; in turn, these movements on the ping-pong ball drove the buggy.

One potential use of these studies is to have remote-controlled cockroaches carry cameras or sensors into dangerous places such as buildings wrecked by explosions or earthquakes.

A compound view Insect eyes have long fascinated scientists, partly because they are very different from our own. Instead of having one central lens per eye, insects have a large array of tiny lenses held together to form a 'compound eye'. The insect sees a mosaic of all the images from these lenses – resulting in sight that may not be as focused as ours, but is far more sensitive to movement and provides a 360-degree field of vision.

Some recent research has focused on the way the compound eyes of moths tend to capture light rather than reflect it. This helps these creatures see at night when they are most active but little light is available. It also helps them avoid being eaten, as they would be more visible if their eyes shone in the moonlight. Scientists at the City University of New York, in collaboration with Massachusetts Institute of Technology and New York University, have created a new type of 'nanomaterial' based on the structure of the moth's compound eye, consisting of crystals encrusted with pyramid-shaped bumps of silicon nitride. Incorporated in medical scanning equipment, this material can capture energy normally lost from X-rays and thereby improve the resolution and accuracy of images – and, in turn, allow X-ray doses to be reduced.

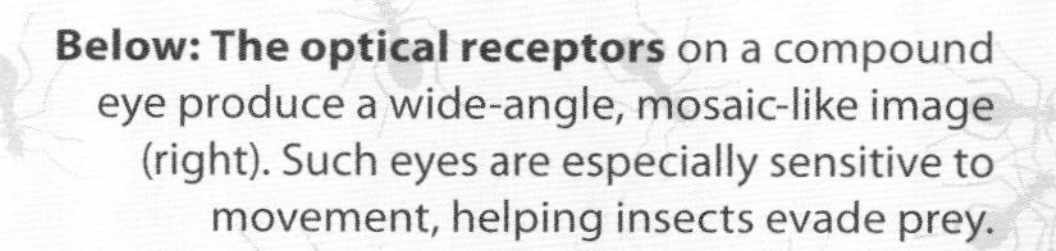

Below: The optical receptors on a compound eye produce a wide-angle, mosaic-like image (right). Such eyes are especially sensitive to movement, helping insects evade prey.

Right: Researchers hope to learn more about obstacle avoidance by studying the fast, frenetic, yet highly accurate movements of swarms of locusts.

FRUIT FLY

Drosophila melanogaster

MEDICAL BENEFITS ◆ Advances in genetics ◆ Enhances understanding of human diseases

They may be annoying when they are hanging round your fruit bowl, but we have a lot to thank fruit flies for – they've been at the forefront of genetic research for the past century, helping scientists to understand and treat human diseases.

Fruit fly

Genetic research using *Drosophila* began in 1910 when Thomas Hunt Morgan, an American biology professor, observed a fruit fly with white eyes. Normally fruit flies have red eyes, so the white-coloured eyes indicated that something controlling the eye colour of the fly had changed. When Morgan bred the white-eyed male fly with a red-eyed female, the offspring all had red eyes. But then when flies from that generation were mated with red-eyed females a white-eyed male was produced. From this he worked out that whatever controlled eye colour was linked to the sex of the fly. In doing this, he became the first person to link a specific trait to a particular chromosome (the female sex chromosome).

Thousands of experiments and breeding rounds later, Morgan and his team went on to confirm his theory that genes (the biological elements responsible for the inherited traits) are carried on chromosomes and some genes occur on the same chromosome and are always inherited together. This was a breakthrough and heralded a flurry of fundamental discoveries about the nature of fruit-fly inheritance and about heredity in general.

in CLOSE-UP

Why fruit flies? Well, though they look very different from us and their systems are much simpler than ours, many of their genes are like those found in humans and serve a similar purpose. This allows scientists to study mechanisms of disease in fruit flies and relate their research to humans. On a practical level, fruit flies are a good laboratory specimen since an individual's life cycle is just 10 days, they are small (millions can be kept in one lab), and they produce numerous offspring – females can lay up to 100 eggs a day.

Thomas Morgan's work helped explain the role of genes and chromosomes in evolution.

One version of the fruit fly genome map plots all the strands of DNA onto a globe-like sphere.

Creating a map As research with fruit flies and inheritance continued, scientists began to realise that the genes on the chromosomes were arranged in a particular order and could be 'mapped'. It helped that *Drosophila* have large chromosomes in their salivary glands. These are easily observed under a microscope and their bar code stripes of light and dark bands allow genes to be mapped easily and accurately.

Mapping the *Drosophila* 'genome' – all the genes contained in the fruit fly's DNA – commenced in 1991 and took nine years. Once it had been sequenced, geneticists were quick to note that of the 289 genetic flaws then known to cause human diseases, approximately 60 per cent had *Drosophila* equivalents. That meant fruit flies could be extremely useful for research into human diseases.

The complete sequence of the fruit fly genome was made freely available to scientists around the world. Thanks to this little insect, researchers have since identified the human genes involved in Parkinson's disease and human cancers, among other illnesses.

Mutant genes Scientists can also use fruit flies to find out how environmental factors can cause genetic mutations. If they expose the flies to radiation, for example, they can then see how genes in their offspring are affected. In 2008 NASA scientists sent fruit flies up to the International Space Station so that nine generations could be bred while in space. The aim was to gain an insight into how genes are affected by weightlessness and the stresses of being in outer space.

OTHER NAMES Pomace fly, vinegar fly, wine fly
ORIGIN Worldwide
PART USED DNA

Evolution in action

Who knows where the research with *Drosophila* will takes us? Recently geneticists from Wilfrid Laurier University in Canada and the University of California declared that they had bred a generation of fruit flies that could count. It took 40 generations to come up with these 'math flies' and now the researchers need to compare their genes with those of ordinary flies to see where the mutation has arisen. The flies developed a 'number sense' after regular 20-minute lessons, which comprised two, three or four flashes of light (with the two or four flashes coinciding with a vigorous shaking of the cage). After a short pause the experiment was repeated. For 39 generations the flies did nothing to prepare for the shaking; then in the fortieth generation they did, because they had evolved to associate the number of flashes with the shaking cage. The findings may support the theory that mathematical ability is an innate feature and it may give insights into dyscalculia (a difficulty with numbers) in humans.

Going head to head here are a normal fruit fly (left) and a mutated fruit fly. Mutation is often achieved by irradiating fruit flies with X-rays.

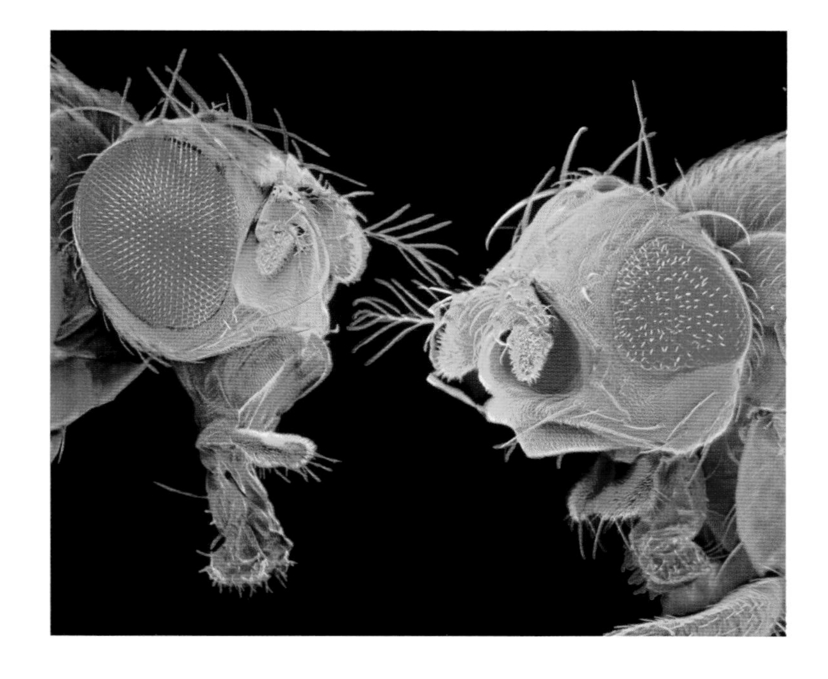

CHILEAN ROSE TARANTULA

Grammostola rosea

MEDICAL BENEFITS ◆ Potential treatment for atrial fibrillation ◆ Potential treatment for muscular dystrophy

Seeing a big, hairy tarantula is enough to make anyone's heart flutter. Ironically, a protein in this tarantula's venom actually calms the heart and may one day be a treatment for a form of arrythmia.

The Chilean rose tarantula is a rather large spider with a 5-cm (2.5-in) body and a leg span of 14 cm (5.5 in). It looks ferocious and yet it is one of the more docile species, making it a popular choice for keeping as a pet – like all tarantulas it does have a venomous bite, but will only use it if threatened.

Of the 40,000 species of spider, fewer than 0.1 per cent have venom harmful to humans.

This tarantula's venom, moreover, has provided a fruitful line of enquiry for medical researchers. After many years of testing venoms from several types of spider with the aim of finding a chemical that would stop cells from triggering atrial fibrillation (the chaotic beating of the upper heart chambers), in 2001 scientists at SUNY, Buffalo, led by Frederick Sachs, found what they were looking for in Chilean rose tarantula venom. Like most spider venom, this tarantula's venom is made up of a cocktail of poisons and bioactive substances, and the researchers had to sift through over 100 chemicals until they identified the most active substance. They called it GsMTx-4.

Calming the heart GsMTx-4 is a protein and it works by blocking 'stretch-activated channels' in heart muscle cells. These channels in the cell walls open when the cell stretches, allowing positive ions into the cell. Normally, the cell then reverts to its original shape, closing the

What You CAN DO

It may be a number of years before GsMTx-4 becomes available as a treatment for atrial fibrillation or muscular dystrophy. Tonus Therapeutics has patented the protein as a 'new molecular entity' and tests are ongoing; the researchers hope to be able to bring GsMTx-4 to clinical trials in the next few years. If you would like to be involved in a trial, keep an eye on the website (www.tonustherapeutics.com).

Normally docile creatures, Chilean rose tarantulas perform a lively courtship display before mating.

channels. But if the channels stay open, as can happen when the heart muscle ages or through disease, the ions continue to flood in and disrupt normal functioning. GsMTx-4 binds itself to the stretched channels, blocking the passage of ions into the cells and thereby restoring the heart's natural rhythm. Importantly, the protein does not bind to unstretched channels in healthy tissue, so it seems to have minimal side effects.

The researchers first observed the effects of GsMTx-4 on single cells then tried it on rabbit hearts. The rabbits were given a jolt of electricity to disrupt their heart rhythm and then given extracts of GsMTx-4 to restore their hearts to normal. Since then the researchers have been able to genetically modify a strain of bacteria to produce the spider venom protein, thus ensuring a steady, and more easily harvested, supply.

OTHER NAMES Rose hair tarantula, Chilean flame tarantula, Chilean fire tarantula, Chilean red-haired tarantula
ORIGIN Chile; also Bolivia and Argentina
PART USED Venom

Muscular dystrophy

Another disease that could benefit from GsMTx-4 is muscular dystrophy. Patients with muscular dystrophy have a faulty gene that means their muscle cells lack a particular protein that helps them to hold their shape. In other words the cells are prone to distortion, and the random opening of stretch-activated channels. In this case the open channels allow an unchecked flow of calcium ions into the cells, leading to muscle wastage and, ultimately, death. In collaboration with Australian researchers, a US company, Tonus Therapeutics, has been testing GsMTx-4 in mice with muscular dystrophy; the first experiments showed the drug improved the animals' strength without harmful side effects. Though it is not a cure, GsMTx-4 could be formulated into a drug that might extend the lifespan of people with the disease.

No outright cure and few treatments are available for muscular dystrophy, which is often first diagnosed in early childhood.

MEDICINAL LEECH

Hirudo medicinalis

MEDICAL BENEFITS ◆ Basis for anticoagulant drugs ◆ Use in microsurgery ◆ Traditional therapy

Leeches have been used therapeutically for thousands of years, and although our theories of medicine have changed radically in that time these bloodsuckers still have an important role to play in healthcare.

The use of leeches in medicine goes back thousands of years – there are even pictures of medicinal leeches in Egyptian pharaohs' tombs. And in the Middle Ages, the practice of bloodletting – applying hungry leeches to the skin of sick people – was a popular treatment. The theory was that, by removing 'bad' or excess blood, certain conditions would be improved.

The four humours In those days medicine was based on the four 'humours' of the body: blood, phlegm, black bile and yellow bile. The aim was to keep the humours in balance and so achieve a state of health. Bloodletting was a way to adjust one of the humours and bring it into balance with the other three. If that sounds like mumbo jumbo, it was at least a step up from the previous doctrine that said all ill health was due to the indwelling of evil spirits. The four-humour theory was the science of its day and used widely by physicians up until the mid-nineteenth century.

Bloodletting could be carried out by cutting a vein, but the application of numerous leeches was a subtler and more controlled process. The leeches would be collected from their natural habitat of ditches and freshwater pools. At the peak of the practice's popularity, in the late 1700s and early 1800s, the medicinal leech became an endangered species such was the demand. Leeches were applied for any condition where the skin appeared red (as this was thought to indicate an excess of blood) and they were routinely used for fevers and swellings.

The surgeon's friend Following the development of a more scientific approach to medicine, the therapeutic use of leeches

Mechanical stand-in

Leeches have their drawbacks. They can be temperamental, sometimes refusing to feed, especially on cold skin. They also have a habit of wandering off after a meal, which can be disconcerting for patients. A more serious problem is the potential for infection, since even leeches raised under strict hygiene can carry harmful bacteria in their guts. For this reason, every leech treatment has to be accompanied by a course of antibiotics. An alternative could be a mechanical leech, developed at the University of Wisconsin-Madison. Based on a vacuum pump, it draws blood after making an incision with a sharp probe and infusing the cut with anticoagulant. Though not as cheap as leeches, it is sterile, so no antibiotics are required. And it isn't slimy.

An adult leech is able to consume about ten times its body weight in blood in a single meal – approximately 15 ml.

This streetseller in Istanbul, Turkey, is offering medicinal leeches for use in self-treatment of a range of conditions.

dwindled; however, in recent years the practice has made a comeback. In particular, leeches have found a new role in the field of micro-surgery – most notably when severed fingers, ears or any other body part needs to be reattached or when skin flaps have to be closed up after plastic surgery. If blood lingers in the body parts, it can go bad, causing a graft to fail or, worse, become infected with gangrene. Strategically placed medicinal leeches encourage blood flow and hence wound healing.

Today medicinal leeches are raised in sterile conditions and are kept by the patient's bedside in a fridge. A typical application might be one leech every four hours. Feeding usually takes about 20 minutes before the leech is full. At that point, the leech is removed and killed – it cannot be reused, as this would risk cross-contamination of blood-borne diseases.

ORIGIN Europe and Asia
PARTS USED Whole body, saliva

in CLOSE-UP

Viewed up close, a leech's mouth resembles that of the monster in the movie *Alien*: it has three jaws and lots of sharp teeth. When it bites, it leaves a Y-shaped incision. The leech's saliva contains an anaesthetic so that the prey doesn't even notice the bite, chemicals that widen the blood vessels to let more blood out, and an anticoagulant to prevent clotting. The active anticoagulant substance, hirudin, was indentified as early as the 1880s; following advances in biotechnology in the 1970s, scientists were able to determine the structure of the compound and now several anticoagulant drugs based on hirudin are used for treating deep vein thrombosis, bruising and blood coagulation disorders.

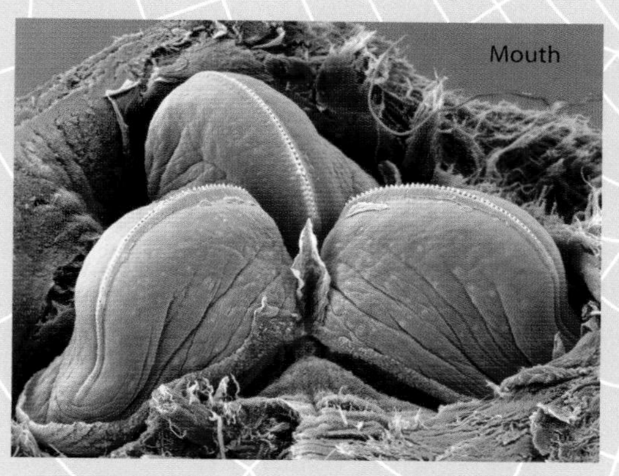

A WEB OF INTRIGUE

Spider silk is an amazing substance. It forms from a liquid into one of the strongest materials on Earth and yet retains elasticity. And the more scientists study it, the more potential uses they find for it.

Weight for weight, spider silk is stronger than steel and Kevlar (an ultra-tough synthetic material used for body armour) and more elastic than rubber. Even more important for the field of human medicine, it does not provoke a reaction from the immune system. With such useful properties, spider silk has enormous potential for medical applications, including use as sutures and wound dressings, 'scaffolding' on which to grow tissue, artificial tendons and ligaments, and microcapsules.

STRONG AND STICKY

Spiders need to produce strong, elastic silk so that they can build sturdy webs capable of catching their prey. Spider silk is made up of different combinations of proteins that produce various types of silk with different properties. They include dragline silk, attaching silk, sticky and nonsticky silk, egg-sac silk and swathing silk for wrapping around prey (spiders even produce a type of glue). The two types of silk of most interest to scientists are dragline silk and sticky silk. The strongest type of silk, dragline silk is used for abseiling down from a twig or branch and making the main framework of a web. Sticky, or flagelliform, silk is used for most of the rest of a web. Also pretty strong, it is especially flexible and can stretch to twice its size without breaking.

A spider's web is a perfect combination of strength and flexibility. Here an orb weaver feasts on a grasshopper.

Sourcing a steady supply No matter how well spider silk performs, however, there is always one problem: supply. Spiders are not silkworms: it is just not possible to 'farm' them – they tend to eat each other if kept in close proximity. So scientists have had to use their ingenuity to come up with ways of gaining a plentiful supply of the silk.

In 2010, a team of researchers at the University of Wyoming came up with the idea of spider goats. It may sound like some hideous chimera, but spider goats are not as grotesque as they sound (and they don't have eight legs). They are simply goats that have been genetically engineered to produce the spider silk proteins in their milk, which can then be collected, purified and spun into silk. When the researchers tested spider goat silk, however, they found it was stronger than steel and Kevlar but still not as strong as real spider silk. It seems that spiders know an extra trick or two about spinning the silk proteins – and of course they have had a 350-million-year head start.

Spider silk is five times stronger than steel of the same diameter.

Tough stuff Nevertheless, another team at the University of Wyoming, in collaboration with scientists from the University of Notre Dame, France, reckons it has solved the supply problem – by genetically tweaking silkworms so that they spin cocoons of spider silk. When analysed, this silk was found to be as tough as the strongest spider silk. And this approach has another advantage: the material comes ready spun.

This is an important breakthrough and could result in the mass production of the revered spider silk. Indeed, if all goes well, in a few years' time there will be spider silk components in all sorts of products, from surgical implants to bulletproof vests.

Right: One team of researchers at the University of Wyoming has succeeded in genetically modifying plants so that they produce spider silk.

Below: It took four years to weave the Golden Spider Silk Cape, made from the silk of more than a million golden orb weaver spiders, native to Madagascar.

Right: German researchers at Munich's Technical University engineered bacteria to produce the silk threads on this frame.

Above: Spinnerets, located at the end of the spider's abdomen, are the organs that produce silk, extruding the liquid that sets to form a sticky thread.

HOW TO WEAVE A WEB

When a spider makes a web, it starts by creating a frame, anchored to twigs or other objects, using dragline silk. Then it runs radial threads, made of nonsticky silk, out from the centre to the edge, like spokes on a wheel. Next it lays a nonsticky auxiliary spiral from the centre outwards; this allows it to move freely as it works on the web. When the spider has finished the spiral, it retraces its path to the centre, eating the nonsticky silk and replacing it with sticky silk, so that it is left with a sticky spiral and nonsticky radial threads that it uses to move across the web. A web is strong enough to withstand winds and rain, though the spider may have to repair it on a daily basis. It's also highly flexible, so that when an insect flies into the web, the silk gives a little and wraps its sticky lines around the insect rather than bouncing it straight back out.

FIREFLY

Lampyridae

MEDICAL BENEFITS ◆ Possible screening tool to test for tuberculosis

The firefly flashes its tail to attract a mate in the dark. Now scientists are harnessing the insect's ability to light up to help diagnose antibiotic-resistant tuberculosis.

Fireflies produce their characteristic glow through a simple chemical reaction. It involves the enzyme luciferase, which acts on the chemical luciferin and turns it into oxyluciferin plus light. With advances in genetic engineering, scientists have been able to move the gene for luciferase into the DNA of mice, making them glow like fireflies. Now scientists are putting the same genes into the bacteria that cause tuberculosis (TB).

You may wonder why this is such an important breakthrough. The answer lies in the two-pronged problem of antibiotic-resistant tuberculosis and the significant amount of time currently required to diagnose the disease. Normally a sputum sample is taken and then the cells have to be cultured, which may take several days. Once the culture is ready, various antibiotics are applied to see which one works, which requires yet more time. And time is crucial when trying to stop the spread of such a virulent disease, especially if that strain is antibiotic resistant.

Speedier diagnosis A bioluminescence test promises to be far quicker. With this, scientists use a bacteriophage (a virus that attacks specific bacteria, see p. 300) to carry the luciferase gene into the TB bacteria, which then produces a glowing light. When an antibiotic is added, the light goes out if the antibiotic is effective, telling scientists which antibiotics work. And the time taken to get a result is just two hours. Researchers at Albert Einstein College of Medicine in New York first developed this idea back in 2007. They were able to show results using cultured samples of TB, but when used directly on sputum samples the reporter phage wasn't bright enough to see. The researchers didn't give up, however, and, using the latest genetic engineering techniques, have developed a phage (2GFP10) that can be used directly in samples of spit, effectively lighting up TB even when very small numbers of bacteria are present. Yet bigger trials are ongoing.

OTHER NAMES Lightning bugs, glowworms
ORIGIN Worldwide
PART USED Bioluminescent chemical

Firefly

En masse, as in this image of thousands of the insects in a tree in the Philippines, fireflies can create a spectacular effect.

Moveable test

Now that a method has been developed for detecting TB in sputum, the next step will be to develop this into a portable kit. One such test kit is currently being developed by the National Institute for Research in Tuberculosis in Chennai, India.

DEATHSTALKER SCORPION

Leiurus quinquestriatus

MEDICAL BENEFITS ◆ Potential treatment for glioma ◆ Possible use in gene therapy, cancer diagnosis ◆ Possible aid for brain surgery

With a name like 'deathstalker', it is not surprising that this scorpion has a highly poisonous sting. But scientists have discovered that one of the chemicals in its venom may in fact be a life-saver through its affinity for brain tumour cells.

Scorpions are generally feared, and understandably so. Most carry venom in their tails that is capable of at least causing pain in humans and in some cases paralysis and death. The deathstalker scorpion is a dangerous one, packing an array of neurotoxins into its venom. It has been known to kill children and frail or elderly people, and in anyone else its sting causes extreme pain and localised numbness. However, among its neurotoxin nasties, there is a chemical that may save lives.

A beneficial attachment The chemical is called chlorotoxin and the property that has been exciting researchers is that it seeks out and clings to the cells of a difficult-to-treat type of brain tumour called glioma, while leaving healthy cells unaffected. By binding to the cancerous cells, chlorotoxin stops them from infiltrating and spreading through the brain.

In 2006 the biotechnology company TransMolecular, Inc., based in Cambridge, Massachusetts, made a synthetic version of

After mating, a female deathstalker scorpion (right) gives birth to about 30 young, which for the first weeks will travel around on her back.

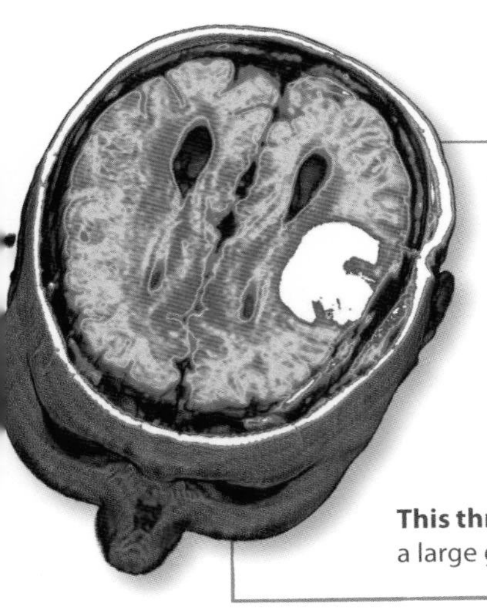

The treatments are still in the process of being clinically tested and may not be available for a few years. Should you need treatment for a brain tumour, you could, however, ask your doctor for the latest information on the tests. Sometimes patients can take part in clinical trials, and your doctor will be able to guide you on whether this is appropriate in your particular case.

This three-dimensional image, produced by combining a number of MRI scans, shows a large glial tumour on the left side of this patient's brain, highlighted in white.

chlorotoxin known as TM-601 and attached a radioactive substance to it. This can be injected into the bloodstream, where it will find its way to glioma cells and attach itself to them, effectively taking the radiation treatment right to the tumour. In 2009, the chlorotoxin-based radiation treatment passed a phase II clinical trial.

Gene therapy Other researchers have been looking at the potential of utilising chlorotoxin in gene therapy. This therapy involves introducing healthy sequences of DNA into cancerous cells to try to repair the damage, usually by attaching the DNA to a carrier that travels via the bloodstream to the tumour. Scientists from Washington University, Seattle, discovered that cholorotoxin's affinity for glioma cells made it a particularly efficient vehicle for carrying the DNA into the tumour, resulting in the delivery of more DNA than had been achieved with conventional carriers.

in CLOSE-UP

A scorpion's body can be divided into three parts: the head, abdomen and segmented tail. At the tip of the tail there is a sharp sting (telson), which is loaded with venom. The venom is used by the scorpion as defence and as a means of killing its prey (often a spider or an insect, but in some larger species it may be a lizard or small rodent). The scorpion holds the prey in its large pincer claws and then arches its tail over to sting it. The toxins in the venom are designed to immobilise or kill the prey and so they are generally fast-acting. Like spiders, scorpions can only digest their food in liquid form, so once they have subdued a victim they add their digestive juices to the carcass and then suck up the nutritious fluid.

Identifying the target Researchers at the Seattle Children's Hospital have found another cancer-beating use for chlorotoxin. They attached a fluorescent dye to the chemical and injected it into mice with brain, prostate and intestinal cancers. In each case, and most successfully with the brain cancer, the dye marked out the precise area of the tumour. This could be especially helpful to surgeons, who, using fluorescence detectors and magnification, would be able to see exactly which areas of tissue need to be removed. Indeed, the approach would allow them to see cancerous tissue even when only a few hundred diseased cells are present – in comparison, an MRI scan can only reveal a tumour when at least a million cells are affected. Furthermore, the dye will highlight areas of cancer that have broken away from the primary tumour, and could possibly even be used to detect tumours just under the skin.

OTHER NAMES Palestine yellow scorpion, Israeli desert scorpion
ORIGIN North Africa and Middle East
PART USED Venom

GREEN BOTTLE FLY

Lucilia sericata

MEDICAL BENEFITS ◆ Assists healing of wounds

It may seem counterintuitive, but if you pack a wound with flesh-eating maggots it gets better, not worse. In fact, maggot debridement therapy, or MDT, as such treatment is known, has been in use since the Middle Ages.

It was not until the 1920s, however, that doctors began to research the therapeutic effects of maggots properly. MDT became especially popular in the 1930s and was widely used in hospitals until the advent of antibiotics in the 1940s. With the emergence of antibiotic resistance in the 1980s, it was used again as a treatment of last resort for recalcitrant wounds where every other treatment had failed.

In 1989, researchers at the University of California, Irvine, decided to undertake a series of clinical trials to test the effectiveness of MDT against other wound therapies. The results showed that the therapy was safe and effective. Since then many studies have been carried out and MDT is now used all over the world. It continues to be a favoured treatment for problematic wounds such as pressure ulcers, burns, foot ulcers and surgical incisions that fail to heal. There have been many cases where the use of maggot therapy has saved a limb that would otherwise have been amputated.

Picky eaters The therapy works because green bottle maggots only eat dead flesh. So when they are let loose on a wound they eat the necrotic parts that harbour bacteria, leaving the undamaged tissues alone. The maggots eat by secreting enzymes onto the dead tissue and sucking up the liquid. Scientists believe that

The usual source of medicinal maggots, the green bottle fly is a widespread species, and especially common in Africa and Australia.

in CLOSE-UP

Maggots are the larval stage of the green bottle fly. The fly usually lays its eggs in a carcass or decaying tissue, and the maggots have evolved to eat only dead flesh. In warm climates they can hatch within eight hours and will feed for up to ten days. Maggots used in MDT are raised in laboratories and sterile when applied to wounds. Usually between five and eight maggots are used per square centimetre (0.15 sq in) of wound. After application, gauze is used to cover the wound, followed by a waterproof dressing that has been perforated to let air in. Maggots need to be able to breathe, so they will never burrow deep into flesh (as some patients fear). The maggots are removed after between 48 and 72 hours.

the action of the maggots changes the wound from acidic to alkaline, stimulating new tissue growth and healing around the wound. The maggots also secrete an antimicrobial substance that is effective against many types of bacteria, including some that have built up resistance to commonly used antibiotics.

Scientists would love to know exactly how maggots inhibit bacteria. They know that some of the bacteria are simply eaten and others do not survive in the alkaline conditions, but the latest research is focusing on the substance secreted by the maggots.

Using the goo In 2008, scientists from Swansea University in Wales collected the brown goo secreted by green bottle maggots as they fed. They isolated a compound called

Forensic scientists can tell how long a dead body has been lying in the open by checking the size of any maggots present.

Seraticin that was active against 12 different strains of bacteria. The substance made short work of nasty bugs such as MRSA (methicillin-resistant *Staphylococcus aureus*), *Clostridium difficile* and *Escherichia coli*. Research is ongoing to determine the structure of the substance and clinical trials would be needed before it could be produced as a drug.

There is one type of bacteria that the maggots have trouble with, however. Known as *Pseudomonas aeruginosa*, it is a common bacterium found in hospital settings. *P. aeruginosa* forms a biofilm (slimy sheets formed by microorganisms hooking up together) and Danish scientists believe that this may hold the key to its ability to kill maggots. The scientists are currently trying to determine the mechanism.

OTHER NAME Blowfly
ORIGIN Temperate zones
PARTS USED Larvae

You may be offered MDT in hospital if you have a problematic wound, such as a deep burn or diabetic foot ulcer. Most patients say they can't feel the maggots. And if it is a question of losing a limb or putting up with a few maggots – which would you prefer? Not all fly larvae are suitable for maggot therapy and you should never try the therapy yourself. Always seek medical assistance.

BRAZILIAN WANDERING SPIDER

Phoneutria nigriventer

MEDICAL BENEFITS ◆ Possible treatment for erectile dysfunction

One of the world's deadliest spiders offers a surprising gift to mankind: a substance in its venom that may prove to be an effective treatment for erectile dysfunction.

The Brazilian wandering spider likes to roam the jungle floor, on the hunt for insects, lizards and small rodents. It is also known as the banana spider due to its habit of hiding out in banana plantations in its home range of Central and South America. Spiders have been known to turn up in crates of bananas in the fresh produce section of supermarkets as far away as the United Kingdom – a worrying prospect since their venom can be deadly. A bite from such a spider causes severe pain, high blood pressure, loss of muscle control and difficulty breathing. Without the antivenom, death can soon follow due to asphyxiation.

A bite from a Brazilian wandering spider can cause death within an hour.

Guinness World Records lists the Brazilian wandering spider as the arachnid with the most venomous bite of all.

Causes of dysfunction But there is a more bizarre symptom of the bite that could offer a new type of medicine: when a man is bitten, he is likely to experience a long and painful erection, a condition known as priapism. Even though the raw venom has been known to permanently damage the penises of men who have survived being bitten, scientists still wondered if there was the potential for a drug that could treat the condition known as erectile dysfunction (ED).

ED affects 4 per cent of men in their 50s and more than 50 per cent of men over 75, and men with diabetes are two to three times more likely to be affected. Other factors that can contribute to the condition include depression and certain drugs prescribed for it (notably selective serotonin reuptake inhibitors, or SSRIs); high blood

Named for its habit of venturing across the forest floor at night, the Brazilian wandering spider rests in dark corners by day.

pressure and related medications; and other drugs including those used against hair loss and prostate enlargement.

An alternative to Viagra? Researchers set out to isolate the erection-causing chemical from the toxins in the wandering spider venom and see how it worked. In 2008 a team of Brazilian and US scientists identified the chemical and called it PnTx2-6. They started by giving it to rats with diabetes and hypertension and the rats' erections improved. In 2012 they tested it on rats with age-related ED and the results were similarly encouraging: the rats had improved erections and appeared to suffer no side effects.

Upon analysing how the chemical works, the researchers discovered that PnTx2-6 uses a different pathway from Viagra. So it could offer a useful alternative to conventional treatment and will be especially welcomed by the one in three men for whom Viagra does not work.

OTHER NAMES Banana spider, armed spider
ORIGIN South and Central America
PART USED Venom

in CLOSE-UP

An erection is the result of a complex interplay between psychological and physical stimulation. Its mechanics are controlled by a series of chemical reactions. During arousal, the brain sends signals to the nerves of the penis and a series of chemicals are released that cause the walls of the blood vessels in the penis to relax and become engorged with blood. The erection is reversed by another chemical, phosphodiesterase type 5 (PDE5). The drugs Viagra (sildenafil), Levitra (vardenafil) and Cialis (tadalafil) block the action of PDE5, so that the erection is maintained longer. These drugs do not work without stimulation; they simply keep the relevant chemicals in the system for longer. PnTx2-6, on the other hand, boosts the release of nitric oxide in cells – the first step in the chain of chemical reactions that normally initiate an erection.

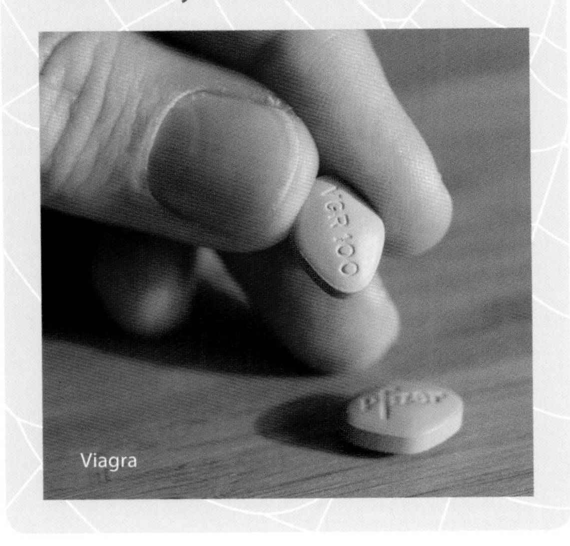

Viagra

You can't yet acquire a medicine based on PnTx2-6. But a synthetic version of the toxin has been made and the next step will be to see if there are any nasty side effects. Once these have been identified and, it is hoped, ruled out, the chemical may then go on to be tested in humans and eventually a new drug will be released on the market.

CHINESE MEDICINAL ANT

Polyrhachis lamellidens

MEDICAL BENEFITS ◆ Potential treatment for rheumatoid arthritis and bacterial infections ◆ Traditional medicine for rheumatoid arthritis and hepatitis

It sounds more like a wilderness survival measure, but eating ants could be good for you. They have long been used in Chinese medicine and now research evidence is backing up some of those centuries-old claims.

In traditional Chinese medicine, *Polyrhachis lamellidens* (known as 'black horse' in Chinese) is prescribed as a tonic to nourish the blood and increase vitality, and it is regularly used in hospitals – ingested whole or as an extract – to treat rheumatoid arthritis and hepatitis. It is also said to promote *qi* (the universal energy or 'life force'), balance yin and yang energies, promote long life, improve virility and fertility, improve digestion and promote sleep.

Such diverse uses for one remedy are not unusual in Chinese medicine, which treats the body holistically. But there are some wilder claims for the use of black ants, too – for example, that the ant extract can increase the amount of DNA in cells. While ideas like that are unlikely to stand up to scientific analysis, there is growing evidence that some of the other supposed benefits of the black ant may be real.

Anticipating relief In 2005, a study on mice by researchers at the China Pharmaceutical University, Nanjing, found that the extract had significant pain-relieving and anti-inflammatory effects – which would explain its use in treating conditions such as rheumatoid arthritis. But because an extract of whole ant was used, the researchers could not tell which particular chemical had had the beneficial effect. In 2008, however, they managed to isolate two chemicals, which they called polyrhacitides A and B. These belong to a group of substances called polyketides, which are unusual in ants but are also found in plants, fungi and bacteria. Studies have shown polyketides to be useful in fighting arthritis, bacterial infections and other diseases.

In 2009, German researchers working for the biotech company Boehringer Ingelheim made synthetic versions of polyrhacitides A and B. This will enable wider testing of the chemicals and may eventually lead to the formulation of a drug.

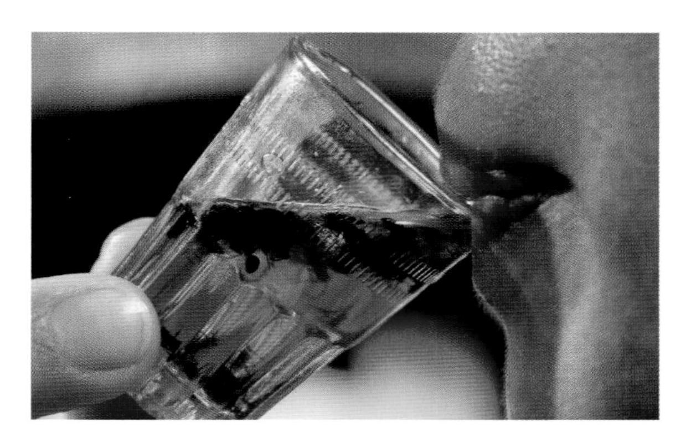

In China, medicinal drinks made with black ants are said to offer diverse health benefits.

What You CAN DO

Chinese medicinal ant is available as an extract in capsule form from Chinese medical practitioners and health food shops. Given the results of recent tests, these may be worth trying for relief from arthritis pain. Follow the dosage instructions on the label. One day your doctor may be able to prescribe a drug based on the ant extract.

OTHER NAME Chinese mountain ant
ORIGIN Eastern Asia
PART USED Whole ant

RELIEVING JOINT PAIN

While compounds derived from ants (see p. 225) and even deer antler (see p. 170) show promise as therapies for joint pain, a range of more readily available natural substances can also provide welcome, albeit temporary, relief.

Joint pain is a common and often debilitating problem, especially in old age. There can be a wide range of underlying causes. Osteoarthritis occurs when the cartilage lining the ends of joints (especially the hips, knees and spine) becomes worn down, eventually degrading the bone beneath; it commonly affects people over the age of 60. Rheumatoid arthritis is an autoimmune disease, whereby the body attacks its own tissue; it causes inflammation around the joints and may occur from as young as 25. Other causes of joint pain include osteoporosis (the gradual decalcification of the bones that accompanies old age) and fibromyalgia, a poorly understood condition that causes general muscle and joint pain.

If you are suffering from chronic joint pain, you should first see your doctor to identify the cause, as this may determine the best way to ameliorate the pain, and medications may be prescribed in acute cases. However, various natural treatments have been shown to bring relief, including the following easy-to-make home remedies. Some of these act directly to block pain, while others help by reducing inflammation.

Chilli pepper ointment Chilli peppers contain capsaicin (see p. 120), which can block pain signals and release endorphins (the body's bliss chemicals). Sprinkle half a teaspoon of powdered dried chilli (or cayenne pepper) into 250 ml of warmed olive oil. Massage around the affected joints wearing rubber gloves (it may sting a little). Never apply to broken skin, keep it away from your eyes, and rinse off well afterwards. Alternatively, simmer 1 tablespoon of cayenne pepper in 500 ml apple cider vinegar for 10 minutes. Cool and then dip a clean cloth in the solution; apply as a compress to aching joints.

Turmeric paste Mix a teaspoon of turmeric (see p. 124) with a tablespoon of grated ginger (see p. 150). Add water to make a paste and apply to a clean cloth and use as a compress over the affected joint. Another way of

NATURAL RELIEF

Research supports the use of these traditional remedies for mild relief:

Blackcurrant The beneficial effects of this berry were backed by a 1994 US study that found blackcurrant seed oil to be potentially effective in treating rheumatoid arthritis. Steep 5 g leaves in 1 l (2 pts) of boiling water for five minutes and drink 2–3 cups per day.

Boswellia A 2000 UK study and a 2002 German study confirmed that resin from this plant helps inhibit inflammation and build cartilage. Take one (150 mg) capsule three times a day.

Celery Recent research supports celery's traditional use as an anti-inflammatory. Steep 1 teaspoon of celery seeds in a cup of boiling water for 10 minutes and then strain and drink. Repeat once a day.

Devil's claw This herb has been shown to contain an active anti-inflammatory compound, harpagoside. Take 300 mg of extract three times a day.

Stinging nettle As a diuretic, nettle increases elimination of sodium and urea and so eases rheumatic and arthritic conditions, as demonstrated in German studies in 1999. Take 20 drops of tincture three times a day after food.

Boswellia resin

Turmeric

harnessing turmeric's anti-inflammatory powers is to add 1 teaspoon to a cup of warm milk before bedtime. The fat content of the milk helps to deliver the active compounds (curcuminoids) in the turmeric. Add a teaspoon of honey to aid restful sleep.

Essential oils Aromatherapists believe certain oils have pain-killing qualities and there are a number that are recommended for painful joints. Add one to a carrier oil (about 2–3 ml essential oil in 30 ml of carrier oil such as almond, olive or sunflower oil) and use in massages or compresses. Alternatively, you may add a few drops (but no more than 10) to a bath. Try eucalyptus (see p. 30), benzoin, chamomile, lavender, juniper or rosemary oil; black pepper, marjoram and ginger oils are also believed to improve circulation.

Soothing supplements Make sure you are eating a balanced diet with plenty of fruit and vegetables. Colourful fruit and vegetables contain antioxidants that help sponge up harmful free radicals in the body and maintain overall health (see p. 146). Consider taking antioxidants such as vitamins C and E as well as zinc. Traditional therapists consider glucosamine, a cartilage-building sugar compound, a highly effective remedy for slowing joint damage and relieving arthritis pain.

TRINIDAD CHEVRON TARANTULA

Psalmopoeus cambridgei

MEDICAL BENEFITS ◆ Potential painkiller ◆ Possible agent for reducing damage due to stroke ◆ Potential antimalarial drug

Spider bites are usually painful, but it turns out that within the venom of the Trinidad chevron tarantula there are chemicals that can also relieve pain – and compounds that may be active against malaria, too.

Spider venoms have evolved to be remarkably diverse, to the extent that they contain toxins lethal enough to harm much bigger creatures than their normal prey – humans, for example. The upside of this is that among the many distinctly nasty substances are other chemicals that might also affect humans, but in more positive ways.

Shutting down pain For example, French and German scientists looked at the activity of one chemical in the Trinidad chevron tarantula's venom, known as psalmotoxin 1, and found that it has potent pain-relieving properties. When given to laboratory mice it had a significant effect on reducing thermal, mechanical, chemical, inflammatory and nerve pain.

The researchers say that psalmotoxin 1 works by blocking acid-sensing ion channels (ASICs) in nerve cells. Many spider venom chemicals act on ion channels, which are like gates that allow ions to pass in and out of cells. In the case of ASICs, the channels open when they sense an acidic environment, which can arise after tissue damage, inflammation or the build-up of lactic acid. This causes the nerve cells to fire off pain signals, which in turn lets us know that something is wrong. Psalmotoxin 1 locks the ASCIs

With surprising speed, tarantulas can attack and immobilise large prey such as this grasshopper.

Though recent developments have been promising, it will be some time before you find medications derived from this tarantula in your local chemist. Psalmotoxin 1 is offering scientists an insight into the mechanism of ASICs, which may eventually lead to a new kind of pain-relief drug. Psalmotoxin 1 may also have an application in patients who are at risk of strokes, though this research is very new and a drug is a long way off, too. The antimalarial substances psalmopeotoxin I and II appear not to have a detrimental effect on human cells in vitro, so could be promising candidates for developing into antimalarial medicines. They will need to go through several years of testing, however, including human clinical trials, before they become available on prescription.

shut so that they are no longer sensitive to pain. Psalmotoxin 1 may also protect the brain during a stroke, since a stroke can cause an acid environment that may lead to brain damage. By locking the ASCIs, the damage may be lessened.

Malaria-fighting chemicals Researchers at Paris's Jacques Monod Institute have found some other potentially useful chemicals in the Trinidad chevron tarantula's venom: substances that kill malaria parasites. Malaria is caused by protozoan blood-borne parasites that are carried by female anopheles mosquitoes. The most virulent species is *Plasmodium falciparum* and this is fast becoming resistant to chemical treatments. Researchers have called the chemicals in the tarantula venom psalmopeotoxin I and II. It is not yet known how they work, but when tested in the laboratory in vitro they acted only on the *P. falciparum* and had no action on human cells. This means that they could be a promising lead for a new class of antimalarial drugs.

in CLOSE-UP

A typical sample of spider venom may contain more than 1000 different chemicals. Why so many? It is thought that over millions of years of evolution spiders have had to update their weaponry continually as prey evolve to resist it, so the chemicals have stacked up. Also scientists have found that the individual chemicals tend to be highly specific, so the variety ensures that the spider has something that will work on most prey species it encounters. The spider's arsenal can be put into two main groups: necrotising agents and nerve poisons. Necrotising agents break down tissue and help spiders to digest their food. The nerve poisons, or neurotoxins, are fast-acting and designed to stop a prey animal in its tracks.

ORIGIN West Indies
PART USED Venom

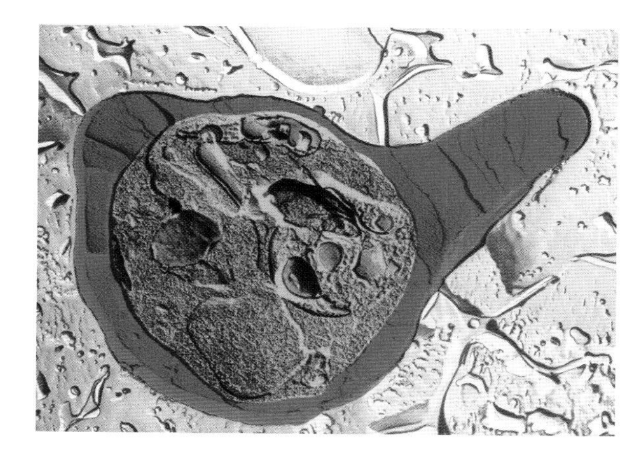

This microscope image shows a malaria parasite growing inside a red blood cell.

WATER JELLY

Aequorea victoria

MEDICAL BENEFITS ◆ Source of method for tagging genes and proteins so that researchers can monitor their activity

This little jellyfish hasn't yielded a cure or remedy for any one disease, but it has provided researchers with one of the most revolutionary laboratory tools of the twenty-first century: green fluorescent protein (GFP).

Since the late 1990s, GFP has literally *illuminated* thousands of crucial experiments and treatments. It's been used, for example, to show how cancer cells spread and how neurones in the brain develop and to investigate the behaviour of the AIDS virus. And it's now routinely used in stem cell research and organ transplant science.

Seeing the light The story begins with Japanese-born scientist Osamu Shimomura. In 1960 he joined a lab at Princeton University, in the United States, where researchers were studying the water jelly. This jellyfish species grows to less than 10 cm (4 in) in diameter and is colourless. But Shimomura was intrigued by its ability to produce a faint ring of glowing green specks around its outer edge and became determined to understand the biochemistry behind this phenomenon. Over the next two decades he reportedly collected about a million of the glowing jellyfish from a Washington harbour. And by 1979 he'd worked out that GFP was the source of the bioluminescence and determined its chemical structure.

Water jellies

In the early 1990s, US molecular biologist Douglas Prasher identified and cloned the gene responsible for producing GFP. Shortly after, Columbia University biology professor Martin Chalfie inserted the gene into the DNA of a bacterium, with the result that it glowed under ultraviolet light. Since then GFP has been used as a biochemical tag in animal cells to investigate how genes and the products of genes – proteins – operate. In 2008, Shimomura, Chalfie and colleague Roger Tsien, shared the 2008 Nobel Prize in Chemistry for their work in this field.

in CLOSE-UP

Researchers attach GFP, like a sticky coloured note, to genes or proteins of interest. Under blue light, the GFP fluoresces, revealing the presence and location of the otherwise invisible molecules. This allows researchers to pinpoint precisely where, when and under what circumstances a gene or protein functions. The GFP is relatively easy to attach to the genes of most organisms and has no side effects.

OTHER NAME Crystal jellyfish
ORIGIN Surface waters of eastern North Pacific Ocean
PART USED A protein

MOSS ANIMAL

Bugula neritina

MEDICAL BENEFITS ◆ Potential treatment for various cancers, HIV, Alzheimer's disease

Sailors worldwide think of moss animals as weed-like pests that foul untreated hulls and jetty pylons. But biomedical researchers have a greater appreciation for these tiny colonial creatures.

Moss animal

Known to scientists as bryozoans, moss animals could be the source of treatments for some of the most debilitating human diseases. One species in particular, *Bugula neritina*, has been under the medical spotlight now for almost 50 years.

In 1968, during a bioprospecting survey in the Gulf of Mexico, US biochemistry professor George Pettit discovered the compound bryostatin 1 in *B. neritina*. Pettit determined bryostatin 1's structure in 1982 and during early laboratory tests it showed enormous anticancer potential, initially against leukaemia cells. Its impact on tumours in animal studies since has been described by researchers as 'pronounced'.

Unfortunately, truly huge amounts of bryozoans are needed to extract a tiny amount of bryostatin and this has restricted further testing. Nevertheless, by 2010, bryostatin 1 had been in dozens of early-stage clinical trials for the treatment of tumours caused by a range of cancers, from ovarian and colorectal to melanoma, and cancer testing continues. Furthermore, the compound has even wider potential. Early stage human trials are now evaluating bryostatin 1 as a treatment for Alzheimer's disease, following reports by US neuroscience researchers that in animal trials bryostatin increased memory capabilities in normal brains. Even more compelling is evidence, again from animal studies, that it could repair and restore memory loss in brains ravaged by Alzheimer's, stroke or head injuries.

Flushing out HIV Meanwhile, Stanford University chemists have been developing synthetically produced compounds based on bryostatin, which they've called 'bryologs'. Lab tests have shown these could activate latent HIV infections. That's important because, while HIV can now be controlled with antiretroviral drugs, sufferers are never completely cured because some of the virus always remains dormant in the body, hidden within certain cells, beyond the reach of drug treatments and ever ready to emerge. Flushing it out could allow doctors to fully eradicate it with drugs.

OTHER NAMES Sea-mat, false coral
ORIGIN Temperate ocean waters worldwide
PART USED Metabolic by-product of bacteria living inside the animal

Early stage human trials are underway to test bryostatin against various cancers, and Alzheimer's disease. If you're interested in becoming involved in these or following their outcomes, ask your doctor. And watch for news of any new drugs based on bryostatin that might come onto the market during the coming years, as a result.

CONE SNAILS

Conus spp.

MEDICAL BENEFITS ◆ Treatment for severe pain

A childhood fascination with the ecology and biology of seashells, and the creatures that live inside them, led to the development of one of the world's most powerful painkillers.

As a kid growing up by the beach in the Philippines in the 1940s and 1950s, Baldimero Olivera was obsessed with seashells and would spend hours scouring the sands looking for them. Gradually his interest focused on cone snails and especially on one species, *Conus geographus*. It is commonly known as the geography cone because of the detailed maplike patterns on its shell; but it's also referred to in the Philippines as the cigarette snail – because when a person is stung by one, they're said to have just enough time to smoke a cigarette before dying from its venom.

Venomous killers Cone snails are part of a marine mollusc family that contains more than 600 different species. They range in length from approximately 1 cm (0.4 in) to more than 20 cm (8 in). Most are found in tropical Indian and Pacific Ocean waters, although there are a few temperate species. All, however, are carnivores: the smaller species eat other invertebrates such as small molluscs and worms, while the larger ones catch and eat fish, octopuses and squid. And all are venomous, and it was this that especially intrigued Baldimero Olivera. When he returned briefly to the Philippines in the late 1960s, after postgraduate studies in the United States in biochemistry and medicine, Olivera began research into the geography cone's deadly venom and found that it contained an extra-ordinarily large number of individual toxins, each one a different small protein-like molecule known as a peptide. His discovery sparked worldwide research interest in cone snail venoms, or conotoxins, which are now known to be equally complex in each different cone snail species.

in CLOSE-UP

Nerve cells are activated by an influx of calcium ions, which causes them to release chemical messages – including signals of pain – that then pass to other nerve cells. The molecules of the medicines based on cone snail venom are exactly the right size and shape to block the tiny pores in the nerve cell membrane through which the calcium ions flow. With these channels blocked, pain signals can no longer be transmitted along nerves.

A new type of painkiller Olivera's own interest in the highly complex venom continued when he returned to the United States in the 1970s and set up a lab at the University of Utah.

In Baldimero Olivera's lab, highly toxic cone snails are held in secure tanks.

Among the stellar staff working alongside him was Michael McIntosh, who, as a 19-year-old undergraduate, discovered and purified a component in the venom of the magician's cone snail (*Conus magus*) that had a profound effect on the mammalian nervous system.

More than 20 years later, a drug called Prialt, based on that compound, is being used to treat chronic pain in people who can't tolerate opioid painkillers, such as morphine. Prialt contains ziconotide, also known as SNX-111, a synthetic version of the compound originally isolated by McIntosh. It was first approved for use in 2004 by the US Food and Drug Administration for the type of intractable pain experienced, for example, by sufferers of cancer, AIDS, back injuries and some nervous system disorders. It's now used, under strict medical supervision, worldwide. Sales of Prialt in 2009, in the United

Like many cone snails, Dall's cone (*Conus dalli*) has an alluringly attractive patterned shell – that conceals a deadly weapon.

What You CAN DO

If you have chronic pain but cannot tolerate opioid painkillers, or are worried about the addiction associated with strong opioid painkillers, such as morphine or pethidine, it could be worth asking your doctor about Prialt. It needs to be administered directly into the spinal fluid, so it is only given under strict medical supervision.

States alone, were $20 million. Yet, because the drug was developed, tested and brought to market by a series of pharmaceutical firms, none of the scientists or universities involved in the original research has shared in the profits.

First of many? Investigations into the many thousands of different cone snail peptides continue today in numerous university and pharmaceutical company laboratories globally. Olivera remains actively involved in conotoxin research and he still collaborates with McIntosh, who is now a research director of psychiatry at the University of Utah.

In drug development terms, it's still early days, but Prialt is tipped to be the first of many drugs likely to emerge from conotoxins. So far, it's the venoms from the fish-eaters that show the most promise. An interesting potential use of conotoxins currently being investigated is for the treatment of disorders with a neurological component, including Alzheimer's, Parkinson's, schizophrenia and depression.

One reason there's so much interest in conotoxins for drug design and development is that they have an extremely small molecular size. This means they're not as likely as larger molecules – such as those found, for example, in snake venoms – to set-off the body's immune system and trigger allergic reactions.

On the hunt

Cone snails are nocturnal predators, and like other snails, slow moving. By day, they tend to hide in rocky crevices and under sand, on and around coral reefs, though they can also be found on sand and around rocks in shallower waters. All sea snails feed by using a rasp-like 'tongue' organ called a radula, which is covered in small teeth. In cone snails, however, this has evolved to become a large toxic weapon. The teeth are greatly reduced in number but each of the few remaining has developed into a large, hollow, barbed 'spear' that functions like a hypodermic needle to inject poison from a venom gland at its base. The cone snail uses one tooth at a time, firing its deadly apparatus like a harpoon, through an extended snout-like proboscis. The paralysed prey is then engulfed by the proboscis and swallowed whole.

OTHER NAME Cone shell
ORIGIN Tropical seas worldwide
PART USED Molecule from venom

The sting of the geography cone snail, which is widespread in the Indian and Pacific oceans, is deadly to humans.

CARIBBEAN SEA SQUIRT

Ecteinascidia turbinata

MEDICAL BENEFITS ◆ Treatment for soft tissue sarcomas and ovarian cancers ◆ Potential treatment for lung, prostate, colon and breast cancers, melanoma and mesothelioma

One of many toxic compounds used by this lowly creature to defend itself from predators has been synthesised to make a cancer-beating drug.

Mangroves are warm, fertile places seething with life. And for the Caribbean sea squirt, a small sac-like creature that lives permanently attached to the roots of mangrove trees – near the bottom of its marine food chain – surviving predation is a constant battle. But this bizarrely pretty marine animal manages with apparently little effort. And it does so, just like many other creatures with similarly sedentary lifestyles and surrounded by an abundance of would-be predators, using an arsenal of chemical weapons. In its case, its very tissues are imbued with distasteful, sometimes toxic compounds.

in CLOSE-UP

Found on the raised roots of red mangrove trees, sea squirts are colonies of interconnected individual animals called zooids. Each zooid is like a small, opaque plastic bag with an upper edge pigmented a shade of orange, yellow or pink – a warning sign to would-be predators that it would make a distasteful, possibly toxic, meal. Unlike most small creatures living in mangroves, sea squirts are not invertebrates but an early offshoot of the evolutionary line that ultimately led to vertebrates, including humans. They produce tadpolelike larvae, each of which has the evolutionary precursor of a backbone, called a notochord. The larvae swim among plankton until they settle as adult sea squirts.

Sea squirts feed by siphoning seawater through their many separate tubes, or zooids, and then filtering out nutrients.

Meeting demand Chemistry professor Kenneth Rinehart was well aware of the sea squirt's antipredator strategies when, during the 1980s and 1990s, he led the University of Illinois' natural products program to collect samples of life from ocean floor and mangrove habitats off Puerto Rico and elsewhere in the Caribbean. In the late 1980s, Rinehart and a graduate student in his laboratory, Tom Holt, extracted and isolated several promising anticancer compounds from sea squirts. One was ecteinascidin-743 (ET-743), from the Caribbean sea squirt. It showed early promise against cancer cells in the lab. But enormous quantities of sea squirt tissue were needed to produce a tiny amount of ET-743: a staggering 1 tonnes (1.1 tons) for just 1 g (0.035 oz).

So, in 1990, Rinehart approached Harvard University's Elias Corey, who had won that year's Nobel Prize in Chemistry, to try and determine a way of synthesising the promising but scarce compound. Corey and a student in his lab, Eduardo Martinez, took six years to achieve this, but they were ultimately successful. The method of synthesis has since been licensed to a Spain-based biotechnology firm with a specific mission to develop cancer drugs from marine resources, PharmaMar. The company had previously tried without much success to farm the Caribbean sea squirt to extract commercial quantities of ET-743.

Targeting tumour cells Trabectedin, the synthetic form of ET-743, is now the active ingredient in a PharmaMar drug called Yondelis that has recently been approved for use against soft-tissue sarcoma – a rare form of tumour – and ovarian cancer across Europe and entered late-stage clinical trials in the United States.

If you or a loved one is afflicted with sarcomas or ovarian cancer, ask your doctor about the suitability and availability of the drug Yondelis, based on the synthetic form of ET-743. If it's not yet approved for use in your country, there may be clinical trials underway in which you could become involved.

Just as ET-743 does, Trabectedin works in two ways to destroy tumour cells. Firstly, it targets and bonds to the DNA in tumour cells, breaking it apart. But then it also interferes with the cells' attempts to repair the damage to their DNA. For this reason, it is thought that the compound might also have a role as an adjunct therapy alongside other anticancer drugs.

OTHER NAME Mangrove tunicate
ORIGIN Warm shallow coastal waters of Bermuda, the Caribbean, Gulf of Mexico, Florida, Mediterranean (seasonal)
PART USED Chemical extract

These mangroves, fringing a shallow bay in Puerto Rico, are typical of the environments favoured by the Caribbean sea squirt.

FUZZY CARROT CORAL

Eleutherobia spp.

MEDICAL BENEFITS ◆ Potential treatment for breast, lung, kidney and ovarian cancers

The comical name and appearance of the fuzzy carrot coral belie its connection to a compound with serious cancer-slaying abilities.

Eleutherobia grayi

This coral was discovered in 1993 by biochemist William Fenical, from the Scripps Institution of Oceanography in La Jolla, California. Fenical, now regarded as one of the great modern marine bioprospectors, was scuba diving in a protected inlet at Bennett Shoal near the Western Australian (WA) tourist town of Exmouth, collecting specimens for a study of chemical defences used by reef animals.

A student in Fenical's lab, Thomas Lindel, later extracted a compound from the 'carrot' that had extraordinary capabilities. Named eleutherobin, it was soon being compared to the cancer wonder drug paclitaxel, marketed as Taxol (see p. 42). During initial laboratory trials on human cell lines, eleutherobin showed that it had as much ability as paclitaxel to inhibit growth in a range of cancers. And it was shown to work in a similar way, binding to and breaking apart cellular structures called microtubules that support the rapid division of cancer cells. Eleutherobin was licensed to Bristol-Myers Squibb and, during the late 1990s, the pharmaceutical company began preclinical trials, reporting that the compound had 'promising potential as a new anticancer agent'.

Eleutherobin is still at the preclinical stage, but now that a new source has been discovered there is renewed interest in its potential and it could soon move into clinical trials. Indeed, there's a good chance that this 'Taxol from the sea', as it was once dubbed, could finally make it into chemotherapy schedules.

An alternative source But the fuzzy carrot coral is rare and its occurrence restricted to an environmentally sensitive location, near WA's Ningaloo Reef World Heritage Area, renowned for its seasonal whale shark population. Hence further progress with eleutherobin stalled – until recently, when a University of British Columbia research team found that another, unrelated, coral, the Caribbean gorgonian coral (*Erythropodium caribaeorum*), also produces the compound. And it turns out that this coral is a popular fish tank feature in the marine aquarium trade and therefore more readily available, and that the level of eleutherobin is equally high in cultivated and wild corals.

ORIGIN Off the northwest coast of Australia
PART USED Chemical extract

COMBING THE SEAS

The oceans provide an opportunity for drug discovery on a scale that far surpasses what's offered on land. But it's not simply the size of the possibilities that's getting scientists excited – there are many other characteristics of marine life that make it appealing from the drug development perspective.

To begin with, marine life overall is old. It's been exposed to the evolutionary forces that drive biological change for at least a billion years more than terrestrial life. Also, while to most of us ocean life means fish, marine mammals such as whales, and large seaweeds, many of the plants and animals are actually small and inconspicuous. Most marine animals, for example, are seemingly insignificant, soft-bodied, slow- or nonmoving creatures. And they survive in places, such as reefs and mangroves, that are crowded not only with competitors vying for space and resources but also with would-be predators and potential pathogens (bacteria and viruses). Just 1 litre (2 pints) of seawater, for example, can contain 20,000 different types of bacteria.

A molecular war chest Faced with this sort of stress, sedentary marine creatures have evolved a chemical arsenal, mostly unlike anything encountered in land-based life. And it's this molecular war chest that scientists have been plundering for new marine sources of drugs.

So far, the soft and delicate bodies of animals such as sponges, sea squirts, molluscs and bryozoans have provided the compounds with the greatest potential pharmaceutical interest. As of 2010, that list of compounds already numbered well over 10,000 and was growing at a rate of hundreds more each year. The US National Cancer Institute, for example, annually adds more than 500 marine samples for testing to a repository of some 70,000 natural compounds it deems of interest. Compounds

THE VAST UNKNOWN

Two-thirds of the planet's surface is covered by ocean, and at least half of all Earth's known living species are found in the marine environment. The first global Census of Marine Life – a massive decade of discovery that ended in 2010 and involved approximately 3000 scientists in more than 80 countries – acknowledged that there are at least 280,000 marine species so far known to science. But, the census concluded, that figure is likely to be just a quarter of what's still waiting to be discovered and described by science in the world's coastal, reef, mangrove, open-water and deep-sea habitats.

sourced from the marine environment already include 10 anticancer drugs as well as pharmaceuticals that target malaria, HIV, inflammation, fungal infections, tuberculosis and dengue fever.

Marine bioprospecting And yet, although indigenous peoples have been incorporating marine life, such as sea cucumbers and seaweed, into their traditional medicines for centuries, intensive bioprospecting of the marine environment has been going on for only a few decades – a short period when it's considered that the development of any drug from a natural source routinely takes more than 20 years from its initial discovery.

Rigorous modern exploration of the oceans only really began with the development of modern scuba equipment in the 1940s and 1950s, and the first marine bioprospecting programs emerged in the United States, Japan and Australia in the 1970s and 1980s. Since then, the United States has been most active in this area, under the leadership of outstanding scientists such as George Pettit, a US biochemist who pioneered the exploration of bioactive compounds from marine sources, as well as land-based plants and insects; Kenneth Rinehart, a former chemistry professor at the University of Illinois; and William Fenical, who rose to become the professor of Oceanography at the Scripps Institution of Oceanography.

So far, much of the collection of marine samples has occurred in coastal areas or shallower waters off the continental shelves. But with the development of sampling technology such as remote-controlled deep-sea submersibles, it's becoming more likely that scientists will discover previously unknown life forms with a biochemistry unlike anything seen before. And that could be where the most promising marine prospects lie for future treatments of human disease.

Above: Fine mesh nets like these can capture minuscule marine creatures almost invisible to the naked eye.

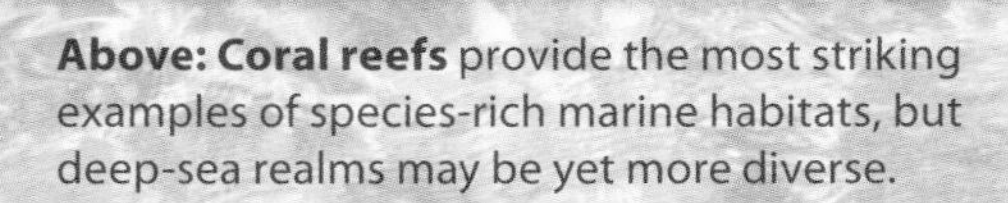

Above: Coral reefs provide the most striking examples of species-rich marine habitats, but deep-sea realms may be yet more diverse.

Right: Marine researchers examine the results of a deep-sea trawl. Such exercises often turn up entirely new species.

SEA CUCUMBERS

Holothuroidea

MEDICAL BENEFITS ◆ Traditional treatment for hypertension, fatigue, impotence, joint pain ◆ Possible treatment for cancer, arthritis, oral infections

Sea cucumbers have long been a dietary staple and trusted component of traditional medicine throughout Asia and the Pacific. Now, scientific evidence is rapidly building to support their purported healing and nutritional powers.

As their common name suggests, sea cucumbers look more like vegetables than animals, but they are in fact close relatives of starfish. There are about 1400 known sea cucumber species and, like their multi-armed cousins, they are mostly bottom dwellers and a common feature of seafloor life throughout the world's oceans, from Antarctica to the Mediterranean. Sea cucumbers move across sediment like oceanic vacuum cleaners, eating it, digesting it, extracting nutrients and excreting sandy or muddy waste in their wake.

Most people come across these creatures in tide pools in the tropics and subtropics. But sea cucumbers also occur in deep-sea habitats, where they can be so abundant that they form slow-moving 'herds'. Adult sea cucumbers range in size, but most grow no longer than about 20 cm (8 in); however, one reef-dwelling species – known as the medusa worm (*Synapta maculata*) – grows longer than 2 m (6½ ft).

Nutritional benefits confirmed Sea cucumbers have been under the scrutiny of Western medicine for about ten years. A recent assessment, by researchers at Portugal's Centre of Marine Sciences (CCMAR), confirmed the nutritional value of five different sea cucumber species on the basis of their high protein and low fat levels. They were also found to have high proportions of healthy polyunsaturated fatty acids. One species in particular – *Holothuria arguinensis* – found in European waters, was confirmed as having especially powerful antioxidant properties.

In other studies, sea cucumber tissue has been shown to be high in vitamins A, B1, B2 and B3 and the minerals calcium, zinc, iron and magnesium. And it's also been found to contain a

Traditional Wisdom

In China, sea cucumbers are known as *haishen*, meaning roughly 'ginseng from the sea', a reference to their role as a health tonic like ginseng. The use of sea cucumbers in Chinese medicine has a 2000-year history. They're valued for their antifungal and antibacterial properties and are used for a range of disorders, including joint pain and high blood pressure. Compounds made from their skin have also been used to treat wounds, asthma, sinus problems and stomach ulcers. They are eaten in China but are more highly regarded as a health tonic than for their taste.

Coastal communities in the Philippines export dried sea cucumbers to China.

Native to Southeast Asia, *Stichopus variegatus* is also known as the curry fish.

vast range of biologically active compounds of potential pharmaceutical interest including: chondroitin sulphate, a compound that's being explored as a treatment for diseases such as arthritis; saponins, which have cholesterol-lowering, anticancer and anti-inflammatory potential; and the anticoagulant heparin.

Lab reports In 2003, University of Texas researchers reported that a fatty acid known as 12-MTA (12-methyltetradecanoic acid), from a sea cucumber extract, slowed the growth of prostate cancer cells in the laboratory. And in 2005, a Shanghai Institute of Materia Medica study documented a new compound called philinopside A, isolated from the thorny sea cucumber (*Colochirus quadrangularis*), which showed signs of being a 'promising anticancer agent'. Five years later, researchers from China's Zhejiang University reported on another two exciting new compounds from the same sea cucumber species: pentactasides B and C. These both also showed 'significant' activity against human tumour cells in the laboratory.

OTHER NAMES Trepang, bêche-de-mer, *gamat* (Malay), *haishen* (Chinese)
ORIGIN Most ocean habitats worldwide
PART USED Skin

Also recently, research at the National University of Malaysia found support for sea cucumbers as a traditional treatment for wound healing. The researchers used compounds known as sulfated GAGs (glycosaminoglycans), sourced from the body walls of two species, *Stichopus vastus* and *S. hermanni*, to successfully promote wound healing in laboratory rats. And in other research, also in Malaysia, a toothpaste based on sea cucumber extracts, also from *Stichopus* species, was found in human trials to effectively treat chronic gingivitis, a bacterial infection of the gums.

Traditionally, sea cucumber powder is prepared as a dietary supplement from dried outer skin of the animal, and today you can buy capsules or tablets made with freeze-dried sea cucumber powder online and in many health stores worldwide. As yet, however, no human trials of sea cucumber compounds have been approved.

ATLANTIC HORSESHOE CRAB

Limulus polyphemus

MEDICAL BENEFITS ◆ Source of a screening test for bacterial infections

Few people today make it through life without having some connection with the Atlantic horseshoe crab – given that it is the source of one of the most widely used tests for the presence of bacterial contamination.

Known as the LAL (*Limulus* amebocyte lysate) test, it's routinely used to check for potentially life-threatening bacterial contaminants in almost all pharmaceuticals or medical devices that come in contact with blood in the human body. That includes vaccinations, blood transfusions and medications that are delivered intravenously.

Wise blood The LAL test makes use of the horseshoe crab's unusual circulatory fluid, or haemolymph – the equivalent of blood in humans – which has been shown to have an extraordinary ability to clot in the presence of bacteria or their potentially poisonous leftover by-products. Researchers have been interested in horseshoe crab haemolymph since the 1880s, when studies first documented its remarkable level of clotting. In the early 1950s, Johns Hopkins University pathologist Frederick Bang discovered that the clotting occurred in response to bacteria. He followed up this work with colleague Jack Levin at the Marine Biological Laboratory in Woods Hole, Massachusetts, and over the next decade several crucial discoveries followed. The clotting response was shown to be due to particular cells in the haemolymph known as amebocytes, which behave like human white blood cells, swarming to attack and engulf foreign matter that poses an infection risk. The amebocytes cause clotting by releasing a compound called coagulogen.

Levin and Bang also discovered that the clotting response didn't require exposure to whole bacteria: it occurred just as intensely

The mass spawning of horseshoe crabs occurs most often when there is a new or full moon.

in CLOSE-UP

Despite their appearance, marine lifestyle and common name, horseshoe crabs are not crabs, but more closely related to spiders, scorpions and ticks. They are best known for their mass spawnings, which take place on the east coast of North America during high tides in spring. At these times, many hundreds of thousands of horseshoe crabs emerge from the ocean and gather just above the low-water mark. Of the 80,000 or so eggs produced by each female during the breeding season, only about 10 per cent make it to adulthood. The rest become critical components of coastal food chains.

in the presence of endotoxins – poisonous compounds produced by bacteria. This was significant because researchers had learned that endotoxins could persist even in sterilised solutions, such as vaccines and drugs, and subsequently cause life-threatening 'injection' fevers in the human body. And the only way to test for them at this time was to give the drug or injection to a live rabbit and see if it became infected – a costly and time-consuming process. Bang and Levin's LAL test offered a convenient, economical alternative.

Solid sign The modern LAL test is much the same as originally developed by Bang and Levin. It uses a freeze-dried product from horseshoe crab blood. This is reconstituted using sterile water in a test tube and then the solution being tested is added and the resultant mixture is incubated for an hour at 37°C (99°F). The formation of a firm gel indicates the presence of bacteria or endotoxins. The US Food and Drug Administration (FDA) first approved the LAL test for use in 1970 and in 1983 endorsed it as the standard endotoxin test for any medical products, devices or pharmaceuticals that come in contact with blood. It's now also used to test for blood infections caused by endotoxins related to diseases such as cirrhosis, cancer, meningitis and gonorrhoea as well as bacterial contamination in food.

To manufacture the test, horseshoe crab amoebocytes are extracted from the haemolymph of horseshoe crabs caught by hand or by trawling. After 'donating their blood', the crabs are mostly returned alive to their habitat. They can be recaptured and bled repeatedly over their lifetime.

OTHER NAMES North American horseshoe crab, beach spider
ORIGIN North American shore of Atlantic Ocean
PART USED Blood cells

High levels of copper result in horseshoe crab blood being blue in colour.

Ways of seeing

The LAL test hasn't been the only contribution of horseshoe crabs to medical science. They have also been ideal research subjects for scientists studying how eyes function, as their eyes are large and have a simple structure, easy-to-access optic nerves, and large photoreceptor cells. Indeed, much of our knowledge of the human eye was derived from early studies of horseshoe crab eyes. American neurophysiologist Haldan Hartline shared the 1967 Nobel Prize in Physiology or Medicine for his contributions to our understanding of vision, based to a large extent on his work with horseshoe crabs.

GREAT POND SNAIL

Lymnaea stagnalis

MEDICAL BENEFITS ◆ Major source of information on nerve function

Much of our understanding of how we learn and create memories comes from studies of the nervous systems of snails and slugs, especially this large, air-breathing, freshwater snail.

The great pond snail has been a major source of information about learning and memory – arguably the most defining features of being human – since about the mid-1980s. As of 2010, at least 30 different laboratories around the world were using the great pond snail for research on the central nervous system. And in the 20 years from 1986 to 2006, at least 1500 different research papers were written about the structure, function or behaviour of nerve cells based on experiments with these snails. In the past decade or so, studies of the great pond snail have increasingly focused on what happens at the cellular and molecular level as learning occurs and, even more intriguingly, as memories form.

Learning how we learn The capability to learn and remember is a critical phenomenon in terms of evolution. That's because it underlies the process that helps animals adapt to changes in the environment. Therefore it makes sense that the basic mechanisms that underpin this would have been preserved right across the animal kingdom, from lowly molluscs to modern humans.

in CLOSE-UP

There are several reasons why researchers use molluscs such as the giant pond snail and the sea hares (*Aplysia* spp.) to study the nervous system. Firstly, their nerve cells, or neurones, are huge – up to 1 mm wide in the sea hares – and in the pond snails they also happen to be bright orange! It also helps that the structure of the nervous systems in these creatures is simple. For example, while the human brain contains billions of neurones, the equivalent in *Lymnaea* is a ring of nine nerve clusters (ganglia). Another appeal of these laboratory animals is that it's easy to train them, making it possible to connect individual neurones or groups of neurones to specific behaviours.

A freshwater species, the great pond snail feeds on aquatic plants and algae. Its shell may be up to 6 cm (2.4 in) long.

Memory in action

Most memory experiments on giant pond snails relate to their breathing. They breathe in two ways: by absorbing oxygen from water through their skin or by taking in air via a breathing tube called a pneumostome into a basic lung. The snails can be trained to keep the tube closed when a researcher taps on it. Researchers then observe how long the snails remember the training for, and monitor the ganglia to see how their memory functions. A long-term memory in these snails is one that lasts longer than 24 hours; an intermediate memory lasts less than three hours.

A colourful type of sea slug, the California sea hare (*Aplysia californica*) can grow up to 75 cm (30 in) in length but is usually much smaller.

Understanding the way that memories are formed and lost and the molecular and cellular foundations of learning has potential applications across an enormous range of areas. What happens, for example, to our ability to form long-term memories when we live in stressful environments? Recent work at the University of Calgary in Canada, has shown that in the great pond snail, at least, stress in the environment due, for example, to overcrowding or the withholding of an important nutritional component greatly reduces the ability to form long-term memories.

Other research in 2012 at the same university hinted at the importance of diet in memory formation and therefore learning. It found that the flavonoid epicatechin – a compound with antioxidant properties found in dark chocolate, green tea and other plant-based foods – strengthened the formation of long-term memories in pond snails.

Pathological memories Research at Washington State University, published in 2010, used pond snails to study the formation of so-called 'pathological memories' that can form in drug-addicted humans. The highly addictive stimulant methamphetamine (meth), for example, is actually a powerful memory enhancer. And the Washington researchers found that memories became harder to erase in pond snails when they were formed while under the influence of meth.

This helps explain why reformed meth addicts relapse so readily. Their recollections of the euphoria generated by the drug are very hard to suppress – the drug, it appears, interferes with the mechanisms in the brain for forgetting.

An earlier model Before the giant pond snail became a popular test subject for research on the central nervous system, there was the California sea hare, *Aplysia californica*, a North American species of sea slug that also has very large neurones that are easy to work with. A pioneer of *Aplysia* research was Columbia University professor Eric Kandel, whose work from the 1960s onwards helped lay the foundations for the studies now undertaken with the giant pond snail. Kandel's investigations into the basic neurological processes underlying memory and learning and his work on the processes that occur at the cellular level in the presence of drugs earned him a share in the 2000 Nobel Prize in Physiology or Medicine.

OTHER NAME Giant pond snail
ORIGIN Freshwater ponds, rivers and lakes throughout Europe, North America and northern Asia
PART USED Nervous system

SPINY STARFISH

Marthasterias glacialis

MEDICAL BENEFITS ◆ Potential treatment for asthma, arthritis, hay fever

This temperate-water starfish produces a protective slime that could help treat serious inflammatory conditions. Not only that, its eggs have provided other important contributions to medical science.

As a young biochemistry researcher working off the west coast of Scotland in the early 2000s, Charlie Bavington became known to local fishermen as 'Dr Slime'. He was interested in osteoarthritis and had been studying molecules known as sugar glycoproteins that are found in human cartilage. With the encouragement of a marine biologist colleague, Bavington had begun looking at these molecules in the marine environment and had become particularly intrigued by a slimy compound produced by the spiny starfish. He obtained his supply of the five-armed creature from the fishermen, who captured large numbers in their nets as by-catch.

in CLOSE-UP

Inflammation – the process whereby white blood cells proliferate and attach themselves to the walls of blood vessels – is a natural, protective response of the immune system to infection or injury. But certain diseases, known as autoimmune disorders, occur when the immune system takes this response too far, causing irritation and even damage to blood vessel walls. Scientists hope to use the nonstick capabilities of spiny starfish slime to prevent excess white blood cells sticking to blood vessel walls during an inflammatory, or allergic, response.

The colour of the spiny starfish varies from tan and orange to pale blue and purple.

Nonstick coating It turned out that spiny starfish slime is a protective antifouling compound that functions, for the starfish, as a kind of Teflon-like armour, to which nothing will attach itself. In turn, it keeps the animal free of disease-causing bacteria and viruses in the surrounding water, as well as discouraging larvae from a variety of marine creatures from settling out of the water and onto their surface, where they could grow to adulthood.

Since this discovery, Bavington and his colleagues have isolated molecules from the slime – previously unidentified anti-inflammatory polysaccharides – and believe these could alleviate human inflammatory disorders by preventing excessive numbers of white blood cells from sticking to blood vessel walls – the usual cause of inflammation (see In Close-up). A Scotland-based company, GlycoMar, formed to develop opportunities for the slime compound, is now collaborating with another company, Verona Pharma, to create treatments for inflammatory disorders of the respiratory system, including asthma, rhinitis (hay fever) and COPD (chronic obstructive pulmonary disease), a lung disease.

Meanwhile, GlycoMar is looking at other potential therapeutic areas for pharmaceuticals based on the slime, including ophthalmic inflammation – the inflammation of the middle part of the eye – caused by autoimmune

ORIGIN Atlantic Ocean, English Channel, North Sea, Mediterranean Sea
PART USED Slime

disorders such as rheumatoid arthritis and ankylosing spondylitis, a chronic type of arthritis that primarily affects the spine.

Halting cell division This isn't the only time that the spiny starfish has come to the attention of medical researchers. Since the 1990s its jelly-like eggs (known as oocytes) have been used in studies of an enzyme involved in regulating cell division, called CDK1.

The enzyme is ubiquitous across the animal kingdom but happens to occur in particularly large proportions in slimy starfish eggs. It has been especially useful in cancer research because it is involved in cell division: when the enzyme is functioning, the egg cells divide rapidly; when it is inactive, they do not divide.

One of the largest Atlantic starfish, *Marthasterias glacialis* can grow to a diameter of more than 70 cm (26 inches).

Inhibitors of this enzyme could therefore prevent division of other cells, the means by which cancer most often spreads.

Partly as a result of their work with starfish eggs, French biochemist Laurent Meijer and his collaborators have been able to identify and develop a cancer drug called R-roscovitine (also called seliciclib) that's now undergoing clinical trials for several types of cancer, including non-small-cell lung cancer and B-cell lymphomas. The drug has also shown promise in laboratory tests against HIV, the virus that causes AIDS, and one of the herpes viruses.

Commercial development of starfish-based treatments for inflammatory disorders is continuing and said to be promising, although practical applications are still several years off. Clinical trials of R-roscovitine are, however, already underway, so practical developments can be expected sooner. Furthermore, R-roscovitine is likely to be only the first of many drugs of this type to emerge over coming years.

COHO SALMON

Oncorhynchus kisutch

MEDICAL BENEFITS ◆ Treatment for postmenopausal osteoporosis, Paget's disease, hypercalcaemia (elevated blood calcium levels) ◆ Possible treatment for osteoarthritis

A hormone produced by a fish is the basis for one of the most widely used and life-changing hormone treatments.

Human bones are in a constant state of flux: old bone is removed, a process known as resorption, and new bone is created, a process called formation. This continues throughout life and is known as bone remodelling. When we're young and healthy, bone formation progresses at a faster rate than resorption. But as a result of disease and advancing years the balance tips and the rate of resorption becomes faster and our bones can become brittle and susceptible to breaking.

Several minerals are involved in the bone remodelling process, but one of the most vital is calcium. In 1961, in a ground-breaking discovery, the North American biochemist Douglas Copp identified, isolated and named one of the major hormones involved in regulating calcium in our bodies, and, therefore, bone remodelling: calcitonin.

Boning up At the time of the discovery, Copp was head of the Department of Physiology at the University of British Columbia. His interest in bones had been spurred by his top-secret involvement at the end of World War II in the Manhattan Project, which developed the first atomic bomb, during which Copp investigated the effects of radiation on bone marrow.

Calcitonin is produced in humans by cells in the thyroid gland and functions to inhibit the release of calcium from our bones and, thus, the process of resorption. A type of calcitonin, it turns out, is produced by all vertebrates: it's produced in the thyroid in other mammals, too, and by the 'ultimobranchial gland' in birds and fish. Copp's lab was also involved in the discovery that one of the most potent forms of calcitonin is produced by Coho salmon, and a synthetic form of this substance was created to

Coho salmon, accompanied by a pink-hued sockeye salmon, swim upriver in Alaska.

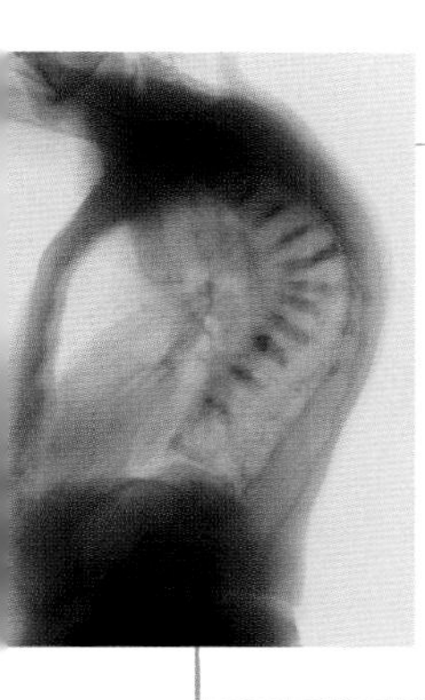

If you have been diagnosed with osteoporosis, your doctor may prescribe salmon calcitonin. It is administered as a nasal spray or by injection (daily or once every two days). Brand names include Calcimar and Miacalcin. Treatment must be prescribed and overseen by a doctor. Clinical trials are currently underway for an oral version of salmon calcitonin.

This CT scan shows severe osteoporosis in a woman's spine.

treat diseases that involve a calcium imbalance, including postmenopausal osteoporosis and Paget's disease, a chronic condition that results in enlarged, misshapen bones. By 1992, world sales of salmon calcitonin exceeded US$900 million, mostly for the treatment of osteoporosis.

A growing problem Osteoporosis is a condition whereby bones become brittle due to minerals, particularly calcium, being lost faster than they can be replaced; this, in turn, makes bones highly susceptible to breaking. Because of hormonal changes (mainly falling oestrogen levels), postmenopausal women are at a higher risk than men of developing the condition.

OTHER NAME Silver salmon
ORIGIN North Pacific Ocean
PART USED Hormone

With the proportion of over-50s in the global population rising substantially over the past century, osteoporosis has emerged as a major health risk worldwide. Indeed, it has become second only to cardiovascular disease as a global healthcare problem, and studies now show that the lifetime risks of death due to hip fracture and breast cancer are similar for a 50-year-old woman.

Unlike osteoporosis, which usually involves the whole skeleton, Paget's disease normally affects just one or two bones. However, it also results in bone pain and can lead to arthritis. Its cause remains unclear, but the condition involves elevated levels of calcium in the bloodstream and increased resorption, so salmon calcitonin can help.

Recent studies on rats have shown that salmon calcitonin may work directly on cartilage as well as bone, so it is now also being explored as a treatment for osteoarthritis, a disease that affects cartilage, and human trials are underway.

in CLOSE-UP

It's not clear why Coho salmon produce such powerful calcitonin, but it may have something to do with the metabolic changes they undergo when switching habitats. These salmon have an anadromous life cycle, meaning that they live in the sea but need to migrate up rivers to breed. Their ability to undergo such arduous journeys – which, in fact, eventually kill them – involves massive shifts in their metabolic activities.

ARCTIC SHRIMP

Pandalus borealis

MEDICAL BENEFITS ◆ Treatment for haemorrhagic bleeding ◆ Potential use in tissue engineering, drug delivery

An extraordinarily effective type of wound dressing is the most high profile of many medical benefits currently being derived from the shells of harvested crustaceans.

The amount of crab, lobster, prawn and shrimp shells thrown away as a waste product around the world is staggering. In Europe alone, for example, 750,000 tonnes (825,000 tons) of crustacean shells are dumped into the ocean each year after the flesh of the animals inside has been removed for use as food. But a recent and growing body of research has been identifying a range of biomedical applications for the natural compounds contained in this waste. One of the most notable so far has been the chitosan bandage, derived largely from the discarded shells of Arctic shrimp. The bandage has been used with huge success since early this century for staunching blood loss in victims of traumatic injury in armed conflicts, most notably the wars in Iraq and Afghanistan.

Military origins The chitosan bandage was developed with the aid of a military grant at the Oregon Medical Laser Centre (OMLC), in the United States. It was approved for use by the US Food and Drug Administration in 2002 and within five years was attributed with having saved at least 120 lives in the Iraq and Afghanistan wars. In 2005, the bandage – sold under the registered name of HemCon (short for 'haemorrhagic control') – was named as one of the world's top inventions of 2004.

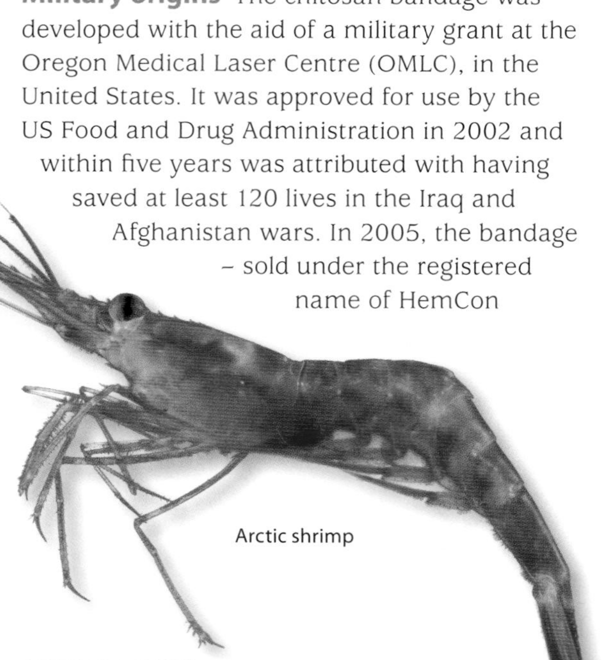

Arctic shrimp

One of the main inventors of the chitosan bandage was a former US Army doctor, Retired Colonel William Wiseman. After unexpectedly

Chitosan bandages are now standard issue for US soldiers in combat zones, and since 2007 a similar type of dressing has been widely available over the counter. Ask your pharmacist or first aid supplier for further information. Because these bandages need blood to make them stick to a wound, blood should not be wiped away before they are applied. There is also a powdered version of the product, available to emergency personnel such as paramedics, that is designed to be poured onto wounds to stop bleeding.

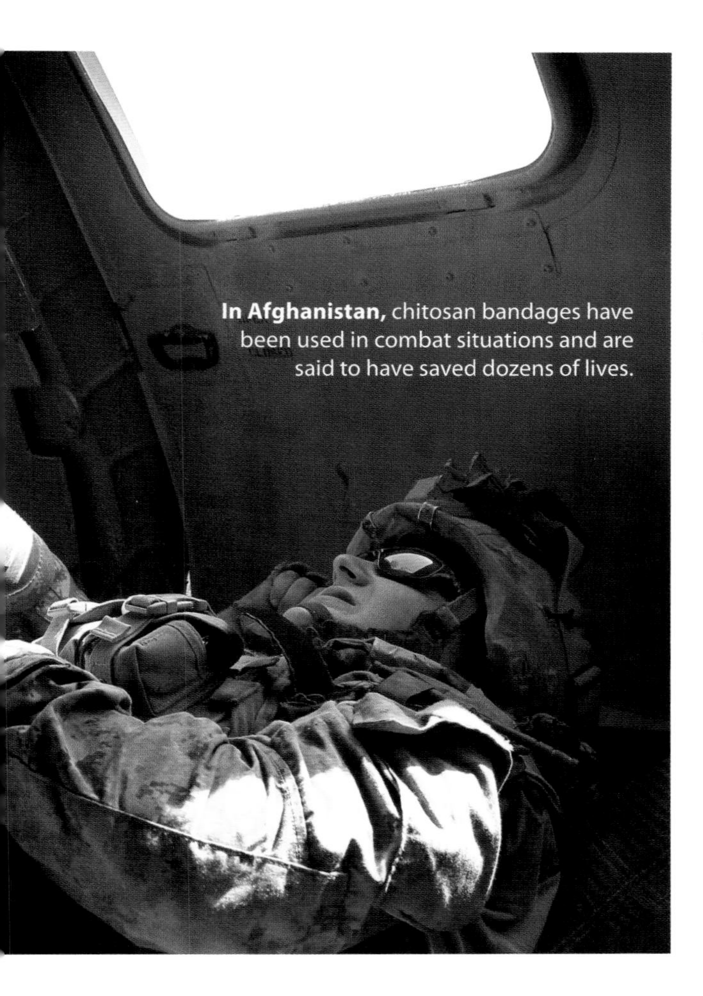

In Afghanistan, chitosan bandages have been used in combat situations and are said to have saved dozens of lives.

high numbers of deaths of US troops in Kuwait and Somalia in 1990s conflicts, Wiseman was coaxed out of retirement and contracted as a medical researcher to find ways to save lives during combat. He set about searching for substances with blood-clotting capabilities and came across a Chinese book that talked of shrimp shells being used to stop bleeding.

Working with OMLC colleague Kenton Gregory, also a physician, Wiseman found that chitosan, a complex carbohydrate derived from the compound chitin in shrimp shells, had an extraordinary capability to stop bleeding. As in a magnetic attraction, positively charged molecules in chitosan are attracted to and bond with negatively charged molecules in blood; it's this mechanism that rapidly staunches bleeding. But chitosan also works in another, secondary, and equally critical, way: it binds with the outer membranes of bacteria, preventing them from multiplying and causing infection.

OTHER NAMES Pink shrimp, great northern prawn
ORIGIN Atlantic Ocean
PART USED Shell

in CLOSE-UP

Chitin, the source of chitosan, is the second most abundant natural polymer on Earth, after cellulose, which is found in plant cell walls. Chitin occurs in the external skeletons of insects and cell walls of fungi, as well as in the shells of crustaceans, where the addition of calcium carbonate from the surrounding sea water makes it particularly tough and durable. Both chitin and chitosan have antibacterial qualities; this and the fact that they are nontoxic and biodegradable has made both the focus of intense interest in two hot areas of biomedical research: tissue regeneration and drug delivery. Chitosan is being used as a scaffold 'building' material for tissue regeneration work in laboratories around the world. And chitosan nanoparticles are being widely explored as drug-delivery systems, particularly for anticancer, gene and proteins drugs. Shellfish skeleton waste also shows promise for use in transdermal patches that slowly deliver medications, such as the local anaesthetic lidocaine, via the skin.

Chitosan bandage production

MARINE SPONGES

Porifera

MEDICAL BENEFITS ◆ Treatments for herpes, acute myeloid and lymphatic leukaemias, HIV, breast cancer ◆ Potential treatments for malaria, fungal infections, asthma, tuberculosis

These sedentary creatures have displayed more pharmaceutical potential than any other group of marine animals and already provide tried and trusted treatments for various cancers and viruses.

Two previously unknown compounds found in a sponge inspired the creation of the first drugs to come from the sea. American organic chemist Werner Bergman isolated the compounds in the 1950s from a sponge that lives almost buried beneath the sediment in shallow water off Florida. It was originally known scientifically as *Cryptotethya crypta* but has since been renamed *Tectitethya crypta*.

Virus protection Bergman and his team speculated that the two compounds, spongothymidine and spongouridine, helped defend the sponge against infection – a vital role, given that the sponge spends most of its time under sand, exposed to disease-causing organisms. And US biochemist Seymour Cohen wondered if the compounds could play a similar role in humans: fighting disease.

Ultimately, the compounds inspired the development of several synthetically created drugs. One, known as vidarabine, is an antiviral that operates against the herpes simplex virus that causes cold sores and against the varicella zoster virus responsible for chickenpox and shingles. Until recently, it was included as the active constituent in medications used against herpes infections, but it has now been largely superseded by other antiviral medications.

Another, cytarabine, was first approved as an anticancer agent by the US Food and Drug Administration (FDA) in 1969. It continues to be used in chemotherapy against certain types of leukaemia and lymphomas. And a third, zidovudine – better known as AZT – was the first licensed treatment for HIV infection and remains an important part of drug protocols against that disease.

A stumbling block One of the most recently developed and approved pharmaceuticals inspired by a sponge is eribulin, an anticancer drug based on the compound halichondrin B, which was first isolated by Japanese chemists from the sponge *Halichondria okadai*, in 1986. Following early reports about its strong potency against cancer cells in laboratory tests, halichondrin B was given high priority status by the US National Cancer Institute (NCI) and became one of the first compounds to be tested by a much-touted screening tool used for drug discovery known as the 'NCI-60 cell line panel', whereby

in CLOSE-UP

Today, an estimated 15,000 different sponge species have been described by science. Except for about 150 freshwater species, they live in marine habitats, from shallow waters to great depths, and from the poles to the tropics. One of the most notable aspects of sponge physiology is that these animals don't have organs or tissues. Instead they have loosely aggregated groups of cells that perform the same function. It's not surprising then that, unlike most other animals, sponges don't have a mouth. Instead they feed via a system of pores, called ostia, which cover their bodies. Specialised cells have appendages called flagella that beat to move water through the ostia. As tiny floating food items pass, they are engulfed and digested by other cells.

Diving on a Caribbean reef, a diver inspects a giant barrel sponge, one of the largest species found in that region's seas.

These yellow tube sponges, on a reef in Belize, are one of the diverse forms of sponge species.

a compound is assessed simultaneously against cells sourced to 60 different human cancers. These include cancers of the central nervous system, breast, colon, prostate, lung and kidney, as well as leukaemias and melanomas.

Despite its early promise, however, halichondrin B was only produced in trace amounts by the sponge in which it was found and progress with its development initially faltered. But ultimately eribulin, a synthetic compound based on halichondrin B's structure, was produced. And in late 2010 it was approved by the US FDA for use in patients with metastatic breast cancer – an advanced stage of the disease – and has since been licensed for the same purpose in Canada, Europe, Australia and elsewhere in the world (under the registered name Halaven). Both eribulin and halichondrin B work by directly blocking cancer cell division.

The palladium approach Discodermolide is another compound from a marine sponge that has shown enormous therapeutic potential but had its progress towards clinical testing stifled by the fact that it occurs naturally in only exceptionally small amounts. It was discovered in the 1980s, by scientists from Florida Atlantic University's Harbor Branch Oceanographic Institute, in the sponge *Discodermia dissoluta*, which lives in deep

Microbe homes

Scientists now believe that many of the unique compounds found in sponges aren't created by sponge cells but by microorganisms living inside these soft-bodied creatures. All sponges seem to house large microorganism communities – experiments have shown that as much as 60 per cent of the biomass of a single sponge can be microorganisms. Many live in a symbiotic relationship with their host: they provide nutrition, waste disposal, chemical protection and other services, and the sponge, in return, offers a functional 'home'. The microorganisms include not only a huge range of bacteria but also fungi, microalgae and possibly even marine viruses.

water off the Bahamas. It showed much early promise in lab tests as a potent anticancer compound that functions in a similar way to paclitaxel, the famed cancer drug originally isolated from the Pacific yew tree (see p. 42). But progress stalled due to its scarcity and the difficulty of synthesising discodermolide, a large and chemically complex molecule.

In the last few years, however, several groups of scientists have been applying a technique that uses the metal palladium to synthesise complicated molecules. (The technique is now widely used for synthesising complex compounds in a range of areas and its originators were recognised for its enormous potential with the 2010 Nobel Prize in Chemistry.) This has permitted the production of sufficient discodermolide for clinical trials to begin in the near future.

The Pacific sponge *Theonella swinhoei* yields a potential anticancer compound, swinholide.

Untapped potential It's been more than 50 years since sponges first began offering up remarkable pharmaceutical promise, but scientists have only just begun to scratch the surface of what's likely to come from this extensive group of mostly marine animals. The list of new compounds being discovered seems to grow daily. For example, the species *Theonella swinhoei* from waters off the Western Pacific island nation of Palau produces a compound called swinholide that may kill cancer cells, as well as one called theopalaumide that has been shown to have antifungal properties.

In 1990, during a bioprospecting program in the waters off Papua New Guinea, Canadian scientists isolated a substance called contignasterol from the sponge *Petrosia contignata*. A patent on it and related chemicals has since been taken out by researchers from the Universities of British Columbia and Alberta because of the potential to treat inflammatory or allergic conditions, as well as cardiovascular disorders. Moreover, animal studies have shown derivatives of contignasterol to have enormous potential for the treatment of asthma in humans and some have already entered clinical trials.

Compounds from sponges also show promise as treatments for malaria, most notably oily alkaloid compounds called manzamines that have been found in 17 different sponge species spread over a wide geographic range. Different sponge-sourced manzamines have also shown promise in laboratory tests as antifungal, anti-HIV, and anti-inflammatory agents. And treatment of tuberculosis is emerging as another possible application for these compounds.

ORIGIN Mostly marine waters worldwide
PARTS USED Chemical extracts

Your doctor should be well aware of the established medications derived from sponges for the treatment of leukaemias, HIV and herpes. But if you or a loved one has breast cancer, it could be worth asking about the availability and suitability of treatment with the recently licensed drug Halaven, based on the sponge compound eribulin.

CARIBBEAN SEA WHIP

Pseudopterogorgia elisabethae

MEDICAL BENEFITS ◆ Treatment for inflammation ◆ Possible use in pain relief, wound healing

Potential medical benefits first noted in sea whips half a century ago are slowly coming to fruition with the development of skin-care products and an ointment that promotes wound healing.

Studies into the natural chemistry of sea whips and other soft corals began in the late 1960s, and it soon became clear that this group of marine creatures produces a high level of compounds of potential interest. From the early 1970s, US marine biologist and biochemist William Fenical – one of the most active and successful bioprospectors of his era – took an interest. Based at the Scripps Institution of Oceanography, he and his team focused on sea whips as part of 'a continuing program to explore the chemical adaptations of marine organisms and to assess the biochemical applications of marine metabolites'.

One of Fenical's most significant finds among soft corals was made and reported in 1985: a newly described class of products that his team named the pseudopterosins, extracted from the Caribbean sea whip *Pseudopterogorgia elisabethae*. In laboratory tests, these compounds displayed anti-inflammatory and analgesic (pain-relieving) properties beyond the capabilities of existing drugs.

So far, about 20 per cent of marine compounds with pharmaceutical potential have come from soft corals such as sea whips.

Pseudopterosins have since been shown to operate in a unique way that involves inhibiting the production of eicosanoids. These are a group of hormone-like molecules that play a vital role in the transmission of cell signals that control and direct major body systems, notably the immune system and central nervous system.

Product development So far, 26 different pseudopterosin derivatives have been identified. OsteoArthritis Sciences Inc., a private pharmaceutical company based in Cambridge, Massachusetts, holds licences to develop at least four of these as anti-inflammatory

As with other corals, sea whips are colonies of living polyps that feed on tiny organisms in the surrounding seawater.

in CLOSE-UP

Sea whips are soft corals common in tropical and subtropical waters; each one is a colony of many tiny coral polyps connected together. Sea whips grow attached to the seabed or rocks and face the oncoming current, and the polyps stretch out their tentacles to catch and feed on microscopic animals as they pass by in the water column. Studies conducted in the 1980s on these creatures indicated that the chemicals they produce protect them from being eaten. And research published in 2012 by scientists from the National University of Colombia, in Bogotá, suggests that the pseudopterosins found in the Caribbean sea whip play a role in keeping the surface of the coral unfouled. They also seem to be involved in regulating the bacterial community that lives inside the sea whip.

compounds. Already, successful clinical trials are reported to have been completed for one of the derivatives, known as pseudopterosin A, or methopterosin, which has been formulated into an anti-inflammatory product with wound-healing properties for external use.

Some manufacturers of personal-care and beauty products have reportedly been using pseudopterosins in skin creams, especially anti-aging lines, for their ability to reduce skin irritation. Some of the pseudopterosins are partially purified extracts from the Caribbean sea whip.

A diver takes a close look at a giant sea whip off Grass Cay, near the island of St Thomas in the US Virgin Islands.

OTHER NAMES Sea plume, sea fan, gorgonian coral
ORIGIN Shallow waters off the Gulf of Mexico and the Caribbean Sea
PART USED Chemical extract

If you are interested in incorporating pseudopterosins into your skin-care routines, look for the terms 'sea whip extract' or 'pseudopterosins' in the lists of active ingredients in cosmetic products. Anti-inflammatory and analgesic medications containing pseudopterosins are expected to enter the marketplace within the next few years.

ATLANTIC SALMON

Salmo salar

MEDICAL BENEFITS ◆ Helps prevent heart attack and stroke associated with atherosclerosis

This popular food fish has been found to be especially rich in omega-3 fatty acids, which not only have been shown to be good for the heart but may also provide a range of other health benefits.

Distinguished by the black spots on their flanks, adult Atlantic salmon can be aggressive, often driving other salmon out of their territories.

The benefits of eating Atlantic salmon were first revealed to medical researchers in the 1970s, when the indigenous people of Greenland were found to have a substantially lower heart attack rate than Western populations. Believing diet was responsible, two young Danish doctors, Hans Bang and Jørn Dyerberg, journeyed on dog sleds across the frozen landscape of Greenland to collect blood samples from the country's Inuit population. They identified high levels in the blood of two particular compounds – long-chain fatty acids with the chemical names docosa-hexaenoic acid (DHA) and eicosapentaenoic acid (EPA), now more widely known as omega-3s. And they established that a major source of these fatty acids was cold-water marine fish, including Atlantic salmon and capelin, a relative of salmon that also featured strongly in the traditional Greenland Inuit diet.

Since the mid-2000s, the American Heart Association and other health advisory bodies have recommended that all adults – even those without a documented history of coronary heart disease (CHD) – eat at least two 100 g (3.5 oz) serves of fish per week, particularly cold-water species such as Atlantic salmon. Grilling, poaching or any other cooking method that doesn't require the addition of oils or fats is recommended. Generally food sources are to be preferred to supplements, but options should be discussed with your doctor.

Good fat, bad fat In the decades since, thousands of studies have investigated the Inuit phenomenon and the role played by omega-3s in cardiac health. This research has shown that the human body needs but can't produce omega-3s and must source them from foods such as the Atlantic salmon and other cold-water marine fish species with oily flesh. And many clinical trials have confirmed that these remarkable fatty acids, also known as n-3 polyunsaturated fats, really do provide significant cardiac protection.

Omega-3s are 'good' fats that reduce the level of a type of 'bad' fat in the blood, known as triglycerides. Small amounts of triglycerides are important for energy production. But high levels in the blood over an extended period of time –

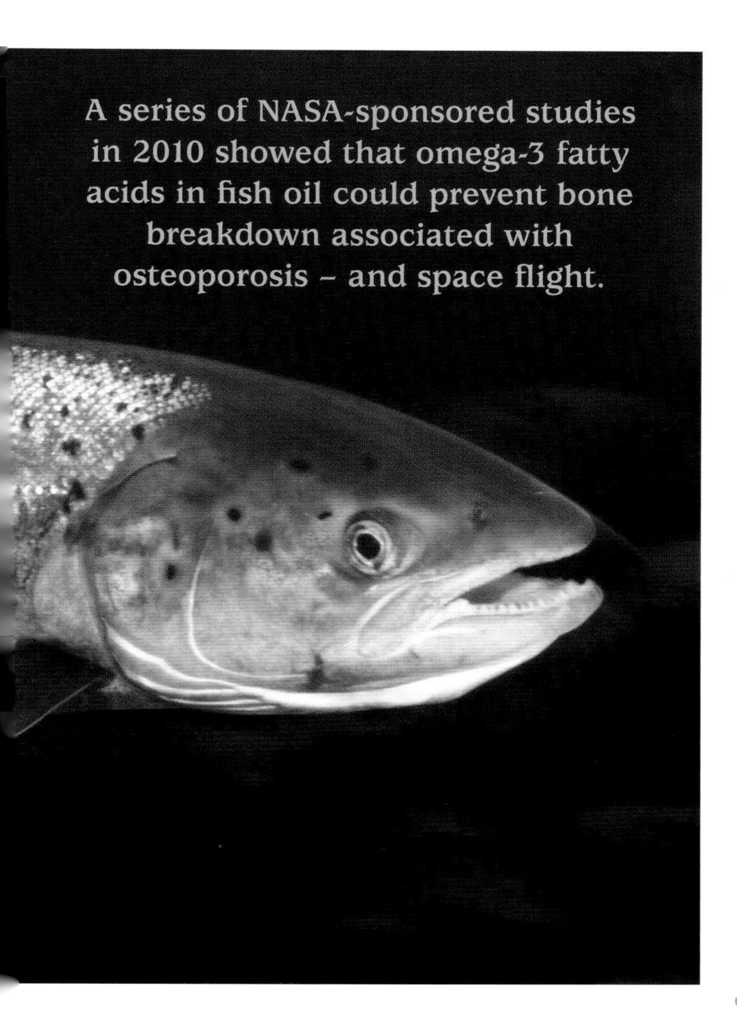

For the Inuit, Atlantic salmon are a vital staple food. Every part of the fish is eaten, including skin, bones and eggs.

through, for example, the overconsumption of alcohol or an excessive dietary intake of saturated fat – can cause narrowing and hardening of the arteries. And this, in turn, increases the risk of heart attack and stroke.

See and think clearly It's not just the heart that's thought to benefit from dietary sources of omega-3s, such as salmon. A large 10-year clinical study, carried out by researchers at the Brigham and Women's Hospital (affiliated with Harvard Medical School in the United States) and reported in 2011, found that women who ate one or more servings per week of fish significantly reduced their risk of developing age-related macular degeneration (AMD) compared to those women who ate less than one serving a month. AMD is a major cause worldwide of blindness in people aged over 50.

Research has also shown that omega-3s, such as those found in cold-water fish, reduce inflammation in the body and play an important role in brain development and performance, including memory.

in CLOSE-UP

Wild Atlantic salmon are born in the rivers and streams of Europe, from Portugal to Russia, and in North America, from the northeastern United States to northern Canada. They remain in fresh water for up to six years, feeding on smaller fish and insect larvae, but eventually undergo a significant physiological transformation into 'smolts', which prepares them for life in salt water. They then migrate downstream to Atlantic Ocean feeding grounds, where they grow and mature for another four years before making a return migration to their freshwater birthplaces. Once there, they breed and most die. The species has been farmed since the 1960s and today, Atlantic salmon is one of the world's most popular aquaculture fish, with large operations in Australia, Canada, Russia, the United Kingdom, Norway and Chile.

OTHER NAMES Bay salmon, black salmon, ouananiche, sea salmon
ORIGIN Atlantic Ocean; also farmed in North America, Australia, Russia and parts of Europe
PART USED Whole animal

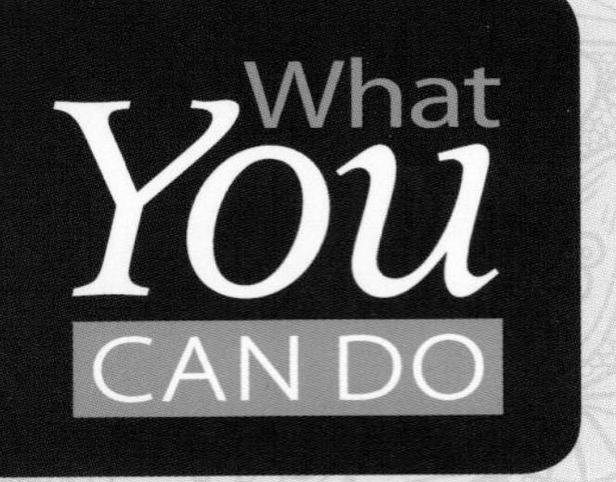

HEART FOODS

Eating oily fish is one of the best ways to protect your heart, according to decades of studies. And even if you don't like fish or are vegetarian, you can choose other foods that provide the same good fats.

Cold-water marine fish, such as Atlantic salmon, which are rich in heart-protecting omega-3 fatty acids (see p. 258) are usually at or near the top of cardiac-conscious diets. Heart associations worldwide recommend a minimum weekly intake of two serves, each a 100 g (3.5 oz) piece or ¾ cup of flaked fish.

This will contain 1–2 g of omega-3s, the recommended daily intake of these beneficial fats for patients with documented coronary heart disease. But if your aim is to reduce triglyceride levels, twice that omega-3 level is recommended, which can be easier to source through supplements. It's important, however, to ask your doctor's advice on this, as taking over 3 g (3000 mg) of fish oil in supplement form per day can have side effects, such as excessive bleeding.

Sardines are another star marine source of omega-3s and other fish species, including herring, mackerel, trout and tuna, are also good options. If fresh fish aren't available, don't overlook the value of canned products, which have the same amount of omega-3s per weight as their fresh counterparts. So it's worth keeping a can or two of tuna or salmon in the pantry.

Fish-free omega-3s For vegetarians, or people who don't like fish, there are good vegetable sources of omega-3s, with tofu and other soya products topping the list, followed by flax and canola seeds, and nuts, particularly walnuts. Omega-3s in these plant-based sources come in the form of alpha-linolenic acid (ALA), which large studies have confirmed is beneficial for heart health. Omega-3-rich seeds and nuts can be readily added to breakfast cereals and salads, whole, crushed or ground. Evidence suggests adding 42 g (1.5 oz) of high omega-3 nuts and seeds to your daily diet may reduce risk of heart disease. Cooking with oils made from them is another way to boost your intake.

Targeting cholesterol While omega-3s reduce harmful triglyceride levels, the other crucial 'bad' compound in the blood affecting heart health is cholesterol. Research shows that one of the most outstanding cholesterol-reducing foods is oatmeal. The scientific evidence has been clear since the 1990s, and recent research has reaffirmed and expanded the value of this food for heart health. A diet featuring oatmeal – as porridge or through the addition of oats to other cereals, breads, cakes and biscuits – reduces inflammation and the risk for elevated blood pressure, weight gain, diabetes and hardening of the arteries.

More recently the heart-protective power of berries has been supported, with the first human trial confirming the blood-pressure-reducing capabilities of pterostilbene – a phytochemical found in naturally high levels in blueberries.

An Eastern influence Proteins in soya beans are also believed to cut cholesterol. Intensive research into the cardiovascular protecting power of soya foods began late last century when researchers noted Asian populations, in which they are a dietary staple, had lower rates of cardiovascular disease than populations with a typically Western diet. The US Food and Drug Administration advised the public in 1999 that 'soy[a] protein included in a diet low in saturated fat and cholesterol may reduce the risk of CHD [coronary heart disease] by lowering blood cholesterol levels'. The American Heart Association followed in 2000, recommending soya protein foods be included in a diet low in saturated fat and cholesterol to promote heart health. Both recommendations remain current.

As well as omega-3 oils, sardines provide high levels of vitamin D and B vitamins as well as iron, calcium, selenium and potassium.

THE MEDITERRANEAN'S BOUNTY

Health advisory bodies the world over recommend that one of the simplest ways to adopt all this evidence-based heart-healthy nutritional advice is to follow the so-called Mediterranean Diet. Recent research has overwhelmingly reaffirmed that this approach – inspired by the traditional cuisines of Greece, Italy, Spain, Portugal and some Middle Eastern nations – reduces the risk of cardiovascular disease *and* the incidence of cancer and Parkinson's and Alzheimer's diseases. Core features include the generous use of olive oil (see p. 136); large quantities of fresh fruit and vegetables; whole, rather than processed, grain products; regular fish servings; and only small amounts of lean red meat.

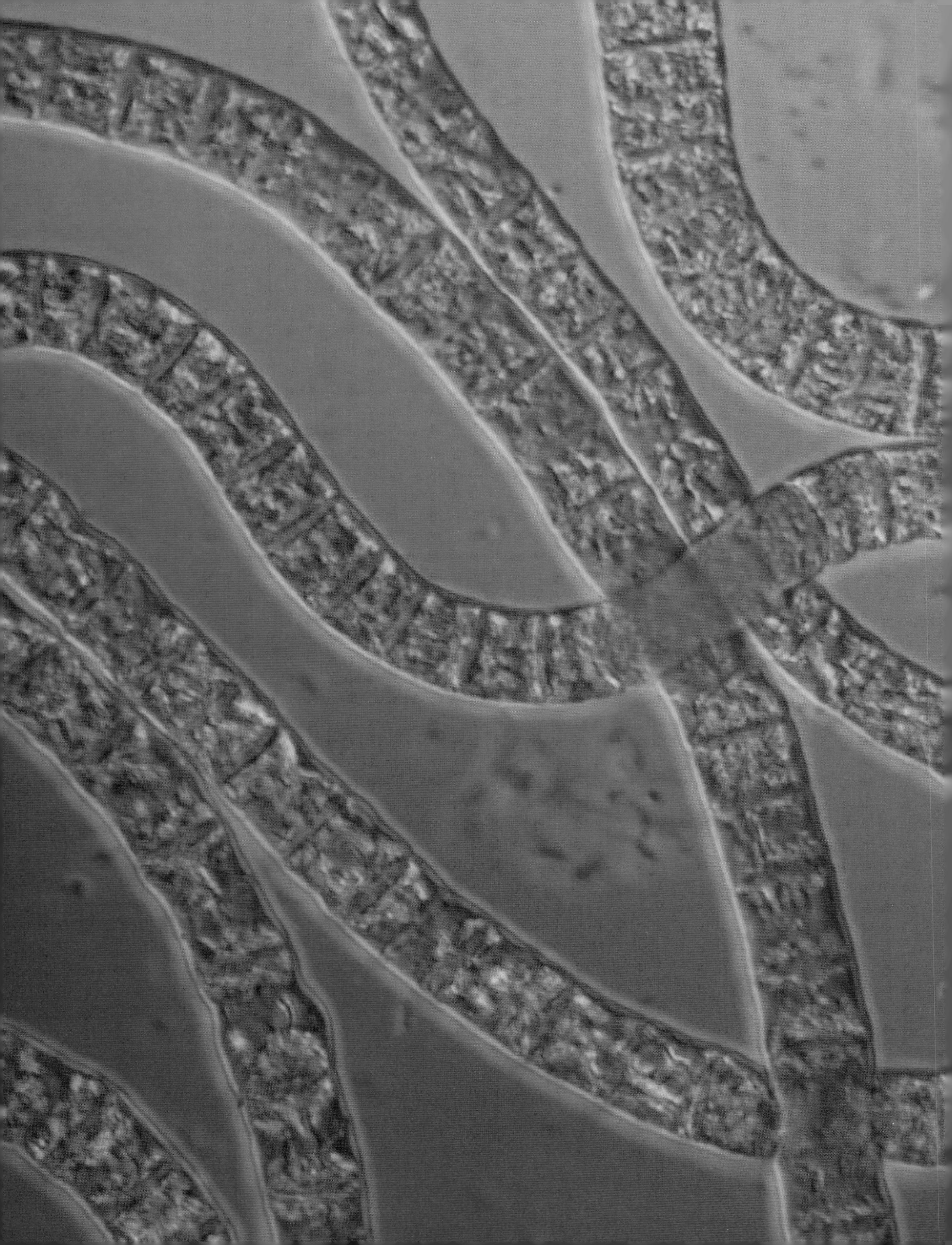

PART THREE

FRIENDLY MICROBES

Spirulina platensis

Brown algae

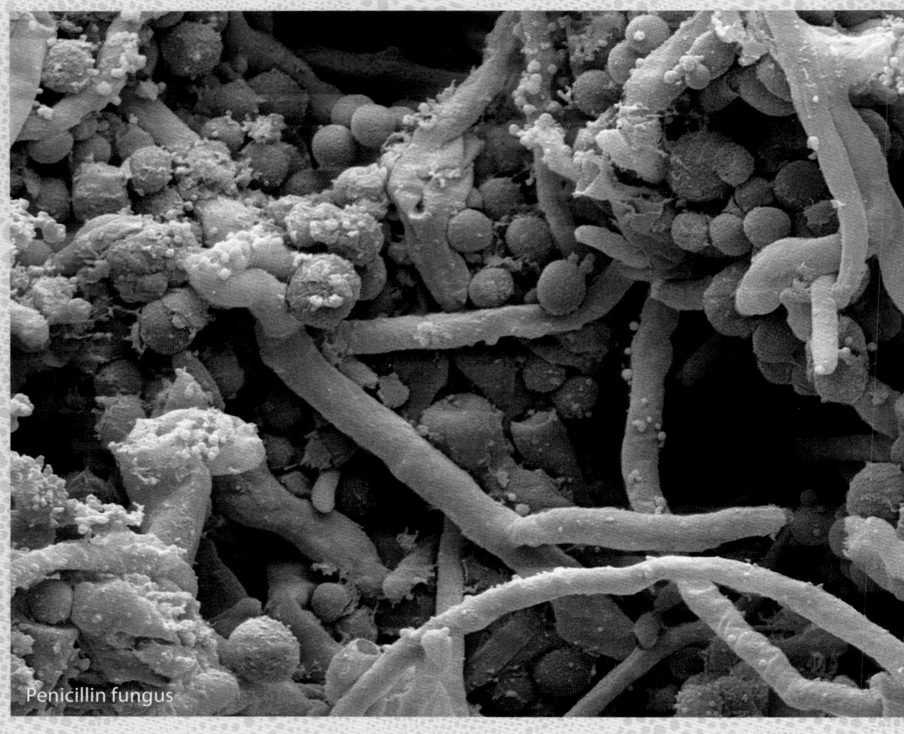
Penicillin fungus

An awareness of the benefits, even the existence, of many microbes only developed in recent times. Yet, in the brief period that their curative powers have been harnessed, these microscopic pharmaceutical powerhouses have saved more lives than any other group of natural organisms.

For thousands of years, microbes such as bacteria, yeasts and fungi have made important contributions to human civilisation by playing a part in processes such as the fermentation that yields wine, bread, vinegar and other staple foods. But it was not until the beginning of the twentieth century that their medicinal benefits began to be deliberately harnessed.

Soon after, in the 1940s, the development of penicillin as an antibiotic ushered in a microbe-powered revolution throughout the pharmaceutical industry – and inspired renewed interest in the healing powers of nature.

Microscopic rescue

In the relatively short time that they have been used as a source of pharmaceuticals, microorganisms have been responsible for saving many hundreds of millions of human lives. The first drugs that microbes provided were used for the treatment of diseases caused by other microbes – especially fungal and bacterial infections, such as tuberculosis and pneumonia, both huge killers during the early 1900s.

It wasn't long, though, before microbes were being explored as a way of fighting cancer. The first antibiotic identified with anticancer potential was actinomycin D, isolated originally from *Streptomyces* bacteria in 1940, which became available as a cancer drug in 1964.

Microbes are now also a source of drugs to treat systemic diseases such as diabetes and cardiovascular disorders. For example, lovastatin, first isolated from the fungus *Aspergillus terreus* in the 1970s became the basis of the world's first commercially available cholesterol-lowering statin drug.

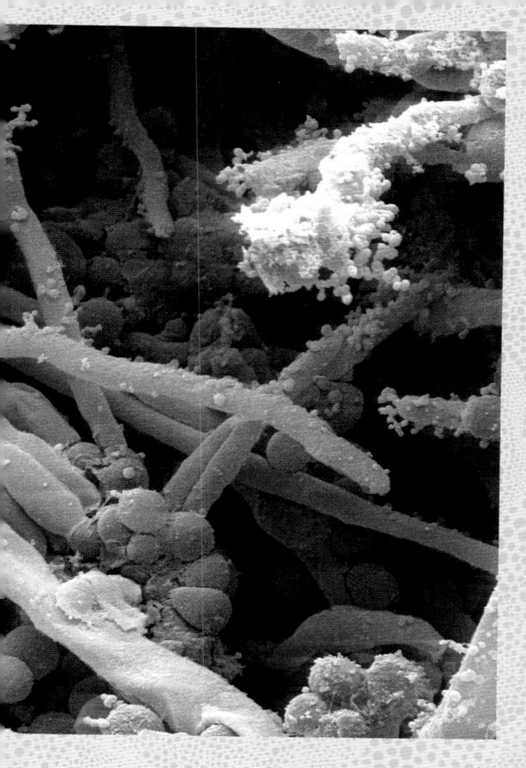

Coriolus versicolor mushrooms

Promising sources

Of the many drugs that have until now been sourced from microbes, approximately 45 per cent have been derived from the actinomycetes, a group of bacteria found in soil and water in diverse environments all over the world. An additional 38 per cent, including penicillin, have come from fungi.

An increasingly important source of microbes with pharmaceutical potential are our planet's oceans. In particular, microscopic algae and symbiotic bacteria living in the tissues of plantlike marine invertebrates show increasing promise.

With experts estimating that the number of bacterial species alone – not to mention other microbes – could be as low as ten million or as high as one billion, the potential to continue exploring microbes as a source of effective pharmaceuticals is truly enormous.

Drug factories

But it's not just as a source of drugs that microbes are being harnessed; they are also contributing in other ways. For instance, certain bacteria are now genetically engineered to produce medically important proteins. These tiny drug factories yield vital substances such as growth hormones, pharmaceutical-grade interferon used to fight tumours, and blood-clotting factors for people with haemophilia (a genetic disorder whereby the blood fails to clot). Having these proteins manufactured by bacteria means they can be produced in conditions guaranteed to be free of disease.

ASPERGILLUS FUNGUS

Aspergillus terreus

MEDICAL BENEFITS ◆ Source of statin medicines, which lower levels of 'bad' cholesterol in blood

Possibly more than any other category of drug, statins have improved the health and saved the lives of countless people in the last 15 years or so. And it's all thanks to a humble fungus.

Statins effectively lower levels of so-called bad cholesterol in the body, which, in turn, reduces the risk of stroke and heart disease. This has led to them becoming the bestselling and most widely used group of pharmaceuticals of recent years. Few users, however, are aware that they were first made from an unusual mould (a form of fungus), called *Aspergillus terreus*.

In nature, the *Aspergillus* fungus lives in warm soil and in grains, straw, cotton and decomposing vegetation. It has gained some notoriety for causing aspergillosis of the lungs, an infection that results in the coughing up of blood.

in CLOSE-UP

There are two kinds of cholesterol in your blood: LDL, or 'bad' cholesterol, which can accumulate in your arteries, and HDL, often referred to as 'good' cholesterol, which helps prevent the bad cholesterol building up. Your body produces all you need of both types, but problems can arise when the blood becomes overloaded with bad cholesterol, often as a result of eating too many foods high in saturated fat, such as meat and full-fat dairy products. The build-up in the arteries reduces the flow of blood to the heart and raises the risk of heart attack. Statins block the enzyme called hydroxy-methylglutaryl-coenzyme A reductase (HMG-CoA reductase), which is produced in the liver and is responsible for making LDL cholesterol.

A childhood fascination In 1979, a natural substance called lovastatin was isolated from the *Aspergillus* fungus by scientists at the pharmaceutical company Merck, which brought the statin to market in 1987 under the brand name Mevacor. Development of lovastatin built on the earlier work of Akira Endo, a Japanese biochemist whose fascination with microbes began during a childhood spent on a farm in northern Japan, where his grandfather taught him about the fungi that grew in the area. Apparently, Endo was particularly amazed by one fungus that produced a substance that killed flies but did not harm people. He was also strongly influenced by Alexander Fleming's famous work on mould fungi, which ultimately led to the development of the antibiotic penicillin (see p. 270).

Straight after college, Endo joined the Japanese pharmaceutical company Sankyo to research food ingredients, with the aim of improving quality. One of his challenges was to find an enzyme (a protein that speeds up a chemical reaction) to minimise the pulp in fruit juice. This honed his skills in investigating fungi and the substances they produce. By the time he found the enzyme to reduce pulp, he had studied nearly 250 kinds of fungi.

His success took him to the Albert Einstein College of Medicine in New York, where he pursued his interest in cholesterol research. The connection between cholesterol and hardening of the arteries had first been observed in 1910,

Round chains of spores crown the fruiting body of an *Aspergillus* fungus in this coloured scanning electron micrograph image.

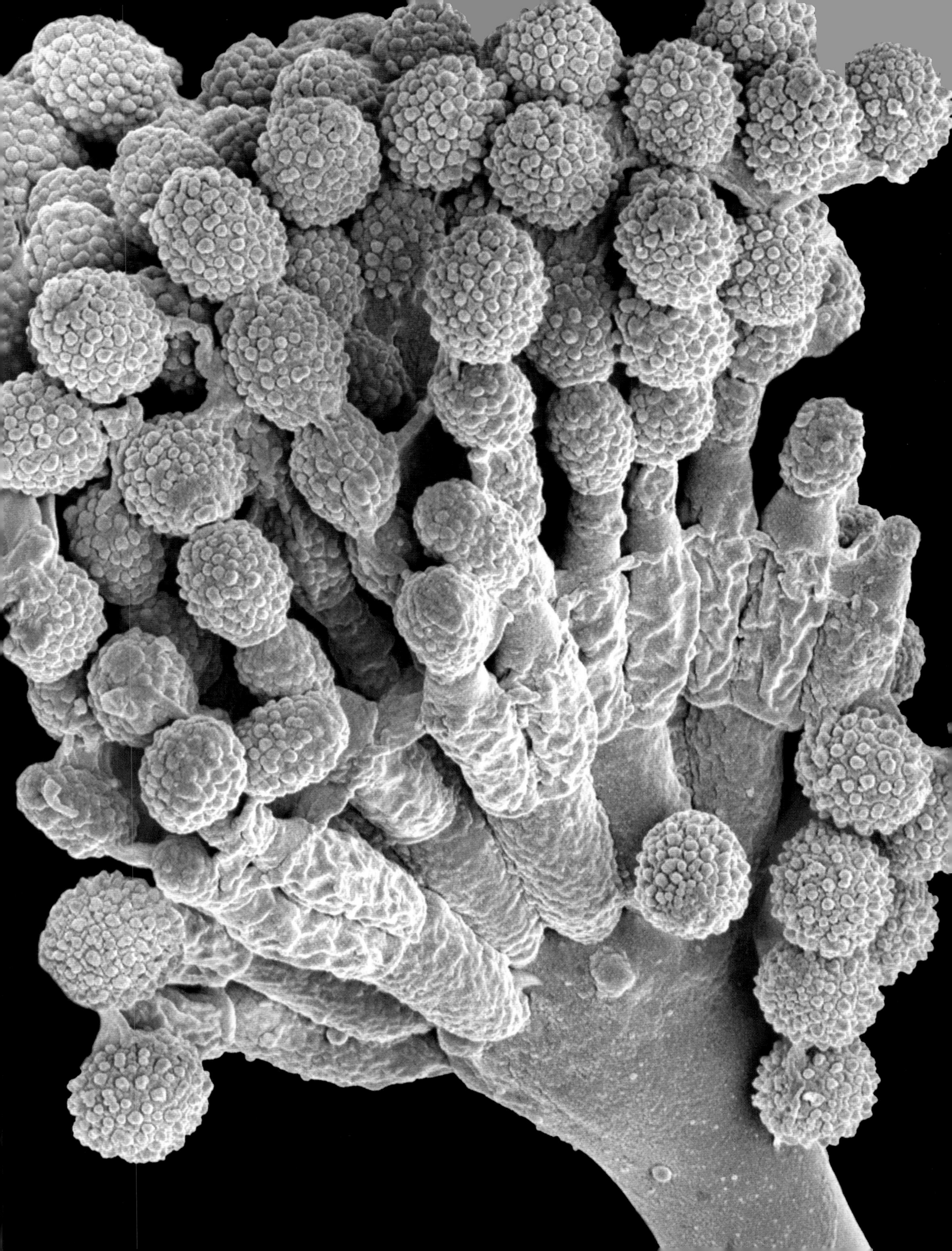

In a factory in India, a technician adjusts a fermentation unit used to grow microbes, including fungi, for medical uses.

and the distinction between 'bad' LDL cholesterol and 'good' HDL cholesterol had been discovered in 1955 by John Gofman, a biophysicist at the University of California, Berkeley. Endo and his colleagues began looking for an enzyme that actually altered and, ideally, reduced, production of LDL cholesterol.

In 1976, Endo discovered a compound, in a broth of *Penicillium citrinum*, called compactin (also known as mevastatin). It was shown to inhibit the activity of the enzyme HMG-CoA reductase, which is involved in making LDL cholesterol in the human body. Endo tested the enzyme on rats, but it was later found to be toxic in dogs. Nevertheless, it was the first major breakthrough in the search for a way to lower cholesterol; moreover, it helped the scientists at Merck identify another natural product in the *Aspergillus* fungus that also inhibited HMG-CoA reductase and became known as lovastatin.

Money-spinners After Mevacor was licensed in 1987 as a cholesterol-lowering medication, many other companies began producing statins

Especially if there is any history of heart disease in your family, you should have your cholesterol levels checked regularly. If your overall or LDL level is high, your doctor may recommend a statin, which is usually taken in tablet form. In addition to drug therapy, there are a number of changes you can make to your lifestyle to reduce your risk of cardiovascular disease and also potentially lower cholesterol, most notably undertaking daily exercise, eating low-fat foods and maintaining a healthy body weight.

Statins reduce the risk of a serious cardiovascular event such as heart attack or stroke by around 39 per cent, according to research published in 2012.

and a wide array is now available. Most are derived from fungi such as *Aspergillus* or consist of synthetic versions of natural compounds. Simvastatin (Zocor, Lipex) and pravastatin (branded Pravachol or Selektine) are made from fungi using a fermentation process.

The market for these products is now vast. One in four Americans over the age of 45, of whom there are 127 million, now take statins, as do between six and seven million people in Britain, where statins account for more than 50 million prescriptions a year. By 2003, atorvastatin, better known as Lipitor, its brand name, had become the best-selling pharmaceutical in history, and by 2008 it was generating a revenue of US$12.5 billion for the multinational drug company Pfizer.

Possible side effects of statins With such high levels of use, any possible side effects are going to have significant health implications. In general, statins are well tolerated, but some users occasionally report inflammation (swelling) of muscles, causing pain, tenderness or weakness, and between 1 in 10 and 1 in 100 people may report nosebleeds, headaches and feeling sick. One recent study also found that high doses of statins are associated with a small increased risk of diabetes, though specialists say the risks are still outweighed by the benefits and may only be relevant in those who already have type 2 diabetes.

Several recent studies have focused on the issue of whether people with a low risk of heart attack or stroke should be taking statins at all. After all, cholesterol plays beneficial roles in the body, too, for example in the production of hormones and the correct functioning of body cells. A 2011 review in the highly respected medical database, *The Cochrane Library*, found that no strong evidence exists to suggest that statins reduce coronary heart disease deaths among people who have not suffered a previous heart attack or other cardiovascular illness. However, in contrast, another large review published in 2012 in the medical journal *The Lancet* suggested that statins reduce the chances of having a heart attack or stroke and save lives in people who are already at a low risk – that is people with a risk of 10 per cent or less of having a heart attack or stroke within the next five years.

Known by the trade names Zocor and Lipex, simvastatin is synthetically derived from a fermentation product of *Aspergillus terreus*.

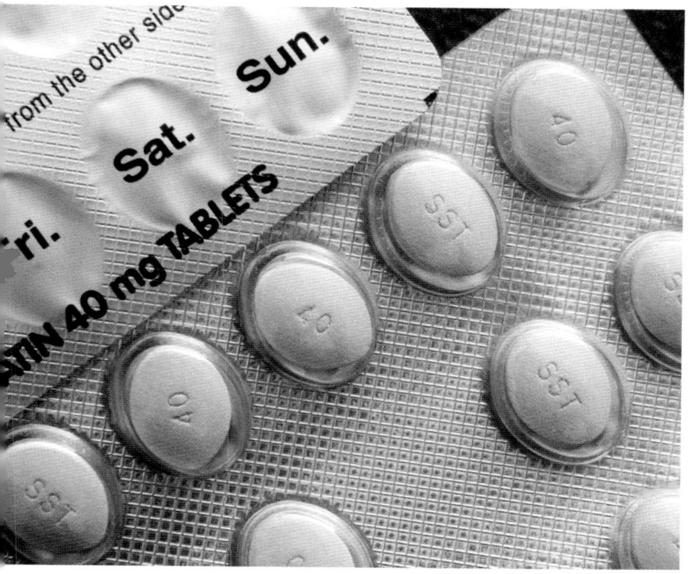

The bottom line While the debates will go on and guidelines will continue to be adjusted in the light of any new evidence, it seems clear at least that heart disease rates have fallen since statins were introduced – a report in the *Journal of the American Heart Association* estimated a decline in deaths from heart disease of 27.8 per cent between 1997 and 2007. And though other factors have no doubt played a part in this, such as lower levels of smoking, improved diets and levels of exercise, and better treatment, it appears that a lowly fungus, *Aspergillus terreus*, has helped large numbers of people around the world enjoy an improved quality of life.

ORIGIN Worldwide
PART USED Substance produced by the fungus

PENICILLIUM FUNGI

Penicillium spp.

MEDICAL BENEFITS ◆ Treatments for a wide range of bacterial infections

The chance discovery of the antibacterial properties of a fungus mould led to the development of penicillin, one of the most effective and widespread antibiotics.

An antibiotic is a substance or medicine that kills or slows the growth of bacteria. Penicillin is probably the most familiar medicine of this kind and one we often encounter early in our lives. Introduced during World War II, it heralded the first hope of treatment, if not cure, for a host of diseases, such as pneumonia, gonorrhea and rheumatic fever – diseases that were previously killers. Indeed, it's amazing to think that 80 years ago, before penicillin, a mere scratch on the leg could often lead to fatal blood poisoning.

There are many kinds of penicillin, but they all are derived from a group of fungi belonging to the genus *Penicillium*. Like many other fungi, *Penicillium* fungi grow in long, branching filaments, or hyphae, creating a network called a mycelium, which is considered a single organism. More commonly, these forms of fungi are known as moulds.

Penicillium moulds grow in cool and temperate realms, almost anywhere there is vegetable matter – in leaf litter and on plants, fruits and vegetables. They thrive on rotting matter and accelerate the decay of foods. At the same

Growing in a petri dish, the fungus *Penicillium chrysogenum* spreads outwards, forming a distinctive radial shape.

in CLOSE-UP

Antibiotics generally kill bacteria by disrupting the processes by which the bacteria gain energy and grow. For example, they may interfere with the conversion of glucose (sugar) into energy, and disrupt the production of new proteins. Penicillin, more specifically, kills a bacterium by attaching to its cell wall and destroying key proteins in the wall. The bacterium then swells with water, bursts and dies.

time these fungi are widely used in the food industry, for example to add white crusts to Camembert and Brie cheeses and to add flavour to sausages and hams.

Ancient civilisations, including the Greeks and Chinese, used moulds of this type to treat infection. Through experience, they found that the moulds produced compounds that helped healing, although they did not isolate and identify any antibiotics. Later, too, in Greece and Serbia, mouldy bread was used as a treatment for wounds and infections.

A chance discovery The discovery of penicillin is usually credited to Scottish scientist Alexander Fleming, who worked at St Mary's Hospital in London in the late 1920s, but a number of other scientists also played crucial parts in the story. In the late nineteenth century, for example, several scientists had noted the antibacterial effect of *Penicillium* fungi. In 1895, a physician called Vincenzo Tiberio from Naples, Italy, even published research about a mould (now believed to have been *Penicillium*) in a water well that demonstrated antibacterial action.

While taking his lead from these pioneers, Fleming actually discovered the antimicrobial powers of *Penicillium* moulds by chance. According to anecdote, he was a brilliant but untidy scientist. One day in 1928 he accidentally left a petri dish, in which he was growing some bacteria, on his laboratory bench while he went on holiday. Upon his return, he noticed that, by chance, a fungus had grown on the dish and

Alexander Fleming said later in life, 'I didn't mean to revolutionise all medicine ... but I suppose that was exactly what I did'.

any bacteria in its immediate vicinity had been destroyed. Fleming then found that this rogue mould, which he initially identified as *Penicillium notatum* (but which was later shown to be *Penicillium rubens*), actually killed a range of different bacteria; he named it 'mould juice'.

At this point in its history, penicillin could easily have disappeared for good because the difficulties associated with extracting the antibiotic compound and producing large enough quantities led Fleming to dismiss it as a potential medicine. However, a few years later, Australian pathologist Howard Florey, German biochemist Ernst Chain, and English biochemist Norman Heatley started developing a method of mass-producing penicillin and successfully trialled it at a hospital in Oxford in the United Kingdom. The first patient was treated with penicillin in 1941.

What You CAN DO

Your doctor will prescribe penicillin-based antibiotics when appropriate, usually for bacterial infections. They may be provided as a tablet, capsule, liquid, cream, lotion, spray or drops or, in more acute cases, via an injection or drip. Even as a patient you can take a number of steps to help limit the emergence of bacterial resistance (see below). Don't, for example, ask for antibiotics for colds or other viral illnesses. Make sure, too, that you complete the full course of any antibiotics you are prescribed; although it's tempting to stop as soon as symptoms improve, this may mean that low levels of bacteria will persist, which will then thrive and may spread to other people. And always remember to wash your hands when entering and leaving a hospital.

The Allies' secret weapon With World War II then underway, it became apparent that having access to antibiotics would greatly improve the chances of survival of wounded soldiers and civilians, who often died from infections of lethal *Staphylococcus* and *Streptococcus* bacteria. Because the United Kingdom's industries and laboratories were under threat of air attack at the time, production of penicillin was shifted to the United States. Initially it proved difficult to manufacture sufficient quantities: the first patient to be treated with US-made penicillin in 1942 was given over half the stocks available. Even a few months later, the United States had only enough antibiotic to treat 10 patients, so scale-up was urgently needed.

In 1943, US researchers discovered a way of increasing production. On a mouldy melon in a market in the town of Peoria, Illinois, they found an especially high-yielding form of penicillin. It was then cultivated in a deep vat containing corn syrup and other growth-promoting ingredients, with satisfying results. By the time of D-Day, 6 June 1944, 3 million doses of penicillin had been prepared for the Allied invasion. It's often said that penicillin was the Allies' secret weapon, and it certainly saved innumerable lives on the Allied side. Although the Germans learned about the discovery of penicillin and even obtained samples of moulds, they were unable to produce useful quantities of the medicine and, as a result, lost large numbers of troops and civilians to infection.

Antibiotic resistance Penicillin has since saved millions more lives and remains a highly effective medicine. However, a growing concern with regard to its widespread use is the

At a Bayer factory in Germany, sterile conditions are maintained for the large-scale manufacturing of penicillin antibiotics.

Production of penicillin became a vital part of the war effort, giving the Allies a distinct medical advantage over the enemy.

emergence of antibiotic resistance. Bacteria, like other living things, constantly evolve, or mutate, in ways that ensure their survival. While most bacteria are killed by antibiotics, a few, due to genetic mutations, manage to resist; in the absence of others, these resistant bacteria thrive and multiply. The more antibiotics are used, the more the resistant bacteria flourish.

Resistance to penicillin was first recorded only a few years after the antibiotic was first mass-produced, in 1947, and the first resistant bacterium was *Staphylococcus aureus*. In 1967, a pneumonia-causing bacterium, *Streptococcus pneumoniae*, was also found to have become resistant, and in the mid-1970s American military personnel in Vietnam were shown to have acquired and spread penicillin-resistant gonorrhea from prostitutes.

According to the US Centers for Disease Control, up to four-fifths of prescriptions issued for coughs and colds are unnecessary.

Since then, excessive and improper use of antibiotics has compounded the problem. Often penicillin is prescribed (sometimes at the patient's insistence) for treatment of colds and other viral illnesses. Antibiotics, however, have no impact on these illnesses; nevertheless they still kill sensitive bacteria and accelerate the spread of resistant microbes. As resistance develops, more powerful doses of an antibiotic may be required to treat an illness, which exacerbates the problem further.

The MRSA threat Today, antibiotic resistance is one of the world's most pressing health problems. Diseases that are becoming harder to treat include pneumococcal infections that cause pneumonia, ear infections, sinus infections and meningitis; skin infections; and tuberculosis. A disturbing development has been the emergence in recent years of methicillin-resistant *Staphylococcus aureus* (MRSA), a bacterium that causes a range of difficult-to-treat infections in humans and which has become immune to many types of penicillin, notably methicillin. To date, 17 strains of MRSA have been identified, each with different levels of resistance and causing different degrees of illness. Outbreaks of MRSA in British hospitals in 2006–8 killed thousands of patients.

ORIGIN Cool to moderate climates, widespread in soil and vegetation
PART USED A metabolic by-product of *Penicillium* fungi

BLACK HOOF FUNGUS

Phellinus linteus

MEDICAL BENEFITS ◆ Potential treatment for various cancers including breast, bladder, lung, liver, prostate

In Chinese art, black hoof fungus, or *lingzhi* as it was originally known, often symbolises immortality, reflecting long-held notions that it enhances health and prolongs life. Now scientific research is beginning to back up these beliefs.

In its natural form, black hoof fungus is a rarity. It grows on tree trunks of old willow, paper mulberry and elm trees, and produces a large mushroom or fruiting body – the medicinal part of the fungus – that takes between 30 and 40 years to develop. Shaped like a hoof (hence its English name), the mushroom is usually black, brown or yellowish and has a bitter taste. Certain specimens resemble a projecting tongue, which has earned it another name: tree tongue.

Despite the difficulties of harvesting large quantities of the fungus, black hoof fungus has long been used by Chinese medicine to prevent a diversity of ailments related to the digestive system, and excessive bleeding following injury. More recently, preliminary scientific studies have demonstrated its ability to fight the growth and spread of tumours by stimulating the immune system.

Black hoof fungus has been shown to have the strongest antitumour activity of the major medicinal mushrooms.

Battling tumours A 2008 American study looked at the effects of black hoof fungus on highly invasive breast cancer cells, which had spread around the body. The results showed that the fungus reduced cell reproduction and disrupted the development of tumour blood supply. A further study of both breast and bladder cancer cells by scientists from Taiwan also showed an antitumour effect as a result of the action of a pigment called hispolon, found in black hoof fungus.

Colon, liver, lung, mouth, prostate and skin cancers have also been reported to have responded to the antitumour activity of the fungus. But although these studies are promising, they have been conducted mainly in the laboratory in cells rather than in living animals or humans. However, there are several published case studies of patients whose cancer diminished upon taking black hoof fungus. One Japanese report provided an account of a 79-year-old patient who had advanced liver cancer that had already spread to his lungs. He took an extract of black hoof fungus regularly for one month and, upon radiographic imaging six months afterwards, all signs of tumour cells had disappeared.

in CLOSE-UP

Biochemical analysis has revealed that black hoof fungus contains an extensive array of compounds that appear to have medicinal properties against various substances, biochemical pathways and genetic mechanisms in the human body. In particular, when proteins in the fungus interact with sugars (polysaccharides) in the body, the resulting combinations or complexes are thought to stimulate the body's immune system and boost levels of cancer-fighting chemicals.

OTHER NAMES Tree tongue, *meshima* (Japan), *song gen* (China)
ORIGIN Japan, China, Korea, southern United States
PART USED Fruiting body of the fungus

In ancient China, black hoof fungus was said to be an elixir of eternal youth. Emperor Qin Shihuang (259–210 BC) once sent 3000 children to Japan to gather it.

Another published case study described a patient with a type of prostate cancer that does not respond to standard hormone treatment. This patient's cancer was also rapidly spreading through his bones; however, upon taking a black hoof fungus extract his condition showed a dramatic improvement.

Black hoof fungus has, moreover, been shown to increase the killing of prostate cancer cells when used in combination with the conventional cancer drug doxorubicin. Wider clinical studies are, however, required to substantiate these promising reports.

If you or a loved one is suffering from cancer, you could ask your specialist about the suitability of black hoof fungus treatment. The fungus is not widely available but can be sourced online. Usually the mushrooms are chopped into small pieces, boiled in water for around 20 minutes and the resulting tea is drunk on a daily basis. Capsules and a liquid containing the extract are also available; a typical daily dose is 10–30 g of the dried mushroom or 2–5 g of the polysaccharide extract.

MEDICINAL MUSHROOMS

Mushrooms, which are the large fruiting bodies of certain fungi, have a long and successful history of medicinal use, especially in China, where more than 100 species are used in traditional medicine. And many are now generating interest among Western researchers.

In particular, it seems that mushrooms may have beneficial effects on the immune system. Some preliminary studies have also demonstrated antitumour activity and an ability to reduce the side effects of cancer therapies.

Caterpillar power A high-profile example of a medicinal mushroom is the 'caterpillar fungus' (*Ophiocordyceps sinensis*). In 1993, three female Chinese runners at the National Games broke five world records. They were tested for illicit drugs, but no illegal substances were found in their bodies. Their trainer put it down to a tonic prepared from this unusual fungus.

Found growing at altitude in Tibet and the Himalayas, in Chinese it is called 'summer grass, winter worm' because over the course of a year the fungus slowly grows inside a living caterpillar larva, killing and mummifying the insect, and then sprouts from its dead body. Records of the fungus date back to the fourteenth century, and it is known in Chinese medicine as an aphrodisiac and a treatment for fatigue, cancer and respiratory ailments. Recent animal and laboratory studies have lent support to some of these beliefs. In one Chinese trial, mice on a high dose of the fungus showed an increase in endurance of up to 73 per cent. Another study, conducted at the Beijing Medical University Sports Research Institute, tested the effects of the fungus on human endurance. It found that athletes given the highest dose experienced improved lactate clearance (which reduces muscle fatigue), resulting in greater anaerobic physical performance.

Immune boosters Exactly how mushrooms exert their health effects is still the subject of research, but there is strong evidence

Left: As it grows, caterpillar fungus gradually assumes the shape of its host insect.

Below: Workers forage for caterpillar fungus on the Tibetan Plateau.

Right: The mushroom *Coriolus versicolor* grows widely in temperate forests, such as this British woodland.

for benefits from people who regularly eat medicinal mushrooms. In one area of Japan, a 14-year survey suggested that farmers who ate a regular diet of medicinal mushrooms had a lower cancer death rate than those who did not (1 in 1000 versus 1 in 600). In Brazil, the *Agaricus blazei* mushroom has been used by folk healers to treat ailments as diverse as hepatitis, high cholesterol, diabetes, blocked arteries, skin conditions and cancer. Researchers have found that it contains compounds that cut off the blood supply (and thus nutrients) to tumours.

It is also a source of polysaccharides, or sugars, that stimulate the immune system. Another mushroom, *Coriolus versicolor*, is known to stimulate the immune system and increase cell death in human leukaemia.

Finally, the shiitake mushroom is thought to protect the liver. An animal study showed that when the mushroom was given for seven days, the liver was protected from damage by acetaminophen, a painkiller. The researchers believed the protective effect of the mushroom is due to its antioxidant properties.

REAL MAGIC

The following are among the most common nutritional benefits of mushrooms:

- **Vitamin D supply** Mushrooms are the only fruit or vegetable source of this critical vitamin.
- **Boost immune function** White button mushrooms (*Agaricus bisporus*) may increase the production of proteins and antiviral molecules that are released by cells while they are trying to protect and repair the body's tissues.
- **High in antioxidants** Mushrooms have high antioxidant activity, on a par with red capsicums. They also contain selenium, which is a component in important antioxidant enzymes.
- **Vitamin B supply** Mushrooms have high levels of vitamins B2 and B3 and pantothenic acid. These are essential for converting food into fuel and for the functioning of the nervous system.
- **Low in kilojoules** Mushrooms are fat and cholesterol free.

Enoki

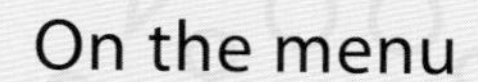

On the menu

Some widely available edible mushrooms have demonstrated medicinal properties:

Shiitake Antioxidant, antitumour, cholesterol-lowering and antiviral properties

Enoki Significant anticancer and immune-enhancing effects

Maitake Anticancer, antiviral and immune-enhancing properties; may also reduce blood pressure and blood glucose

Oyster Strong antioxidant properties, even when cooked; some protection against cancer

White mushrooms Source of vitamin D due to use of ultraviolet light during farming

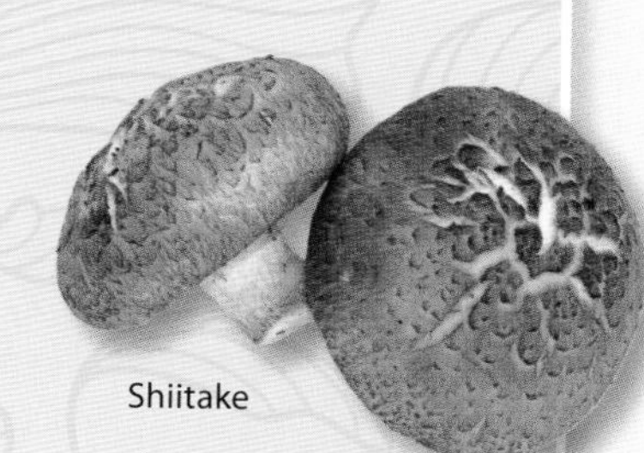

Shiitake

Maitake

Oyster

VAMPIRE FUNGUS

Pythium oligandrum

MEDICAL BENEFITS ◆ Treatment for skin and nail fungal infections including jock itch, ringworm and athlete's foot

An accidental encounter with this highly efficient predator fungus paved the way to an effective new treatment for athlete's foot and other fungal infections.

In its natural habitat, vampire fungus can be found growing within the roots of certain plants, including tomato and sugar beet. Once bound to the root, it stimulates the production of plant growth hormones and induces responses that defend the plant from other harmful fungi.

Vampire fungus is a parasite of other fungi: indeed, it survives by degrading other micro-organisms. When it meets another fungus, it attacks it and sucks the nutrients from it – hence its common name. So far, no microbe resistance to vampire fungus has been discovered; it simply eats up any fungus in its path.

After the fungus and its properties were discovered in the late 1970s, it was quickly adopted in agriculture as a form of pest treatment, used to protect plants from parasitic mushrooms and as a soil treatment to reduce harmful fungal disease around plant roots.

Putting a foot in it In the early 1990s, a group of Czech researchers studying further possible applications of vampire fungus in agriculture made another fascinating discovery: that the fungus would even eat other fungi present on human skin. This came about by chance, when a researcher in the team of Dr Dasa Vesely dropped some of the fungus into her boot. A little later she found that her foot, which had been infected with athlete's foot, was now clear of the condition. Curious, she tried it out on her husband, who also had athlete's foot, and found that it eradicated his infection, too.

The researcher then told her colleagues in the laboratory and they decided to undertake clinical trials. The results were encouraging.

Vampire fungus has been shown to kill more than 20 common harmful fungi.

In one trial, involving 69 people with fungal foot infections, the unpleasant smell due to their conditions decreased in more than three-quarters of the patients, foot sweating was eliminated in almost as many, and athlete's foot was eradicated in more than 80 per cent.

Clearing the skin Once the scientists had demonstrated the effectiveness of vampire fungus in human trials, they developed a medicinal powder that consists of vampire fungus spores mixed with silica. In addition to clearing up harmful fungi and avoiding the development of resistance, the vampire fungus powder is kinder to the skin than chemical treatments, with no reported side effects or toxicity. Once the fungus has exhausted its food source of fungal infection, it dries out and dies. The dead fungus can then be dusted off.

in CLOSE-UP

When vampire fungus detects another fungus, its spores wake up and grow fibres. The fibres then pierce the prey fungus, causing protoplasm – a gel-like substance – to seep out. The vampire fungus sucks this up and grows, while the prey dies.

ORIGIN In soil worldwide, often near plant roots
PART USED Spores, which grow into fungus when applied

Medicinal powders made with *Pythium oligandrum* are available online. The spores last many years when kept cool and dry, and will not grow into the adult fungus unless a prey fungus and sufficient moisture are available. The method of use depends on the problem. To treat athlete's foot, for instance, you stir the powder into the lukewarm water of a footbath then wash the feet in it. The water retains the active fungus, so it can be saved and reused (once only). The European Commission considers the product safe, without evidence of harmful effect on human or animal health, groundwater or the environment, and the US Environmental Protection Agency has also confirmed it is totally safe to use on pets and people.

Right: When the feet are immersed in water containing the spores, the vampire fungus starts to attack any other fungus present.

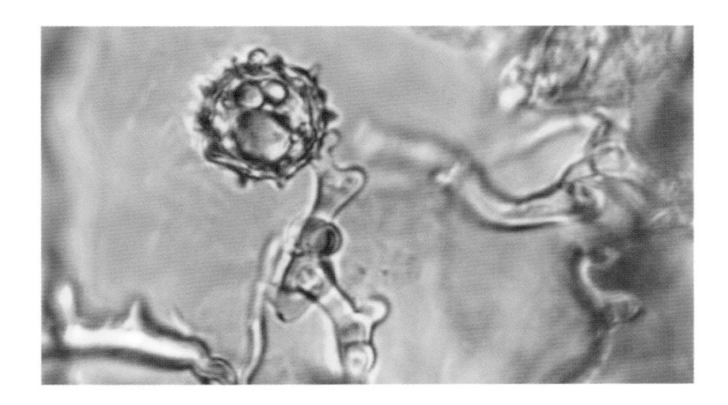

Above: On contact with water, the tiny, round vampire fungus spores grow long fibres.

Above: The vampire fungus wraps its fibres round those of the prey, piercing them. It then sucks out nutrients, killing the other fungus.

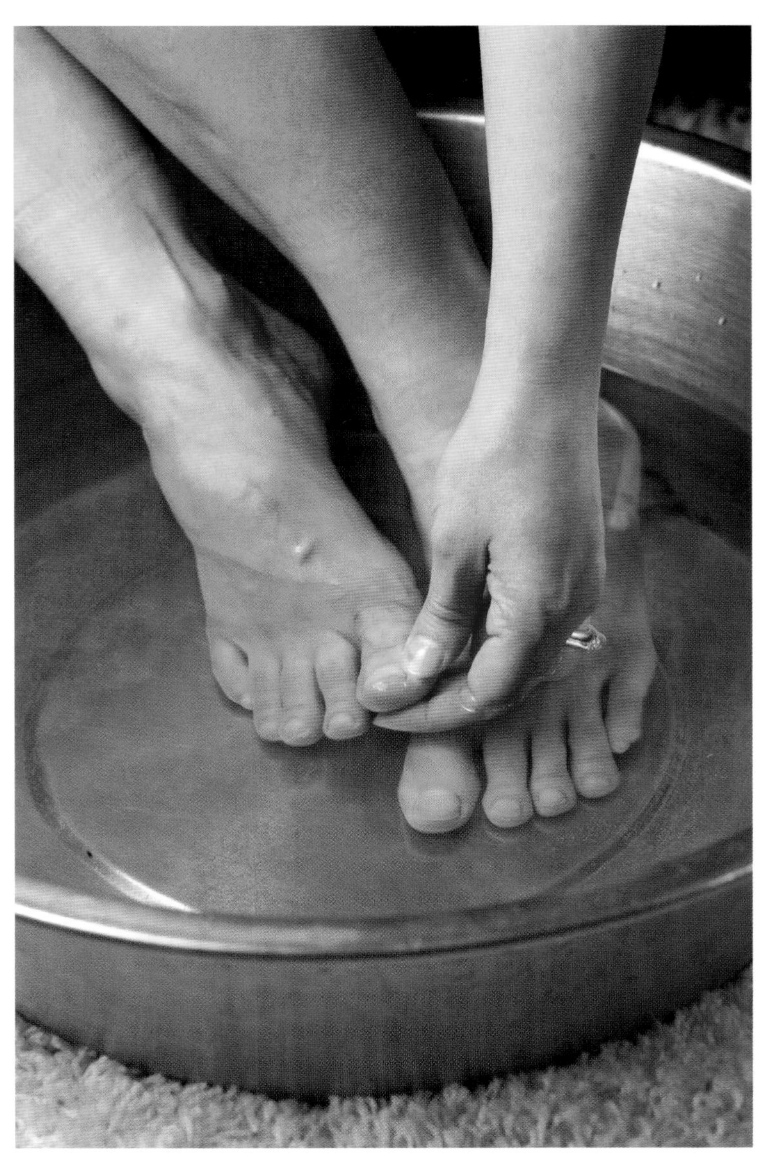

SPIRULINA

Arthrospira maxima, Arthrospira platensis

MEDICAL BENEFITS ◆ Highly nutritious ◆ Potential treatment for high LDL cholesterol, HIV, allergic rhinitis ◆ Possible protection against liver cancer

If you could take only one source of food on a mission to Mars, what would it be? Well, according to the European Space Agency and NASA, spirulina could be a wise choice.

Both agencies have investigated a biological life support system for long-term piloted missions into space, and both concluded that a particular strain of *Arthrospira* could be developed as a convenient source of nutrition.

Widely dubbed a 'superfood', spirulina contains around 60 per cent protein and impressive amounts of beta-carotene (which the body then converts to vitamin A), vitamin B12 and B complex, iron, essential trace minerals and gamma-linolenic acid. And because it contains all nine essential amino acids, it is considered a complete source of protein for vegetarians.

The algae have been used as a food for centuries for their high nutritional value, and the United Nations World Health Organization believes spirulina has enormous potential to combat malnutrition. In recent years, studies have also begun to highlight a number of potential therapeutic benefits. For example, research suggests that spirulina could provide a degree of protection against cancer – one study demonstrated some prevention of liver cancer in rats that received spirulina supplements.

Other research has indicated that spirulina could be used to treat high cholesterol and type 2 diabetes. A study in normal volunteers showed that 4.5 g per day of spirulina for six weeks lowered blood pressure, total cholesterol and 'bad' cholesterol (LDL), and increased 'good' cholesterol (HDL). Two small studies investigated the effects of spirulina supplementation in type 2 diabetes and demonstrated improvement in fasting blood glucose and lipid levels.

Slowing the progress of HIV Researchers are also investigating claims that spirulina can slow the development of HIV into AIDS. The work aims to substantiate various anecdotal reports that people who regularly eat algae in Chad, Korea and Japan have low rates of HIV/AIDS. Currently, there are no conclusive studies in large numbers of patients, but a recent pilot study in which spirulina was given either alone or in combination with a brown seaweed known as wakame (*Undaria pinnatifida*) provided promising results, with no side effects and some suggestion that spirulina may improve signs and symptoms in patients with HIV over time. One patient who received 13 months of spirulina supplements showed a decrease in the particular cells of the immune system (CD4 cells) that indicate the presence of HIV, and also a drop in the amount of virus in his body.

What You CAN DO

Spirulina has been produced commercially for more than 30 years, and its popularity

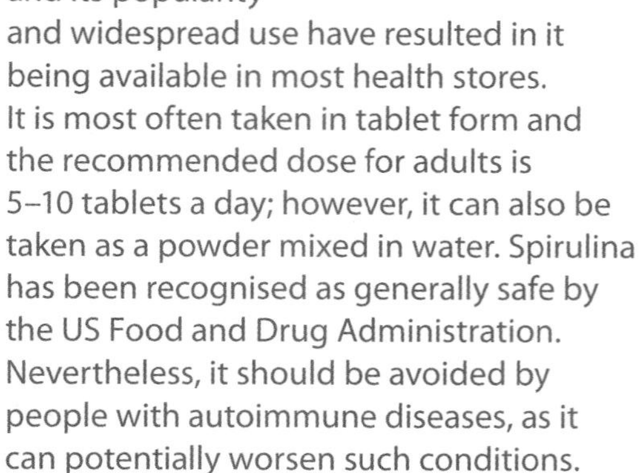

and widespread use have resulted in it being available in most health stores. It is most often taken in tablet form and the recommended dose for adults is 5–10 tablets a day; however, it can also be taken as a powder mixed in water. Spirulina has been recognised as generally safe by the US Food and Drug Administration. Nevertheless, it should be avoided by people with autoimmune diseases, as it can potentially worsen such conditions.

ORIGIN *A. maxima* found in Central America, *A. platensis* in Africa, Asia and South America
PART USED Whole alga

Traditional Wisdom

Spirulina has a long history of use as a food in countries with mineral-rich lakes, where the algae may grow abundantly, often turning the water a bluish-green colour. In the African country of Chad, reports of the Kanembu people harvesting spirulina to make dihe, a dried cake that is in turn used for broths, date back to the ninth century. Similarly, records suggest the Aztecs as well as other Mesoamerican tribes sourced spirulina from Lake Texcoco in Mexico up to 400 years ago. The Aztecs called it Tecuitlatl, which means 'the stone's excrement'. But today's biggest spirulina producers are the United States, Burma, Chile, Thailand and Taiwan.

Harvested spirulina is spread out on wooden boards at Lake Chad to dry it in the sun before it is ground up into a powder.

Spirulina algae bloom in profusion in mineral-rich lakes such as the hot-spring-fed waters of Africa's Great Rift Valley.

A six-month study in patients with allergic rhinitis (inflammation of the nasal passages) found spirulina led to notable improvement compared to a placebo.

CHLORELLA

Chlorella pyrenoidosa

MEDICAL BENEFITS ◆ Highly nutritious ◆ Possible treatment for blood toxins, fibromyalgia, high blood pressure, inflammatory bowel disease, some cancers

Thought to have been consumed by humans for millennia, chlorella may have been one of the most important and nutritious foods of our early ancestors.

in CLOSE-UP

If you take a look at chlorella through a microscope, each individual algal cell will appear green and spherical and be 2–10 micrometres (a micrometre is 1×10^{-6} of a metre) in diameter. By dry weight chlorella contains 45 per cent protein, 20 per cent fat, 20 per cent carbohydrate, 5 per cent fibre and 10 per cent vitamins and minerals. It also contains high levels of antioxidant phytonutrients – beneficial compounds also found in plants (see p. 146).

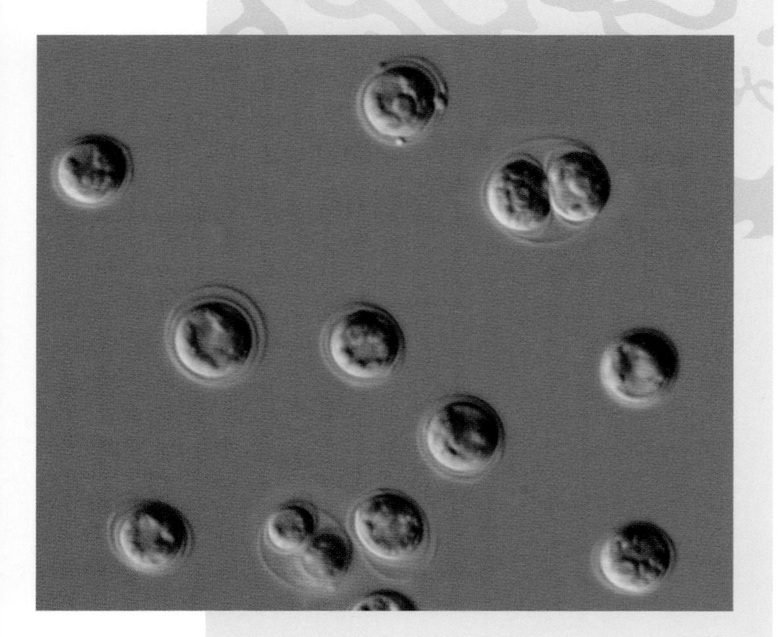

This microscope view shows the typical round, green form of individual chlorella algae growing in water.

This green, fresh water alga is considered to have the highest chlorophyll content of any edible plant, and has twice the protein content of spinach, about 38 times the protein content of soybeans, and 55 times that of rice. Today, it is usually consumed as a nutritional supplement, in tablet, powder or liquid form, and the most commonly used species is *Chlorella pyrenoidosa*, which is grown and processed mainly in Japan and Taiwan.

In the 1940s, the extraordinary nutrient profile of chlorella meant it became widely known as a potential 'superfood', at a time when there were fears that a global population boom would outstrip the availability of food. Production difficulties meant the alga never solved any anticipated food shortage, however, and eventually better crop efficiency overcame the potential problem.

In one Japanese study, a chlorella diet significantly prevented the decline of cognitive ability in mice.

Practitioners of alternative medicine use chlorella to treat a diversity of illnesses, and as a preventative measure. Robust clinical evidence for many claims relating to the medicinal benefits of chlorella is needed, but one study in rats with liver cancer that were given chlorella showed that the supplement helped protect against further development of the liver cancer cells because the chlorella killed some tumour cells while inhibiting the growth of others.

Chlorella is available in capsules, powder, liquid and tablets, and may also be found in some herbal detoxification products. Many people mix the powdered form into salad dressings or smoothies. Chlorella is relatively safe, but mild side effects may occur in addition to interactions with some medications such as blood-thinning agents. Also, some people (especially those allergic to iodine) experience serious allergic reactions to chlorella, including breathing difficulties and swelling of the mouth. The human digestive system cannot break down the hard outer cell wall of chlorella, so make sure any product you buy has already been processed to make it digestible.

It might look unappetising, but chlorella's benefits make it appealing as a health food.

A detox aid Detoxification in the body's cells appears to be the most widely accepted beneficial use of chlorella. The alga seems to have a unique ability to bind with mercury, lead and cadmium, and has become increasingly popular as a heavy metal detoxifier. This ability to detoxify is partly due to the high chlorophyll content, which joins with molecules in environmental toxins, inactivating them.

A small Japanese study suggested that women who took chlorella supplements during pregnancy showed a reduction in levels of dioxin (a toxin found in herbicides and the insecticide DDT) in their breast milk, reducing the transfer of dioxins to the infant. Also, levels of a protein in the immune system known as immunoglobulin A (IgA), were found to be increased in pregnant women who took chlorella.

The results of another study, which looked at the effectiveness of chlorella as a daily dietary supplement in patients with fibromyalgia (chronic, widespread pain in the muscles and joints, of unknown cause), high blood pressure, and ulcerative colitis (a type of inflammatory bowel disease) suggested that the alga might reduce high blood pressure, lower cholesterol levels, accelerate wound healing, and enhance immune functions.

ORIGIN Fresh water worldwide, but mainly Japan and Taiwan
PART USED Whole alga

BROWN ALGAE

Phaeophyceae

MEDICAL BENEFITS ◆ Promotes wound healing ◆ Potential treatment for obesity ◆ Traditional treatment for thyroid disorders

Brown algae are a familiar sight along the shores of the North Atlantic, New Zealand and parts of Australia. But the potential medical benefits of these seaweeds are still not widely appreciated.

One component of brown algae, called alginate, is increasingly being used for a range of medical problems, most notably as a wound dressing and weight-loss agent. Another, fucoxanthin, is also under investigation for aiding weight loss. In addition, it has been claimed, though with less supporting evidence, that brown algae could provide treatments for a range of other ailments including thyroid disorders, cancers, arthritis, heart disease and high cholesterol.

In certain ocean habitats, brown algae may grow to more than 30 m (100 ft) in length. There are about 2000 species worldwide.

Mopping up A long carbohydrate molecule found in the cell walls of the algae, alginate can absorb vast amounts of water and it is this property that makes it effective as a wound dressing, particularly for burns, diabetic wounds, cavity wounds and some bleeding wounds. The alginate helps limit secretions and minimises bacterial contamination; healing is promoted by the creation of a moist environment, which prevents the wound from drying out, and means the dressing can be removed with less pain than with conventional dressings. Alginate dressings have been used widely in hospitals since World War II and a range of commercial products is available internationally.

in CLOSE-UP

Alginate dressings absorb water due to an exchange between calcium ions in the alginate in the dressing and sodium ions in the blood or fluid of the wound. When sufficient calcium ions are replaced by sodium ions, the alginate fibres swell, partially dissolve and form a gel.

Fat burners It has been claimed that both alginate and fucoxanthin can increase metabolism of fat as well as create a sensation of fullness, thus resulting in weight loss. The results of a study carried out at the University of Newcastle, United Kingdom, in 2010, suggested that alginate can reduce fat digestion in the gut by more than 75 per cent. This is better than most anti-obesity treatments currently available over the counter. The work was carried out in an artificial gut, but the researchers are currently testing the ability of alginate added to bread to reduce fat digestion in humans.

Some recent and ongoing research suggests that fucoxanthin may burn fat in the body, in particular belly fat. One trial showed that a mix

Large quantities of *Laminaria* brown algae are harvested off the coast of Brittany in France, much of it for use in health products.

of fucoxanthin and pomegranate seed oil promoted weight loss and reduced body and liver fat content in obese nondiabetic women.

Scientists from the University of Copenhagen, Denmark, also found that dietary fibres from brown algae boost the body's sensation of satiety, helping people eat less. The study was conducted in nearly 100 obese people who were given alginate in liquid form.

Treating thyroid disorders One type of brown alga known as bladderwrack (*Fucus vesiculosus*) has long been a staple of traditional and alternative medicine. Rich in iodine, it is used to treat iodine deficiency and thyroid disorders such as an underactive thyroid or an oversized thyroid gland (a condition also known as goitre). It has been employed, too, to treat such diverse conditions as arthritis, hardening of the arteries, digestive disorders, anxiety and abnormal menstrual cycles. Conclusive evidence for the effectiveness of such treatments is still lacking, however.

ORIGIN Mainly temperate or cold seas but also found in some tropical waters

PARTS USED Alginate, a component of the cell walls, and fucoxanthin, a pigment

Alginate dressings can be bought in some pharmacies or online. Because they are highly absorbent, they are regarded as particularly good for lightly weeping or bleeding wounds and will also reduce the chance of a scab and scar forming. Seaweed pills for weight loss are available in some health stores, but bear in mind that the efficacy of this treatment is still under investigation. Using brown algae, including bladderwrack, without medical supervision is not recommended, as, used incorrectly, they can cause thyroid problems, allergic reactions and other problems.

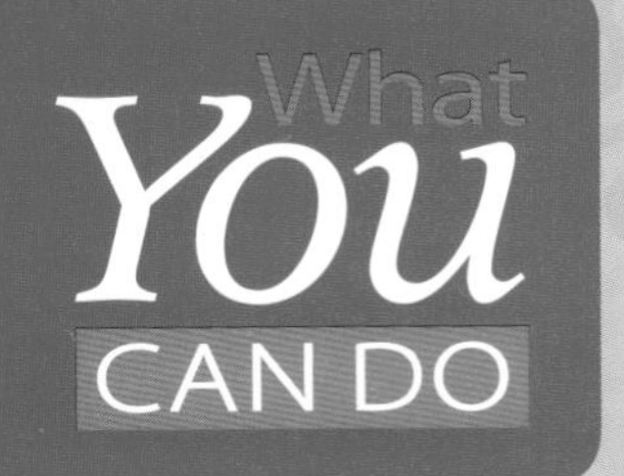

SUPER SEAWEEDS

Positive reports on the nutritional and other health benefits of seaweeds have led to a wide range of seaweed supplements becoming available. But there are other, more creative ways to get your seaweed fix.

Packed full of vitamins, minerals and other nutrients, seaweeds are now commonly used in various cuisines. Japan has brought us miso soup, which often contains brown seaweed; Chinese cooking is known for dishes such as crispy fried seaweed; and, increasingly, even European and American diets are incorporating these and other types of seaweed.

Filling up If you don't fancy seaweed soup or fried seaweed, you could always try a seaweed salad, which will provide healthy doses of iodine, vitamin K and magnesium. Or perhaps some seaweed bread? According to a study at Sheffield Hallam University in England, as well as being nutritious, seaweed bread may help people lose weight.

The study found that, by fortifying bread with seaweed (*Ascophyllum nodosum*), the fibre content was enhanced, with the result that those eating it felt fuller more quickly than they did with standard bread. In a trial, overweight men ate the seaweed bread for breakfast, toasted and topped with scrambled eggs. Compared to men who had the same breakfast served on wholemeal bread, participants said they felt less hungry and subsequently ate less at lunch and dinner that day.

Salt substitute In another study at Sheffield Hallam University, seaweed granules made from Arctic wrack seaweed, found in the North Sea, were used as a substitute for salt in baked goods, and tests showed that consumers could not detect any difference in taste. This has led to proposals that seaweed granules be used instead of salt in a range of processed foods. Seaweed granules are considered healthier because their sodium level is just 3.5 per cent compared with approximately 40 per cent in the salt that is commonly used by the food industry. Seaweed granules are available online and from some health food stores.

Wrapping up If seaweed soups, salads and bread are not your thing, you could always try a wrap. No, not a lunchtime snack, but the process of coating your skin with seaweed paste. With some such treatments, the entire body is covered with the paste, encased in cling film and left to sweat out impurities for an hour. By all accounts, this leaves your skin firmer and smoother – although the smell of seaweed has a tendency to linger!

The iodine-rich seaweed wrap is thought to stimulate the body's metabolism. Nutrients from the algae are absorbed into the skin, and toxins are eliminated. The process of washing off the wrap removes dead skin cells and draws any remaining toxins to the surface. The heat generated by the wrap is claimed to redistribute fat deposits, which may account for the smoother appearance of the skin and reduced cellulite.

To try this out in a more limited way, you can make a seaweed face mask (see below left), which is said to similarly smoothe, tone and moisturise the skin. Ready-made masks are also available.

Finally, you may wonder where all this super seaweed is coming from, given the strong demand for it as a food, beauty treatment and medicine. Fortunately, on a planet two-thirds covered by water, brown algae are abundant, though certain species, such as Australia's giant kelp, have been classified as endangered.

SEAWEED FACE MASK

Buy some dried sheets of wakame or nori (available from health food stores). Grind the sheets into a powder. Mix 1 tablespoon of powder with 1 tablespoon of warm water to make a paste. Add either 1 teaspoon of aloe vera gel or 1 teaspoon of honey, or both. Smoothe the paste across your face, leave for 20 minutes, then rinse off. For best results, use twice a week.

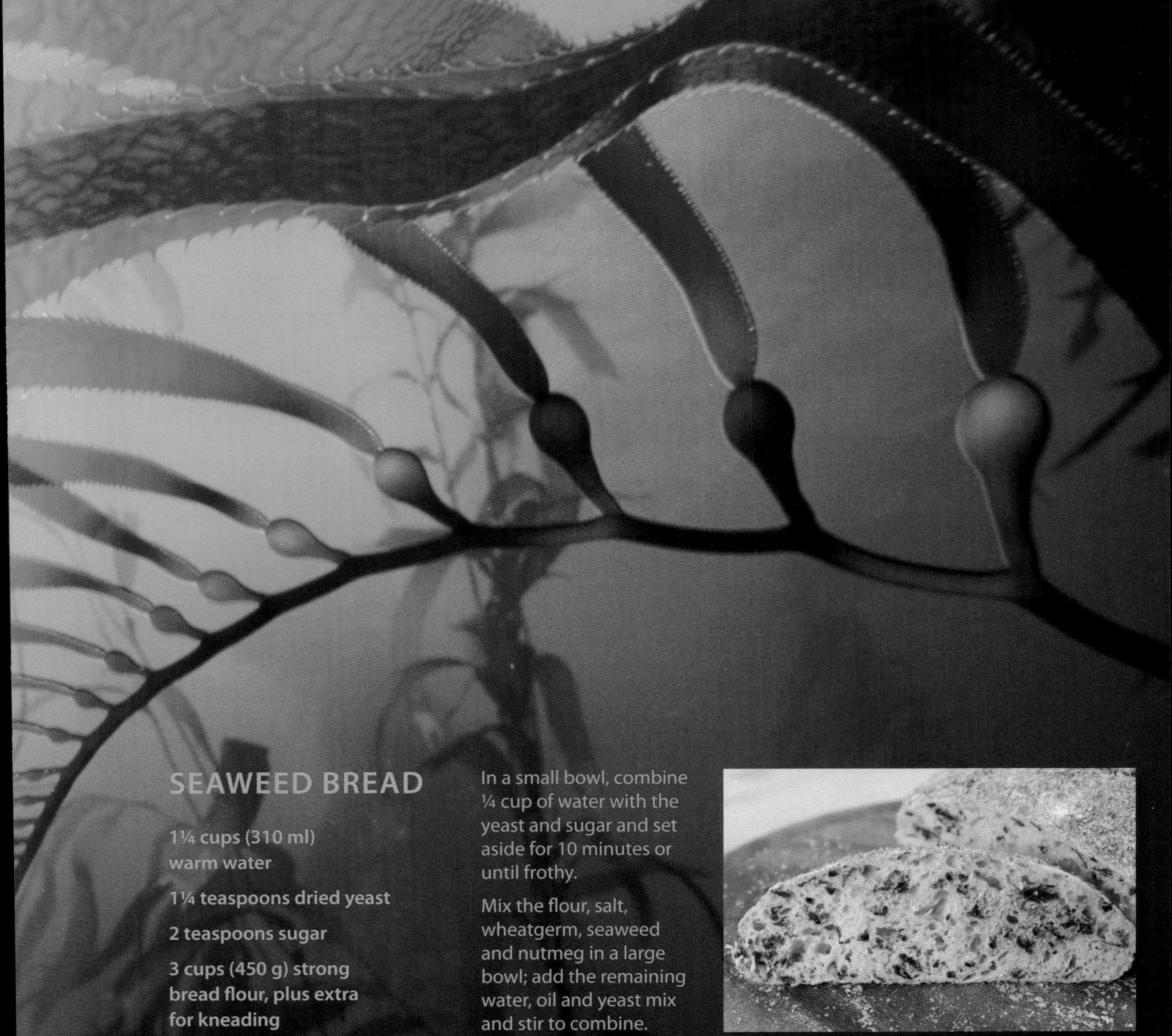

SEAWEED BREAD

1¼ cups (310 ml) warm water

1¼ teaspoons dried yeast

2 teaspoons sugar

3 cups (450 g) strong bread flour, plus extra for kneading

1 teaspoon salt

3 tablespoons wheatgerm

150 g (5 oz) rehydrated seaweed (wakame or similar), drained and chopped

¼ teaspoon ground nutmeg

3 teaspoons sunflower oil

In a small bowl, combine ¼ cup of water with the yeast and sugar and set aside for 10 minutes or until frothy.

Mix the flour, salt, wheatgerm, seaweed and nutmeg in a large bowl; add the remaining water, oil and yeast mix and stir to combine.

Turn the dough onto a lightly floured surface and knead until smooth and springing back when pressed. Place in a large, oiled bowl then cover and set aside in a warm place until doubled in size (1½–2 hours).

Next, turn the dough onto a lightly floured surface, gently knead two or three times, place in an oiled loaf tin (6-cup capacity) and set aside until risen (45–60 minutes).

Preheat your oven to 180°C (350°F/Gas 4) and then bake for 45 minutes.

ACTINOBACTERIA

Actinobacteria

MEDICAL BENEFITS ◆ Treatment for tuberculosis, various cancers, bacterial infections of the skin, ear and eyes ◆ May improve mental alertness

Especially abundant in the soil beneath your feet, actinobacteria have provided a range of medicines that have saved millions of lives in recent times.

A single teaspoon of soil contains billions of bacteria. The species present will depend on the level of moisture, the temperature and the availability of food, but the dominant ones will be those bacteria with a survival advantage. Part of this competitive advantage is conferred by the release of natural antibiotics produced as a defence against other bacteria. These natural antibiotics have made soil bacteria the focus of much research and, in turn, the source of some of the world's most widely used medications.

Actinobacteria are among the most abundant and best-known soil bacteria. Though you may not be aware of it, you are likely to be familiar with their distinctive scent, which is especially strong in woods after heavy rain. Actinobacteria produce spores as the soil dries, then, when rainfall hits the soil, the spores are kicked up into the air, creating a strong, sweet smell. It's also likely that you have encountered medicines derived from actinobacteria, as they include some of the most widely used antibiotics.

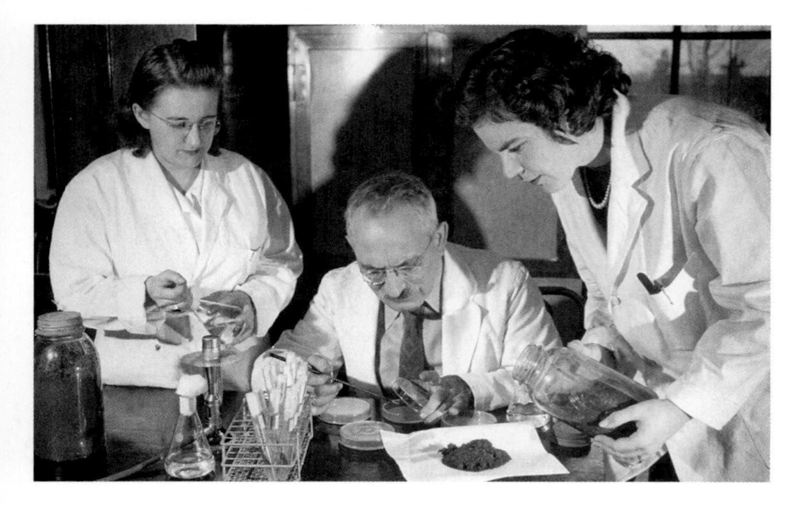

Pioneering microbiologist Selman Waksman is seen here in his laboratory.

Digging for drugs The antibiotic properties of actinobacteria were first identified by a Ukrainian-American biochemist, Selman Waksman, working at Rutgers University in New Jersey in the early twentieth century. There he studied bacteria in culture samples from different soil layers. He noticed that actinobacteria appeared to compete for nutrients in the soil by making compounds that destroyed other bacteria, and this prompted him to test whether any of these substances might also work against bacterial infections in humans.

In 1940, Waksman and his colleagues at Rutgers isolated the antibiotic actinomycin from actinobacteria of the genus *Streptomyces*. They found it possessed both bacteriostatic properties (that is, it stops bacteria reproducing) and bactericidal properties (it kills bacteria). Waksman and his team subsequently went further and separated out two forms of actinomycin, using petroleum ether: the orange-red coloured actinomycin A and the colourless actinomycin B. Actinomycin A demonstrated strong bacteriostatic and bactericidal properties, whereas actinomycin B displayed only bactericidal characteristics.

Actinomycin B ultimately proved to be too toxic for use in humans; however, actinomycin A, which is active against most bacteria as well as some fungi, was developed as an antibiotic drug, approved by the US Food and Drug Administration in 1964, and released onto the market with the trade name Cosmegen. Waksman received the 1952 Nobel Prize in Physiology or Medicine for the discovery of actinomycin and went on to discover a further 21 antibiotic compounds before his retirement in 1958, including neomycin (from the actinobacterium *Streptomyces fradiae*), another widely used drug.

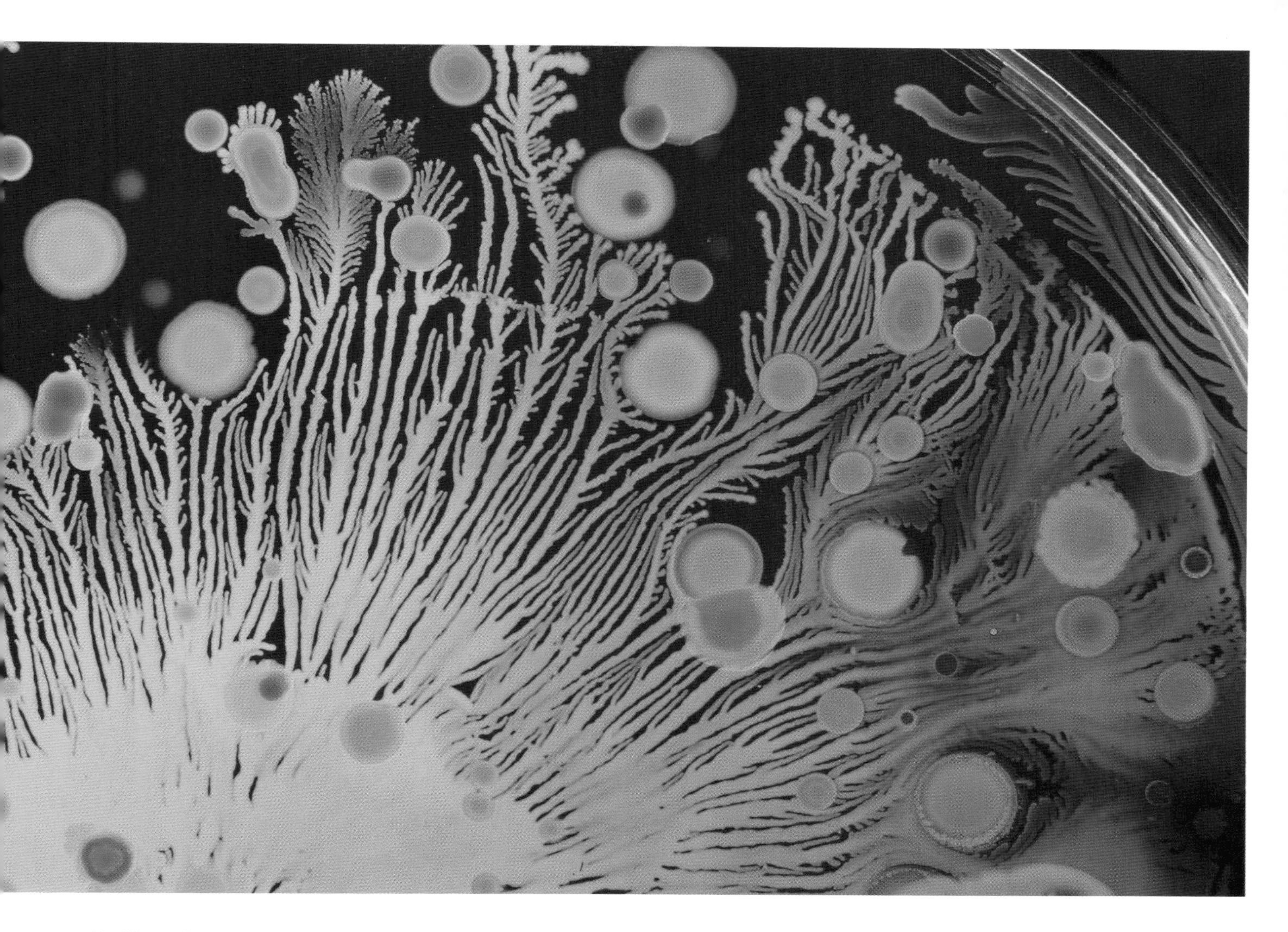

Rolling them out Waksman's research ambitions were matched by those of another American scientist, Albert Schatz, who, while working at a US hospital during World War II, witnessed the suffering of soldiers with tuberculosis (TB). Schatz's experience encouraged him to search for an alternative antibiotic to penicillin, which had failed to work in many patients with infections, like TB, that had developed resistance to the drug.

Here, too, actinobacteria looked promising. In 1943, when he was 23, working as a graduate student in Waksman's laboratory at Rutgers, Schatz isolated the antibiotic streptomycin from the actinobacterium *Streptomyces griseus*. It became the first effective treatment for TB, and was initially produced on a large scale by the pharmaceutical company, Merck & Co.

ORIGIN Worldwide
PART USED Metabolic by-products of the bacteria

Viewed up close, cultured samples of actinobacteria reveal branching filaments similar to the growth patterns of fungi.

in CLOSE-UP

The antibiotics developed from soil bacteria work by disrupting the reproductive activity of other bacteria that infect our cells. As a chemotherapy drug for cancer treatment, actinomycin works by damaging the DNA (genetic material) of cancer cells. After DNA damage, a cell has difficulty reproducing and that prevents the cancer growing. Streptomycin works slightly differently: it disrupts the production of new proteins by harmful bacteria, but not the production of proteins in human cells.

Gold standards Together, actinomycin, neomycin and streptomycin came to be seen as the gold standards of antibiotic treatment and are still major mainstream drugs today. Actinomycin is used to treat various cancers, including pregnancy-related tumours, a kidney cancer called Wilms' tumour, a cancer related to skeletal muscle cells, a cancer of bone or soft tissues called Ewing's sarcoma, testicular cancer and melanoma.

Neomycin is commonly used as an ointment or cream, to treat bacterial infections of the skin, ear and eye, and is also used in many vaccines to prevent bacterial contamination during the manufacturing process. By killing bacteria in the intestinal tract, it keeps ammonia levels low and prevents hepatic encephalopathy (brain damage due to the liver failing to remove toxins from foods), so it is often administered prior to surgery on the intestines.

Streptomycin is still used for TB but usually only if other drugs fail or in combination with other anti-TB medications; however, it is also employed for a wide range of other infections.

Vital defences Other early antibiotics derived from actinobacteria include vancomycin, isolated in 1956 from actinobacteria in a soil sample collected in a Borneo jungle. Due to its powerful action, it is currently used as a last line of defence against bacteria that have become resistant to other antibiotics – though in the past few years there have been worrying signs of resistance to vancomycin, too.

Quinupristin-dalfopristin, known under the brand name Synercid, is a combination of two antibiotics derived from the actino-bacterium *Streptomyces pristinaespiralis*. It is used to treat life-threatening staphylococcal infections. Extracted from the actinobacterium *Streptomyces venezuelae* and first released onto the market in 1949, Chloramphenicol became the first synthetically produced antibiotic. It works against a broad range of bacterial infections and is frequently used in the developing world because it is inexpensive.

Brain boosters? In addition to their antibiotic effects, actinobacteria might also have other benefits. A 2010 study showed that if mice ate actinobacteria they seemed to become smarter. Scientists at The Sage Colleges in Troy, New York State, in the United States, gave mice peanut butter laced with *Mycobacterium vaccae* and compared the activity of those mice to that of others given peanut butter alone. They found that the mice that had consumed the actino-bacteria ran through a maze twice as fast as the other mice. This reaction continued for 18 further trials over the next 6 weeks.

The researchers also found that the bacteria triggered a response from the immune systems of the mice, which in turn activated clusters of neurones (nerve cells) in the brainstem known as the dorsal raphe nuclei. These connect to areas of the brain involved in mood, behaviour and cognitive function – hence the improved mental performance.

A rich seam

Actinobacteria have yielded many other antibiotics that are used for well-known diseases. These include tetracycline and erythromycin to treat respiratory infections, and the rifamycins for tuberculosis and leprosy. Another, rapamycin, is used to suppress the immune system and help prevent rejection of organ transplants. One of the major advantages of actinobacteria antibiotics is that they generally do not affect human cells and therefore have few serious side effects.

After World War II, the United States sent streptomycin to Allied nations in Europe.

PROBIOTICS

Bifidobacterium spp.,
Lactobacillus spp.,
Saccharomyces boulardii

MEDICAL BENEFITS ◆ May help prevent and treat diarrhoea, antibiotic-associated diarrhoea, inflammatory bowel disease, eczema, dermatitis, female urinary tract infections

Bacteria are often considered harmful and generally best avoided. Yet probiotics, which are beneficial microbes, are rapidly changing our perception of the role bacteria play in our bodies.

Probiotics are microorganisms that thrive in the human gut and are thought to benefit health; the most widely known and studied are the bacteria *Bifidobacterium* and *Lactobacillus* species, and the yeast *Saccharomyces boulardii*. Our guts provide a reservoir for a large and dynamic microbe community. You need a balance of different types of good and bad microbes and it is this diverse but balanced mix of flora that maintains a healthy digestive system. Bacteria residing in the gut contribute to metabolism, absorb nutrients, help to maintain immune structure and function, and aid protection against invasion by potentially harmful foreign microbes.

Out of balance Sometimes, however, the balance shifts, often as a result of illness, changes in diet, medications or environmental factors. Then more harmful bacteria come to dominate, causing inflammation, producing pH-altering toxins and damaging membranes, which, in turn, further increases susceptibility to harmful microbes. Indeed, it's thought that this chain of events may play a part in the development of a range of conditions, including diarrhoea, gastroenteritis, inflammatory bowel disease (IBD), colon cancer and even multiple organ failure.

Increasing the quantities of probiotics, or 'friendly microbes' in the gut may help restore balance and help prevent such diseases.

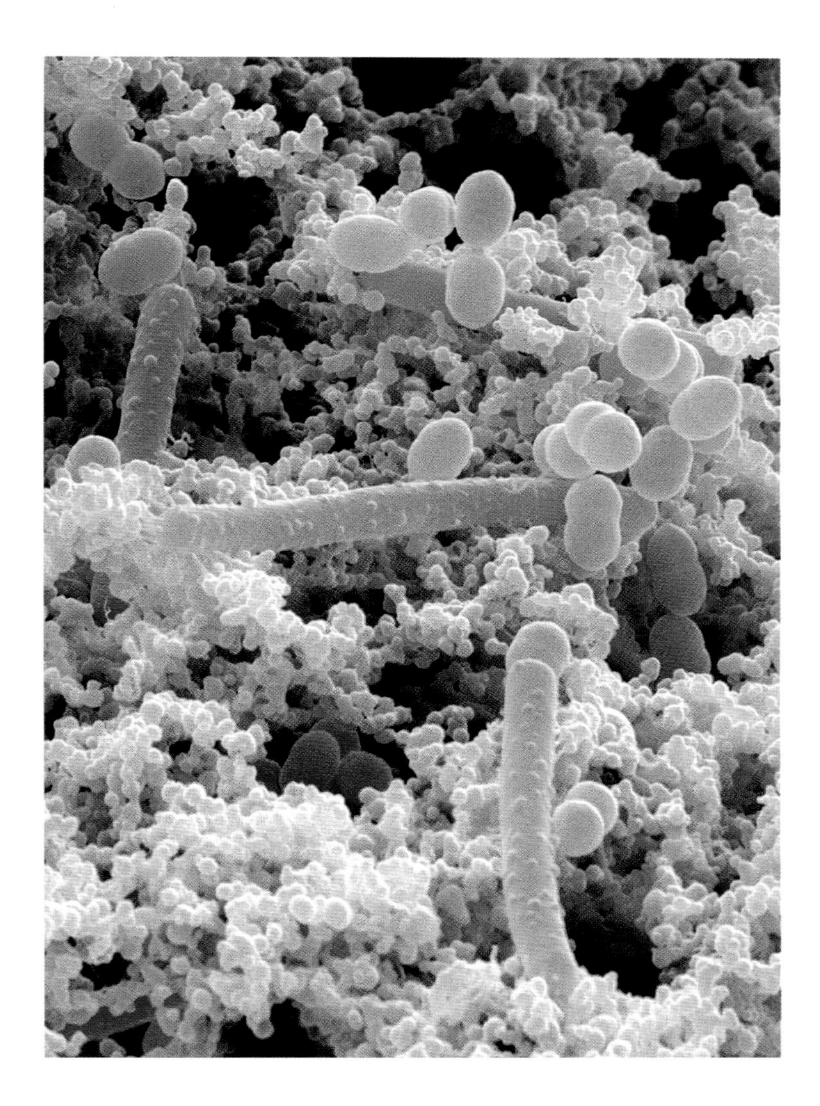

Two forms of beneficial bacteria are visible in this microscope image of yogurt: rod-shaped bacilli and spherical cocci.

Yogurts are especially rich in *Lactobacillus bulgaricus* and *Streptococcus thermophilus*.

Russian biologist Ilya Mechnikov's early 1900s research into gut bacteria inspired the later development of probiotic products.

in CLOSE-UP

Cereal, juice, frozen yogurt, granola, chocolate bars and even cookies may advertise that they contain probiotics, and an extensive array of probiotic supplements is also available in health food stores or online. However, remember that the type and quantity of probiotic microbes are important if you are using them as a possible treatment and there is no guarantee these products will contain the appropriate mix. You can try contacting the manufacturer for further information, but the best approach if you wish to use probiotics to treat or prevent illness is to consult a specialist gastroenterologist.

Consequently, health experts now encourage the consumption of additional probiotics in the form of supplements or in foods in which these microbes are naturally abundant or to which they have been added, most notably certain kinds of yogurt.

Alleviating bowel disease A wide range of probiotic products is now available, including myriad supplements and treatments. But how much benefit do they confer and what does the latest research show?

Evidence from animal studies indicates that the bacterial make-up of the gut can play a part in inflammatory bowel disease (IBD), although more research needs to confirm if this is true also for humans. If it *is* the case, then probiotics may have a beneficial effect for sufferers of IBD. Backing this up, an Italian study of 32 patients

An average adult has between 1 and 2 kg (2.2 and 4.4 lb) of bacteria in the intestine at any one time.

with Crohn's disease (a type of IBD), published in 2000, showed that those who received probiotics along with an antibiotic called aminosalicylic acid had a significantly lower recurrence of symptoms than patients not receiving probiotics. The probiotic used was *Saccharomyces boulardii*.

Probiotic treatments A comprehensive review of the use of probiotics to treat illness was published in the *Medical Journal of Australia* in 2008. It highlighted significant supporting evidence for the use of probiotics in treating acute infectious diarrhoea and preventing antibiotic-associated diarrhoea, with the microbe species *Lactobacillus rhamnosus* GG and *Saccharomyces boulardii* appearing to provide the greatest benefits.

Your intestinal tract is home to more than 100,000 billion microorganisms.

A quarter of people taking antibiotics experience diarrhoea because healthy bacteria in the gut can be killed off along with harmful ones, upsetting the balance. Several probiotics have been evaluated specifically for treating or preventing antibiotic-associated diarrhoea. A 2012 review of 82 studies found that people who took such probiotics – especially *Lactobacillus, Bifidobacterium, Saccharomyces, Streptococcus, Enterococcus* and *Bacillus* species – in combination with antibiotics were 42 per cent less likely to develop diarrhoea.

Many of the most positive findings regarding probiotics relate to the treatment of diarrhoea in children. A review published in *The Cochrane Library* in 2004 looked at more than 20 international studies of almost 2000 children and found that probiotics reduced the risk of diarrhoea and its severity by two-thirds. There is also good reliable evidence for probiotics preventing traveller's diarrhoea.

ORIGIN Worldwide
PART USED Whole bacterium

Beyond the gut While most studies of probiotics have investigated their impact on the gut, some have looked at their use in the prevention and treatment of conditions affecting other parts of the body. Studies suggest the consumption of *Lactobacillus* GG during pregnancy may help prevent eczema and dermatitis in newborns. And urinary tract infections in women have also been shown to benefit from use of certain probiotic bacteria, namely *Lactobacillus rhamnosus* GR-1 and *Lactobacillus reuteri* RC-14.

Traditional Wisdom

Fermented foods that we would term 'probiotic' today have been part of traditional diets for thousands of years. Some peoples, mainly in North Africa, ate camel dung as a treatment for dysentery (inflammation of the colon that causes diarrhoea). Scientists believe the therapeutic ingredient is a bacterium called *Bacillus subtilis*, which lives in plant material and water. In the human intestine, the dung bacteria stimulate production of beneficial bacteria, which in turn, triggers the immune system to fight the dysentery infection. Camel dung therapy was discovered during World War II by German scientists who visited North Africa to find out why their soldiers were dying of dysentery while most local people survived.

BOTULINUM BACTERIUM

Clostridium botulinum

MEDICAL BENEFITS ◆ Treatment for cervical dystonia, migraine, eyelid spasms, crossed eyes, severe underarm sweating, muscle stiffness, overactive bladder ◆ May relieve spasticity related to stroke, cerebral palsy, multiple sclerosis

A toxin from this bacterium, known by the name Botox, is widely used to create wrinkle-free skin. But this versatile microbe has even greater powers – to both heal and destroy.

The toxin produced by the bacterium known to scientists as *Clostridium botulinum* is the most lethal poison known in nature, with significant powers of paralysis. However, these paralytic properties can be harnessed for good and, used in tiny amounts, botulinum toxin can offer relief from a wide range of medical disorders that affect the body's nerves and muscles.

A force for good Long before cosmetic use (circa 1989) and beneficial medical applications, botulinum toxin was already known for less desirable associations: with botulism, a serious condition often contracted through eating contaminated food, which can lead to paralysis and even death without prompt treatment; and as a potential bioweapon that could be released into the air, causing widespread botulism. On balance, however, the toxin's benefits outweigh the potential dangers. Today it is associated with the treatment of more than 50 medical conditions, ranging from muscle spasms to migraines. Usually, it provides relief by interfering with the way nerves trigger muscle contractions.

Botulinum toxin is actually found in seven different forms, but the most commonly used in medicine is called onabotulinum toxin A. In clinical trials involving significant numbers of patients, botulinum toxin has been shown to be particularly effective in treating the involuntary and painful contraction of the neck known as

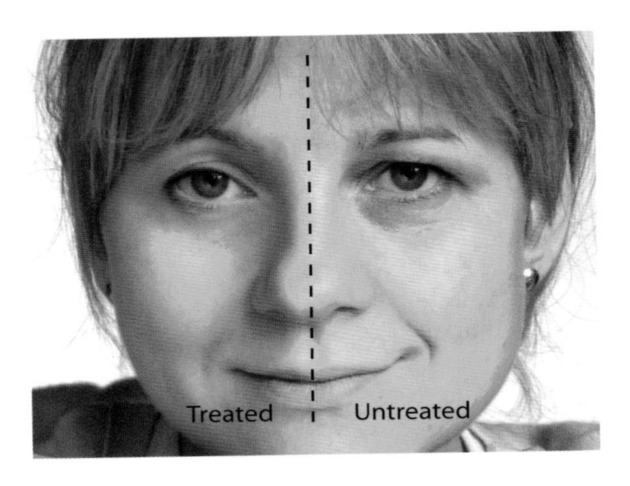

Injecting botulinum toxin beneath the skin can iron out wrinkles associated with ageing.

The availability of botulinum toxin for medical applications will depend on the country you live in, and for certain medical uses your clinician will need to be involved in research. Clinical uses approved in the United States, for example, include treating overactive bladder, excessive underarm sweating, cervical dystonia, crossed eyes, contracting or twitching of the eyelid, and spasticity in an upper limb. The recommended dose depends on the type of botulinum toxin used and the size of the muscle or gland being injected. Repeat doses are usually required, as the effect wears off after three to four months.

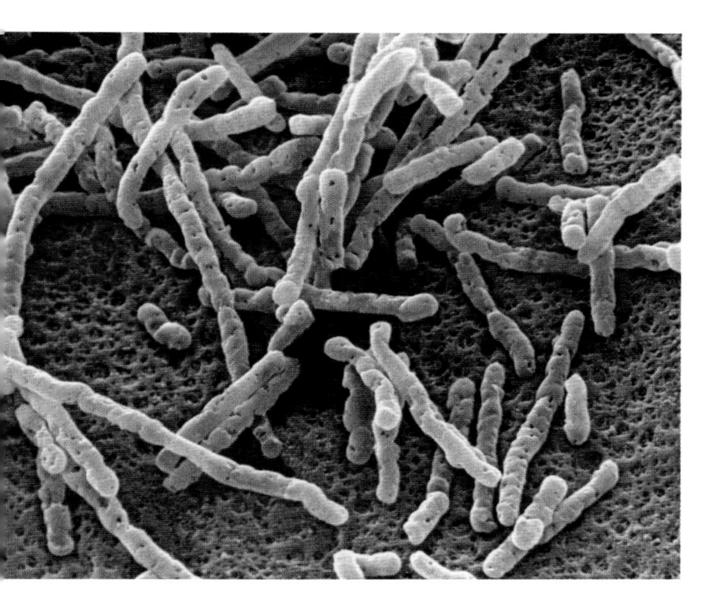

Botulinum bacteria can develop in poorly prepared or stored food, but are also present in soil and even in house dust.

cervical dystonia. In this disorder, regular botulinum toxin injections prevent the neck muscles from contracting, alleviating the twisting and pain.

Muscle relaxant Another disorder for which botulinum toxin is increasingly used is chronic migraine (chronic migraines are diagnosed if a patient experiences severe headaches on at least 15 days a month, eight of which have to be migraines). Botulinum toxin's success as a migraine therapy was discovered when Californian cosmetic surgeons noticed some of their patients, who were being treated for wrinkles, found their migraines also improved.

in CLOSE-UP

Botulinum toxin interferes with the release of a chemical called acetylcholine, which carries nerve signals from the brain to muscles and glands. In large doses, the toxin causes paralysis, but in minuscule, controlled doses it can prevent overactive muscles from contracting involuntarily and allow them to remain in a relaxed state. Similarly it can restrict gland activity – injection into the skin, for example, reduces sweat gland secretion.

Doses of botulinum toxin can help sufferers from diseases such as cerebral palsy achieve greater control of their movements.

The reasons why botulinum toxin seems to alleviate migraines are not clear, but it may be that it relaxes the head muscles, reduces blood pressure within the brain, or reduces the nerves' ability to send pain signals or other signals that lead to a migraine.

Growing evidence also points to the effectiveness of botulinum toxin injections in treating major nerve-muscle dysfunction, as seen in conditions such as multiple sclerosis, cerebral palsy, stroke, traumatic brain injury and spinal cord injury. In one trial in patients with arm spasticity due to stroke, up to five treatments with botulinum toxin A significantly improved muscle tone, lessened disability, and improved patients' quality of life.

ORIGIN Worldwide
PART USED Nerve toxin produced by the bacterium

CYANOBACTERIA

Cyanobacteria

MEDICAL BENEFITS ◆ Possible protection against sunburn and skin cancers ◆ Potential treatment for leukaemia and lung, renal, colon and prostate cancers

Scientists are looking to harness substances produced by these common bacteria to create more convenient and protective forms of sunscreen and, perhaps, new drugs to treat a range of cancers.

Skin cancers, particularly the type known as melanoma, account for a large number of deaths worldwide every year. Sun lotions, creams and sprays provide good protection if used properly, but they are messy and need to be reapplied regularly to be fully effective. It would be so much easier and more reliable if we could pop a pill that would prevent sunburn – as well as the skin cancers caused by it. Now scientists in the United States, United Kingdom, Australia and Sweden are making progress towards finding just such a solution, by studying how cyanobacteria living on coral reefs protect themselves from the sun.

Turning light into energy Because they use photosynthesis to obtain energy in the same way as algae, cyanobacteria are often referred to as blue-green algae, but they are in fact a group of bacteria. They live in an extremely broad range of habitats, including seawater, fresh water, soil and even rock. You may have seen them as a blue-green coloured scum on the surface of seawater or fresh water; in such locations they can grow rapidly when nutrients are plentiful. Some such blooms are toxic to animals and humans.

To produce energy by photosynthesis, cyanobacteria need to be consistently exposed to sunlight, so in seawater they usually inhabit areas close to the surface, such as coral reefs. This means that they are constantly subject to harmful types of ultraviolet rays, notably UVA and UVB radiation. However, cyanobacteria existed for billions of years prior to Earth forming an oxygen-rich atmosphere that blocks most ultraviolet light, so they had a long, long time to evolve advanced protective mechanisms. Upon exposure to ultraviolet rays, cyanobacteria produce a range of chemical compounds that

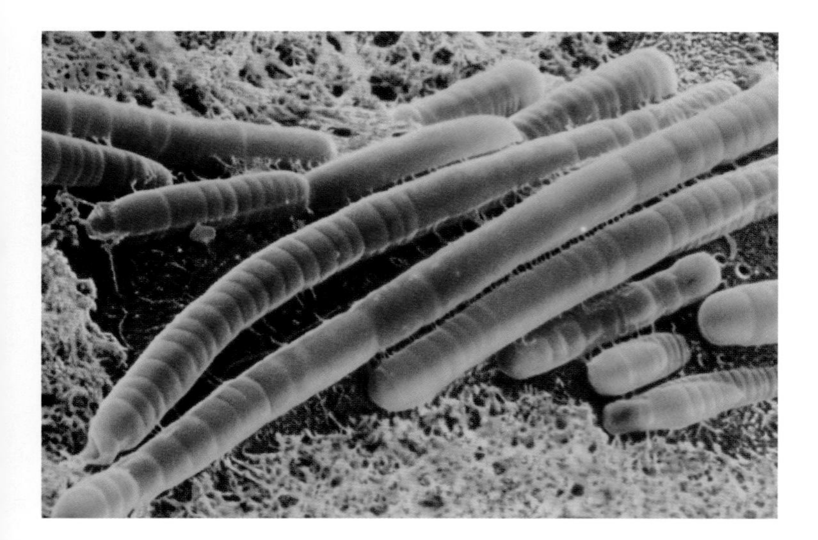

As they develop, cyanobacteria cells form long strands known as trichomes.

Bacterial bonuses

Other compounds made by cyanobacteria hold promise, too. Substances from the cyanobacterium *Lyngbya majuscula*, which lives in tropical seas, have been shown to have anticancer effects: compounds called aurilides B and C, for example, collected from Papua New Guinea, were active against leukaemia, and lung, renal and prostate cancer cells. Another compound called largazole, isolated from *Symploca* cyanobacteria, found off the coast of Florida, was demonstrated to be active against colon cancer cells in mice and in breast cancer cells in the laboratory. Largazole has also been found to stimulate production of bone cells, and is being evaluated as a therapy in osteoporosis.

Cyanobacteria add their blue-green hues to hot springs such as this one in Yellowstone National Park in the United States.

shield them from the harmful effects of the sun and, in turn, protect the coral or any other living structure that the bacteria inhabit.

On the bright side Current scientific studies are moving closer to identifying the chemicals that provide protection. Researchers from King's College, London, working on Australia's Great Barrier Reef, have isolated sun-shielding compounds produced by cyanobacteria living in a tropical coral called *Acropora microphthalma*. In the United States, researchers at Harvard Medical School have deciphered the proteins responsible for making the natural sunscreens produced by certain cyanobacteria; they found the proteins consisted of compounds called mycosporines and mycosporine-like amino acids (MAAs), produced in response to UVB rays. This knowledge could enable scientists to make the molecules synthetically and possibly develop a sunscreen pill. Meanwhile in Sweden, scientists have also identified another class of natural sunscreen compound produced by cyanobacteria, a pigment called scytonemin, which blocks UVA light. The researchers noted that a sunscreen made from scytonemin, being a natural product, could be especially beneficial for people who are allergic to chemical-based lotions.

OTHER NAME Blue-green algae
ORIGIN Worldwide
PARTS USED Substances made by the bacteria

You can't yet buy any sunscreens derived from cyanobacteria compounds, but they may not be too far off. The idea of a sunscreen pill is being pursued and King's College, London, recently entered into an agreement with skincare company Aethic to develop a sunscreen based on compounds from cyanobacteria. That means clinical trials are likely to take place in the next few years.

SALMONELLA

Salmonella spp.

MEDICAL BENEFITS ◆ Potential treatment for cancers of the gut and skin

The bacteria commonly called salmonella might be best known for causing food poisoning, but, perhaps surprisingly, they also show promise as a treatment for certain types of cancer.

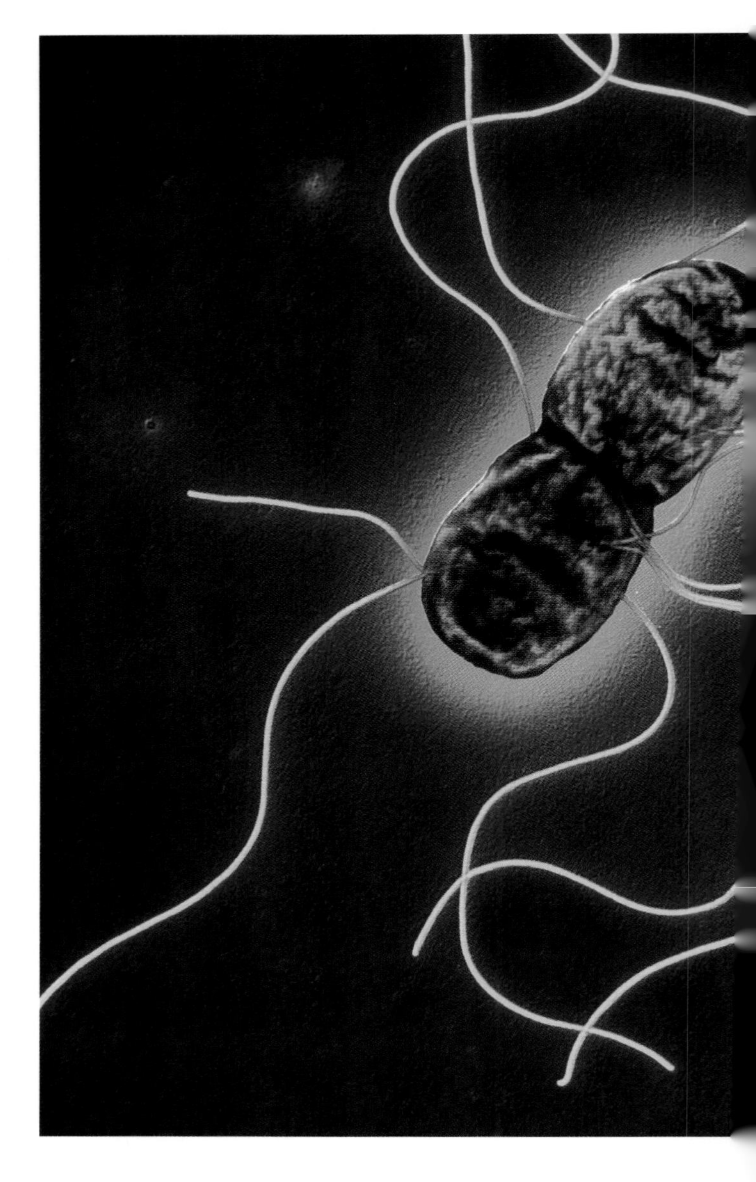

One particular type of salmonella bacteria called *Salmonella enterica* Typhimurium, which causes gastroenteritis in humans, is of special interest to scientists with respect to fighting cancer and possibly improving patient survival. Although it's early days, it's thought that research into its effects could even lead to a new human vaccine for various cancers.

Catching a cure Salmonella bacteria live in the gut of infected humans and animals, as well as in contaminated water and foods such as eggs, meat and poultry. The bacteria are usually transferred between different hosts as a result of poor personal hygiene and frequently cause illness.

However, scientists have known for some time that cancer sufferers may actually experience improvements in their condition after exposure to an infection. An Austrian report from the 1860s noted that a hospital patient with a large tumour found his cancer shrank after he contracted an infection from another patient in a neighbouring bed. Paradoxically, his tumour disappeared but he died of the infection.

Treatment of cancer using salmonella bacteria is only available under the auspices of a clinical trial. One is currently being conducted at the Masonic Cancer Center at the University of Minnesota, in the United States; check the clinic's website for the latest developments: www.cancer.umn.edu/cancerinfo/trials.html.

Triggering destruction Now, nearly 150 years later, scientists are deliberately infecting cancer patients with salmonella to see if the bacteria will shrink their tumours. They are using a weakened form of the bacterium designed to avoid adverse effects on healthy cells while still triggering cancer-cell destruction.

In 2010, researchers at the European Institute of Oncology in Milan and the University of Minnesota Masonic Cancer Center in the United States injected *Salmonella* Typhimurium into mouse tumours and found that the tumours shrank; a similar result was recorded when the bacterium was tested in cancer cells from humans. Human trials are now being conducted.

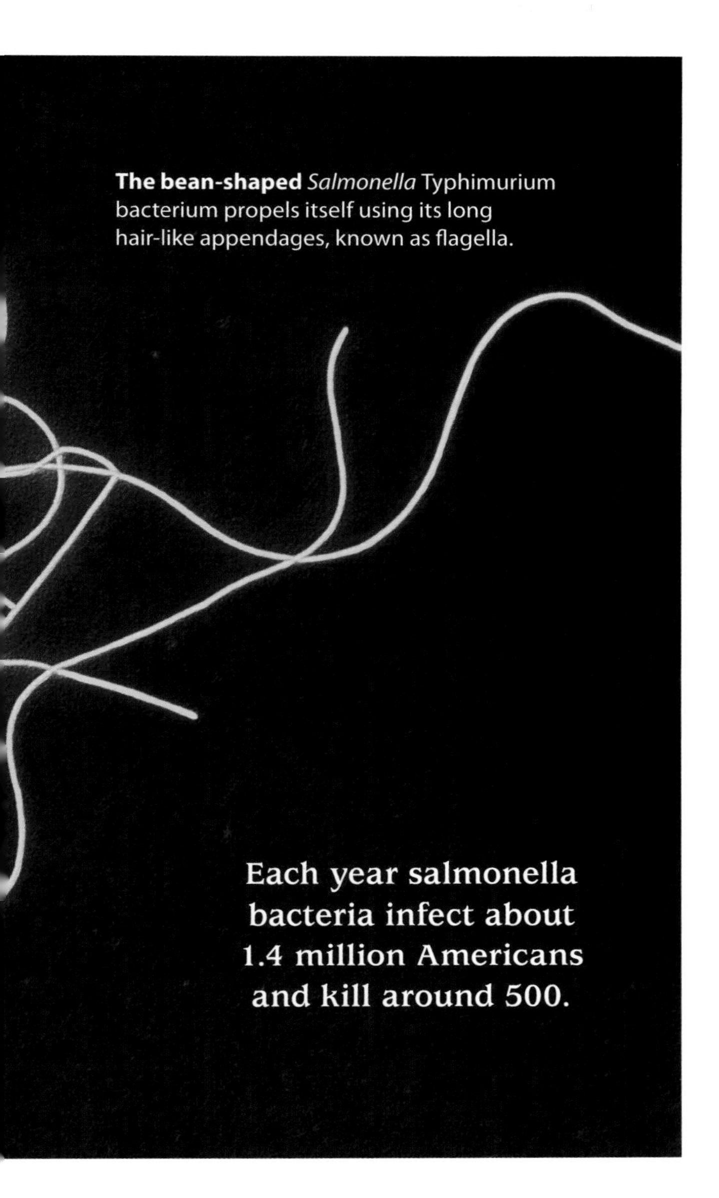

The bean-shaped *Salmonella* Typhimurium bacterium propels itself using its long hair-like appendages, known as flagella.

Each year salmonella bacteria infect about 1.4 million Americans and kill around 500.

Medical researchers use foods such as eggs to cultivate a range of salmonella bacteria in the laboratory.

Anticancer vaccination In the studies so far, researchers have used cancer cells from melanoma, which is one of the deadliest forms of skin cancer, but they believe that salmonella bacteria could potentially be used to treat other forms of cancer, too. These include cancer of the liver, spleen and colon, which are all located in the area that salmonella bacteria naturally migrate to once inside the human body.

Recently, the University of Minnesota took its use of salmonella against cancer further and launched a clinical trial using a new 'weaponised' form of the bacteria against cancers of the gut. In effect, this means the bacteria have been genetically engineered to carry a type of 'messenger protein' called interleukin-2. The human immune system contains interleukin-2, which is important for kick-starting production of T-cells and other disease-fighting cells, and in the case of engineered salmonella the interleukin-2 triggers production of these agents against the cancer cells. The overall effect is a double whammy: the salmonella both directly targets the tumour cells and carries an agent that spurs the body's immune system into attack mode.

Eventually, the researchers hope to develop a salmonella vaccine, which would trigger a cancer patient's immune system to attack the cancer cells. Known as immunotherapy, this type of approach is relatively new in the field of cancer treatment. If approved, it could also be cheaper and have fewer side effects than current therapies.

ORIGIN Contaminated food, humans and animals
PART USED Whole bacterium (modified)

in CLOSE-UP

The way salmonella bacteria kill tumour cells is fascinating. Tumour cells are clever. Effectively, they 'hide' from the body's immune system so that they are not destroyed by it but left to grow uncontrollably. However, when tumour cells are infected with salmonella, the immune system recognises them as part of the infection and attacks and eliminates them.

HARNESSING VIRUSES

We think of viruses as a cause of illness. But scientists have recently been looking at ways to employ the destructive capabilities of viruses against bacteria that make us sick.

One of the most promising strategies currently being investigated is the use of a particular category of viruses called bacteriophages. These viruses penetrate bacteria, and, once inside, hijack the bacteria's cellular machinery to make multiple copies of themselves. This, in turn, kills their host, and releases more bacteriophages to infect yet other bacteria.

Bacteria eaters The term 'bacteriophages' means 'bacteria eaters' and comes from the Greek *phago*, meaning 'to eat' or 'to devour'. Bacteriophages were first identified by British bacteriologist Frederick Twort in 1915 and, independently, by Canadian microbiologist Félix d'Herelle in 1917. The most extensive research was, however, conducted much later, in the 1980s and 1990s, in Russia and Eastern Europe.

Bacteriophages are often found in the soil and in seawater, which both have a rich diversity of bacteria. Once located, they are isolated then purified and grown in sufficient quantity for use in treatments. They can be given orally or applied topically on infected wounds and other surfaces, and are sometimes used during surgical procedures. A review of scientific research published between 1966 and 1996 found that the overall reported success rate for bacteriophage therapy was between 80 and 95 per cent.

Frederick Twort

Félix d'Herelle

FOOD SAFETY

While no medical applications of bacteriophages have yet reached fruition, these tiny assassins are already being employed in other ways to benefit health. In 2006, for example, the US Food and Drug Administration granted approval for a bacteriophage product that is sprayed onto meats to kill the bacterium *Listeria monocytogenes*.

Search and destroy Much recent interest in this work was prompted by the issue of antibiotic resistance. Using bacteriophages may provide an alternative to some antibiotics that now commonly trigger resistance, and a number of medical applications are being investigated.

Researchers and burns specialists at hospitals in Bristol and Bath, in the United Kingdom, aim to introduce bacteriophages into burns infections using advanced dressings. These dressings will be covered with 'nanocapsules' used to contain and stabilise the bacteriophages. Ultimately, the researchers hope to produce a dressing that will only release bacteriophages into a wound when it is infected.

In another study, scientists at the Teagasc Food Research Centre in County Cork, Ireland, have shown in laboratory models how bacteriophages can attack the lung infection *Pseudomonas aeruginosa*, which is a threat to patients with cystic fibrosis, who are particularly susceptible to bacteria. The scientists hope to start trials in patients with cystic fibrosis soon.

And scientists at the University of Leeds in the United Kingdom hope to deploy bacteriophages against a troublesome and very common skin condition, acne. They have deciphered the genetic sequence of the bacteriophage PA6, which infects *Propionibacterium acnes*, the bacterium that causes most acne, taking the first step towards developing a bacteriophage therapy.

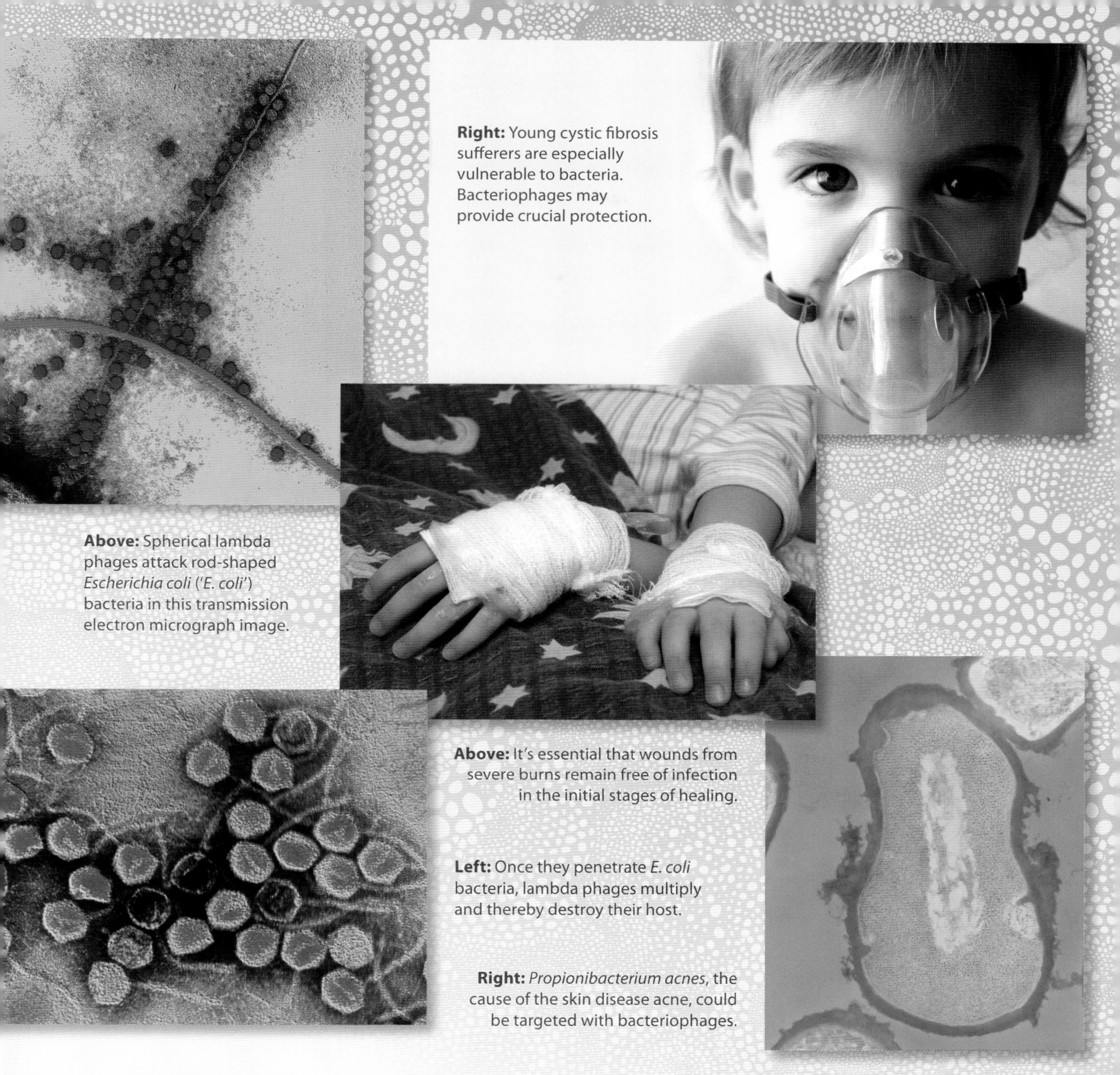

Right: Young cystic fibrosis sufferers are especially vulnerable to bacteria. Bacteriophages may provide crucial protection.

Above: Spherical lambda phages attack rod-shaped *Escherichia coli* ('*E. coli*') bacteria in this transmission electron micrograph image.

Above: It's essential that wounds from severe burns remain free of infection in the initial stages of healing.

Left: Once they penetrate *E. coli* bacteria, lambda phages multiply and thereby destroy their host.

Right: *Propionibacterium acnes*, the cause of the skin disease acne, could be targeted with bacteriophages.

A broad alliance Other kinds of viruses are also being employed in the fight against illness. Scientists have found that the reovirus, which usually causes mild colds or stomach upsets, can have antitumour properties when injected into the bloodstream. It works partly by stimulating the immune system into attacking the tumour and also provides a form of chemotherapy by directly killing cancer cells. To date, patient trials look promising, according to the researchers at the Institute of Cancer Research in London.

Another approach to using viruses to prevent cancers is that of vaccination against viruses that may cause cancers. Vaccines for hepatitis B virus, associated with liver cancer, and human papillomavirus, associated with cervical cancer, are already available and in widespread use. Scientists are also looking at the possibility of reprogramming viruses to attack cancer cells directly, an approach called virotherapy. One such therapy, OncoVEX GM-CSF, is now in phase III (large-scale) clinical trials.

STREPTOCOCCUS BACTERIA

Streptococcus salivarius

MEDICAL BENEFITS ◆ Potential preventative treatment for tooth decay, bad breath, upper airways infections

Brushing, flossing and mouthwash are the mainstays of oral hygiene. But a bacterium called *Streptococcus salivarius* may offer another strategy for protecting against cavities, diseases and infections.

As adults we all have a mixture of good and bad bacteria in our mouths. Together they form dental plaque, and some of the bad bacteria are responsible for tooth decay and bad breath. Moreover, these bacteria may also play a role in other diseases. According to immunologist Trevor Marshall from Murdoch University, Western Australia, molecules produced by bacteria disturb the human body's antimicrobial defences. In response, the immune system increases production of certain genes linked to chronic diseases such as heart disease and diabetes, which then drives the illness.

Regular brushing helps minimise bacteria and therefore the build-up of dental plaque.

Streptococcus salivarius is the first bacterium to grow inside a baby's mouth and upper airways; indeed, during the first 24 hours of life, oral streptococci bacteria comprise between 60 and 90 per cent of plaque in the mouth. Fortunately, *S. salivarius* is one of the good bacteria that, throughout our lives, help keep the bad ones in check. By understanding how this abundant bacterium does this, scientists hope to develop new treatments in oral health.

Natural antibiotics Research shows that the mouths of individuals who are less prone to dental problems are more likely to contain a particular type, or strain, of *S. salivarius*. This strain produces two natural antibiotics, or bacteriocin-like inhibitory substances (BLISs), called salivaricin A and salivaricin B. In various studies, notably a 2012 report from the University of Otago, New Zealand, these have been shown to reduce bacterial infections

Bacterial roll call

Several hundred species of bacteria are present in the human oral cavity. A major research program based at the Forsyth Institute in Boston, the Human Oral Microbiome Database (HOMD), aims to provide the scientific community with comprehensive information on a large number of these bacteria. Effectively, HOMD will classify the bacteria and link DNA sequence data with other characteristics of the species. Genomic and other genetic information will also be added to the database.

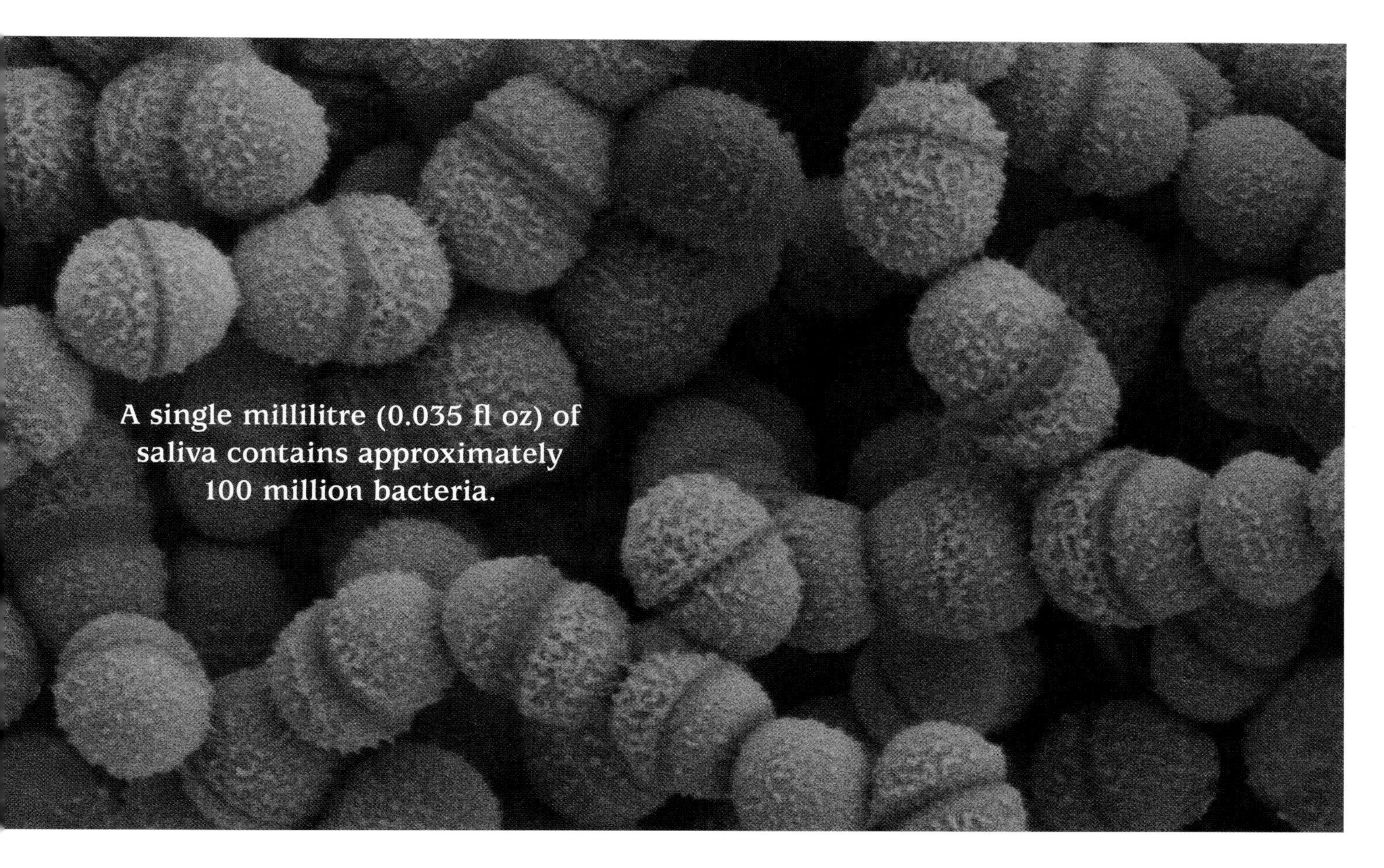

Spherical in shape, *Streptococcus salivarius* bacteria can multiply rapidly in the body.

of the oral cavity, as well as bad breath and infections of the upper airways. A study published in the journal *Future Microbiology* in 2009 reported that people with high levels of the same strain of *S. salivarius* are, furthermore, less prone to strep throat infections caused by *S. pyogenes*.

In 2011, infectious disease specialists from Japan published a laboratory-based study showing that *S. salivarius* also produces enzymes (proteins that catalyse chemical reactions) that help reduce the formation of layers of plaque made by another oral bacterium, *S. mutans*. The scientists identified one of these enzymes and named it exo-beta-d-fructosidase (FruA). The same scientists have also found that a commercial form of FruA, made by the bacterium *Aspergillus niger*, was as effective as FruA produced by *S. salivarius* at inhibiting the build-up of plaque.

And there could even be another benefit: a 2005 study from the State University of New York found that *S. salivarius* prevented entry of the yeast *Candida albicans*, which is known to cause oral thrush, into the mucous membranes of the mouth.

ORIGIN Worldwide
PART USED Substance produced by the bacteria

A handful of companies make lozenges containing *S. salivarius* to help alleviate bad breath and tooth decay, and to support good oral and throat health, and many of these products can be purchased online. Trials of other medical applications are continuing, notably at Teikyo University Institute of Medical Mycology, Tokyo, Japan, and BLIS Technologies at the University of Otago, Dunedin, New Zealand.

Biotechnology researchers in Kenya

PART FOUR

REFERENCE

STOP PRESS

Barely a week goes by without the publication of at least one new study of the potential medical benefits of natural substances. These are some of the most intriguing recent reports from the front lines of research.

AFRICAN SPINY MICE

Acomys kempi, A. percivali

In 2012, reports appeared in the scientific literature of mammals that can regrow large areas of skin, just as some lizards can regrow tails. The phenomenon has been observed in two species of African spiny mice, and it has potentially important implications for the treatment of serious wounds in humans.

Usually mammals, including normal laboratory rodents, regrow scar tissue when skin wounds heal. But when the spiny mice *Acomys kempi* and *A. percivali* lose their skin, it regenerates complete with new hair follicles, sweat glands, fur and cartilage. This sort of regenerative capability is well known in invertebrates such as crustaceans and insects, in some reptiles and in axolotls (see p. 185). But the phenomenon had not been reported before in mammals, until researchers from the University of Florida in Gainesville brought it to the world's attention.

African spiny mice have brittle skin that tears readily, allowing them to make a break for it when grabbed by a potential predator. They can lose more than half of their skin, regenerate it and survive – with, apparently, no ill effects. Scientists would now like to explore the genetic and molecular controls underpinning the phenomenon. One day, it might be possible to activate genes in humans that could trigger similar regrowth.

CARIBBEAN SEA ANEMONE

Stichodactyla helianthus

Human testing recently began on a new drug treatment for the debilitating symptoms of multiple sclerosis (MS). The promising new pharmaceutical is based on a synthetic version of a compound called ShK, which was isolated during the mid-1990s from the venom of the Caribbean sea anemone, *Stichodactyla helianthus*. It entered phase 1 trials in the Netherlands in 2012.

In patients with MS, nerves are attacked by cells within the body's immune system known as T-cells, often leading to paralysis. ShK interferes in a very precise and specific way with T-cell function. Because of this, it offers the opportunity to treat MS by disabling one problematic part of the immune system without affecting other components.

Relatives of corals and jellyfish, sea anemones are perhaps best known for their symbiotic relationships with clownfish, made famous by the children's animated movie *Finding Nemo*. Their venom is contained in stings in tentacles used for both capturing prey and protecting against predators.

The new drug has been developed as a result of a collaboration between researchers at Australia's Monash University and the University of California, Irvine, in the United States.

COFFEE

Coffea spp.

There was reassuring news in 2012 for anyone worried about an addiction to a morning espresso or latte: more evidence that caffeine is good for brain health. Researchers from the universities of South Florida and Miami, both in the United States, reported on a study they say provides the first direct evidence that coffee

MOON JELLY

Aurelia aurita

Scientists have used the form and function of a common jellyfish as inspiration to build a simple muscular pump. It's an achievement that's been applauded as an early step in a process that could one day lead to new types of self-powered pacemakers for the heart.

Bioengineers from Harvard University and the California Institute of Technology revealed the breakthrough in 2012, when they unveiled a 'robot' they dubbed a 'medusoid', an artificial, free-swimming marine creature – originally based on the simple moon jelly *Aurelia aurita* – using heart muscle cells from a rat and a sheet of silicon.

In a process known as 'reverse engineering', the complicated exercise created an independently moving type of 'robot', based on the form and function of a rhythmically pulsing, real-life organism. 'Morphologically, we've built a jellyfish. Functionally, we've built a jellyfish. Genetically, this thing is a rat', explained Harvard biophysicist Kit Parker. It's speculated that this line of research might one day, in the distant future, provide a way to build entire new human organs.

might reduce the risk of dementia, or at least delay its onset.

Over two to four years, the study followed 124 people aged 65 to 88 who had mild memory loss. Usually about 18 people in such a group could be expected to go on to develop Alzheimer's disease, the most common form of dementia, within 12 months. The study found that those who didn't had noticeably higher caffeine levels in their blood.

Like the results of earlier research on mice, the outcome suggests that, as lead author Chuanhai Cao put it, 'moderate daily caffeine/coffee intake throughout adulthood should appreciably protect against Alzheimer's disease later in life'. Two to three daily cups of coffee is considered a moderate intake.

BLACK CARROT

Daucus carota

We're often told it's nutritionally better to eat a couple of carrots than drink a glass of carrot juice. And in 2012, researchers revealed one reason why. In a world-first study, nutritionist Anneline Padayachee, based at Australia's University of Queensland, uncovered a link between fibre in fruit and vegetables and the anticancer antioxidants they contain.

She based her research on black carrots, which are really a very dark purple and the original source of orange carrots. The 'black' version is commonly grown in Asia and is particularly rich in anthocyanin and phenolic acid antioxidants. Padayachee found that when antioxidants remained contained within fibre – as they are in unjuiced, whole vegetables – a large proportion could avoid digestion in the stomach and small intestine and make it all the way to the bowel. Once there, they're believed to play a protective role against colon cancer.

When it comes to fruit and vegetables, the take-home message according to Padayachee is that if you 'consume everything – the raw or cooked whole vegetable or fruit, [and] drink mainly cloudy juices and eat the fibrous pulp – you will not only have a clean gut, but also a healthy gut full of protective polyphenols'.

ZIZIPHORA

Ziziphora spp.

The latest Chinese traditional medicine to attract attention from Western science comes from a shrub-like herb called *Ziziphora*. Early lab study results published this year reveal that it has significant anticancer potential.

A common plant throughout the grasslands and arid areas of Eurasia, *Ziziphora* is used by the Uighur people of northwestern China to treat health disorders ranging from high blood pressure and heart disease to bronchitis and oedema. Extracts from *Ziziphora* and several better-known traditional medicines – aloe vera, ginger and saffron – were tested in the laboratory against gastric cancer cell lines by researchers at Shahed University in Iran. *Ziziphora* was found to be the most effective, and the researchers concluded that the herb 'seems to be a good candidate as an anticancer agent against gastric cancer' and warrants further investigation. Gastric cancer is the second biggest cause of cancer-related deaths worldwide and the fourth most common form of the disease.

SAFFRON

Crocus sativus

The golden reputation of saffron has glowed even brighter since 2012, when the results of a follow-up study conducted in Italy into the ancient spice's eyesight-protecting potential were published.

Saffron has been used in traditional healing for centuries, particularly in Eastern countries, and there's been modern medical interest since the late 1990s in its possible anticancer and antioxidant properties. But there's now new excitement about its potential for improving and protecting vision in sufferers of age-related macular degeneration (AMD), the leading cause of blindness in people over 50.

In 2010, an Italian-based study reported that all 25 early-AMD sufferers in a six-month trial of a saffron supplement experienced vision improvements. The results of the longer follow-up study reported in 2012 were similarly positive, with researchers concluding that saffron supplementation shows promise as 'a long-term treatment of early retinal dysfunction associated with AMD'.

Saffron, the dried stigmas of crocus flowers, imparts a vibrant yellow hue and is used to colour and flavour food. It's labour intensive to harvest, each flower producing only a few stigmas, which helps make it one of the most expensive spices.

GLOSSARY

algae (*sing:* alga) Single- or multicelled plantlike organisms that contain chlorophyll and are capable of photosynthesis. The best known are seaweeds.

alternative medicine A group of treatments and therapies that fall outside those taught at mainstream medical schools. Also known as complementary medicine, they include herbal medicine, homeopathy and acupuncture.

Alzheimer's disease A degenerative disease of the brain involving a build-up of plaques on brain cells (neurones). It is the most common form of dementia.

analgesic A substance that reduces the body's ability to sense pain.

antibacterial Capable of killing bacteria or inhibiting its growth.

antibiotic A chemical substance capable of killing or inhibiting the growth of microorganisms such as bacteria and fungi. A major challenge in healthcare is antibiotic resistance, whereby bacteria become resistant to existing antibiotics as a result of overuse.

antibody Any of various proteins produced in the blood in response to the presence of harmful microorganisms such as viruses and bacteria. By attaching themselves to microorganisms, antibodies render them harmless.

anticoagulant Any substance that prevents or delays the clotting of blood.

anti-inflammatory Capable of reducing inflammation, the body's natural response to injury or infection.

antimicrobial Capable of killing or limiting the growth of microorganisms, especially potentially harmful ones such as bacteria and viruses.

antioxidant Any substance that prevents or delays damage to an organism due to oxidation (the process whereby oxygen combines with a substance). Imbalanced oxidation – also known as oxidative stress – is thought to be a cause of serious diseases such as cancers and heart disease.

antiseptic Any substance that kills microorganisms such as bacteria and viruses.

arrhythmia An irregular heartbeat. Some arrhythmias may be life-threatening or increase the risk of stroke.

atherosclerosis A life-threatening condition involving the accumulation of fatty deposits on artery walls. Resulting blockage can cause heart attacks and strokes.

autoimmune disease A condition whereby the body's immune system overreacts and starts to attack healthy tissues.

Ayurveda Indian traditional medicine, based originally on ancient Hindu writings.

bacteria (*sing:* bacterium) Any of a large group of microorganisms, the prokaryotes, many of which are parasites and cause disease.

bioprospecting The search for compounds in nature that might provide or form the basis of new medicines. Often this involves field work in remote realms and consultation with indigenous healers and therapists.

blood glucose Glucose circulating in the bloodstream. Excessive or persistently high levels, known as hyperglycaemia, may be caused by diabetes. Low levels are known as hypoglycaemia.

cardiovascular Pertaining to the heart and blood vessels. Therefore cardiovascular disease is a disease of the heart or blood vessels.

chemotherapy The treatment of a disease, usually a form of cancer, with chemical substances.

cholesterol A white, waxy substance produced by the body, which is an important component of cell membranes. Overproduction of cholesterol is thought to increase fat deposits in arteries and thereby contribute to heart disease.

clinical trial Controlled testing of a medicine on human patients.

diabetes A condition characterised by excessive levels of blood sugar. Type 1 diabetes is caused by a deficiency in insulin, which regulates carbohydrates and fats in the body. Type 2 diabetes is due to a failure of cells to respond to insulin.

DNA Deoxyribonucleic acid, a material living in cells that carries the genetic instructions followed by organisms as they grow.

enzyme Any of a group of proteins produced by living cells which act as catalysts in chemical processes vital to life.

essential oils Oils found in plants, which carry the flavour or scent of the plant. They are used in perfumes and health products.

flavonoid Any of a group of plant pigments. They are often beneficial to health because they act as antioxidants in the body.

free radical A damaging compound produced by the body

as a result of oxidation, frequently in response to foods or environmental factors such as smoke or sunlight. Free radicals are thought to contribute to illnesses such as cancers and heart disease.

fungus (*pl:* fungi) Any of a large group of single- or multi-celled organisms that do not contain chlorophyll and usually reproduce by spores. They include mushrooms, moulds, mildews and yeasts.

gene A unit of DNA that determines a particular characteristic of a living organism. An entire set of genes passed on by an organism to its offspring is known as a genome.

HIV A virus, the human immunodeficiency virus, that causes the disease known as AIDS.

hormone A chemical produced by the body that triggers an effect in another part of the body. Human hormones, for example, regulate functions such as sleep, hunger and sexual desire.

hypertension Another name for abnormally high blood pressure, which causes the heart to work harder and is a cause of heart attacks, strokes and aneurysms.

immune system The processes the body uses to protect itself against disease, including the production of antibodies in the blood. An ability to resist disease is known as immunity.

inflammation A normal response of the body to injury or infection, characterised by redness, heat, swelling and pain, all of which are the result of protective processes set in motion by the body.

in vitro Describes a type of scientific testing carried out in laboratory equipment – often test tubes – rather than on living things.

in vivo Describes a type of scientific testing carried out on living organisms.

metabolism The whole system of chemical processes that occurs in and controls a living organism. A person's metabolic rate is the amount of energy expended to run this system.

microbe Any type of microorganism, but particularly one that causes disease.

neuralgia Severe pain caused by nerve irritation or damage.

neurone The type of cell that makes up nerves and transmits nerve impulses.

osteoarthritis A disease that involves the breakdown of cartilage in the joints, often causing chronic inflammation. It is the most common form of arthritis.

parasite An organism that lives in or on another living creature and derives its nourishment from it. Parasites often cause damage to or illnesses in their hosts.

pigment A substance in an organism that imparts a colour to that organism, such as green chlorophyll in plants.

placebo An inactive substance given to selected patients during a scientific test in order to compare those patients with others receiving the compound being tested.

protein Any of a class of large molecules made up of chains of amino acids, which are vital to the functioning of living organisms.

side effect Any effect, over and above the intended one, caused by a medicine.

statin A medication used to lower levels of cholesterol in the blood.

stem cell A body cell with the potential to develop into any of the main types of cell, such as muscle cells or nerve cells.

synthetic drug A medication produced without natural substances; it may, however, be modelled on a natural compound.

traditional medicine Any system of medical diagnosis and treatment based on knowledge accumulated before the advent of modern scientific medicine. Sometimes referred to as folk or indigenous medicine.

toxin A poisonous substance produced by a living organism, especially a microorganism.

venom A poisonous substance secreted by an animal such as a snake or spider and normally delivered by a bite or sting.

virus A submicroscopic organism or molecule that replicates within the cells of plants and animals and often causes disease.

INDEX

C

D

E

M

N

O

ACKNOWLEDGMENTS

Front cover main Darryl Torckler/Getty Images; Insets l Philip Dalton/Nature Picture Library, cl Shutterstock, cr Snapper Media, r Chris Newbert/Getty Images; Back cover l Shutterstock, cl SPL/Getty Images, cr Shutterstock, r SPL/Getty Images; 1 l Tim Gainey/Alamy, cl Erlend Haarberg/Nature Picture Library, cr Studio Wilke/Getty Images, r Photo Researchers/Getty Images; 2–3 Shutterstock; 4 Stephen Dalton/Minden Pictures; 6–7 Hiroya Minakuchi/Minden Pictures; 8 Frans Lanting/Auscape; 10 l Nashworld/Flickr, r iStockphoto; 11 tl Mahesh Kumar/AP Photo/AAP, tr iStockphoto, br Ashley Cooper/Corbis; 12 bl Mark Moffett/Minden Pictures, tl Shutterstock, tr APOPO; 13 tl Steven David Miller/Nature Picture Library, tr iStockphoto, cr Swim Ink 2, LLC/Corbis, br Photo Researchers/Getty Images; 14–15 Shutterstock; 16 l GFC Collection/Alamy; 16–17 t Karen Kasmauski/Science Faction/Corbis; 17 Photomall/Xinhua Press/Corbis; 19 t Jean-Christophe Bott/Keystone/Corbis, b Shutterstock; 20 t Jay Directo/AFP/Getty Images, b SPL/Getty Images; 21 Bettmann/Coris; 22 tl Mary Evans Picture Library/AAP, r Mary Evans Picture Library/AAP, bl Science & Society Picture Library/Getty Images; 23 Fumio Tomita/amanaimages/Corbis; 24–25 Panoramic Images/Getty Images; 25 tl Arco Images GmbH/Alamy, br Tony Wharton/Frank Lane Picture Agency/Corbis; 26 SPL/Getty Images; 27 c AP/AAP, br Gary Retherford/Getty Images, tl Norbert Wu/Minden Pictures, tr Mark Moffett/Minden Pictures, cl Carr Clifton/Minden Pictures; 28–29 t Ashley Cooper/Corbis; 28 b SPL/Getty Images; 29 r iStockphoto; 30 Stephen P Parker/Getty Images; 31 tr Peter Crome/Alamy, bl Dorling Kindersley/Getty Images; 32 Bettmann/Corbis; 33 tl Wil Meinderts/Minden Pictures, tr William Osborn/Nature Picture Library; 34 Classic Image/Alamy; 35 l Carol Sharp/Flowerphotos/Alamy, r Andre M. Chang/Alamy; 38–39 t Michiel Schaap/Minden Pictures; 39 dpa/Corbis; 40 t Alison Miksch/FoodPix/Getty Images, b iStockphoto; 41 bl Bojan Brecelj/Corbis, tr Willem Kolvoort/Nature Picture Library; 42–43 Michael W Davidson/Getty Images; 44 Minden Pictures/Masterfile; 45 Gerry Ellis/Minden Pictures; 46 Shutterstock; 47 tl Macduff Everton/Science Faction/Corbis, tr Owen Franken/Corbis, bl Shutterstock; 48 Science Faction/Getty Images; 50–51 FoodPix/Getty Images; 50 Photocuisine/Alamy; 51 t Ina Peters/Getty Images, b Shutterstock; 52 DeAgostini/Getty Images; 54 bl Gallo Images/Getty Images, r Bettmann/Corbis; 55 Steffen Hauser/Botanikfoto/Alamy; 56 AFP/Getty Images; 57 Scott Camazine/Alamy; 58 AgStock Images, Inc./Alamy; 59 Arco Images GmbH/BSIP; 60 Shutterstock; 61 Shutterstock; 62 tr Larry Crowe/AP Photo/AAP, bl Inmagine Asia/Corbis; 63 Shutterstock; 64 FLPA/Alamy; 65 Mark Harmel/Getty Images; 66 SPL/Getty Images; 67 tr Image Source/Getty Images, bl Shutterstock; 68 Wichita Eagle/Getty Images; 69 tl Demange Francis/Gamma/Getty Images, r Hamid Sardar/Corbis, bl Bill Bachman/Alamy; 70 Shutterstock; 71 Tim Gainey/Alamy; 72 Alamy; 74 t Shutterstock; 75 b Cyril Ruoso/JH Editorial/Minden Pictures/Corbis, t Lydie/Sipa/Snapper Media; 76 tl Lydie/Sipa/Snapper Media, tr Lydie/Sipa/Snapper Media; 77 tl Lydie/Sipa/Snapper Media, tr Lydie/Sipa/Snapper Media; 78 SPL/Getty Images; 79 t SPL/Getty Images, br SSPL/Science Museum/Snapper Media; 80 Scott Camazine/Getty Images; 81 Wikipedia Commons; 83 Shutterstock; 84–85 Shutterstock; 86 Snapper Media; 87 Colin Roy Owen/Alamy; 88 Garden Picture Library/Getty Images; 89 Science Photo Library/Getty Images; 90 tr Mirek Weichsel/AgStock Images/Corbis, bl iStockphoto; 91 Eric and David Hosking/Corbis; 92 tl SPL/Getty Images, br Bon Appetit/Alamy; 93 iStockphoto; 94 SPL/Getty Images; 95 tr Imagebroker/Getty Images, cr Photo Researchers/Getty Images, bl SPL/Getty Images; 96 tr Yonhap News Agency/AAP Image, bl Shutterstock; 97 tr Getty Images, bl Eye Ubiquitous/Corbis; 98 bl Reza/Getty Images, br Michael Freeman/Corbis; 99 tl SPL/Getty Images, tr Hulton Archive/Getty Images; 100 Kyodo/AP Images/AAP; 101 iStockphoto; 102 Universal Images Group/Getty Images; 103 tl Firoz ahmed/Demotix/Corbis, tr Shutterstock; 104 Bettmann/Corbis; 105 tl Shutterstock, br Mary Evans Picture Library/AAP; 106 Shutterstock; 107 tl Photo Researchers/Getty Images, tr Wichita Eagle/Getty Images, c Paco Chuquiure/epa/Corbis, br Liz Cole/Garden World Images, bl SPL/Getty Images; 108 tr SPL/Getty Images; 109 br Geoff Simpson/Nature Picture Library, bl StockFood/Getty Images; 110 Shutterstock; 111 tr Shutterstock, br Image Source/Getty Images; 112 bl StockFood/Getty Images; 112–113 main Shutterstock; 114 iStockphot; 115 t Nicolas Thibaut/Getty Images, c Heritage Images/Corbis, b Shutterstock; 116–117 Shutterstock; 117 iStockphoto; 118 AgStock Images/Corbis; 119 t iStockphoto, b Michael Ciesielski Photography; 120 Shutterstock; 121 t Floris Leeuwenberg/Corbis, b Shutterstock; 122 t Robert E. McGinnis/National Geographic Creative/Getty Images, b Shutterstock; 123 Shutterstock; 124 Bloomberg/Getty Images; 125 Shutterstock; 126 Gillians Food; 126–127 Reuters/Picture Media; 127 Bloomberg/Getty Images; 128 Tim Spence/Getty Images; 129 t Dorling Kindersley/Getty Images, b FotoosVanRobin/Getty Images; 130–131 iStockphoto; 131 Shutterstock; 132 Noah Berger/New York Times; 133 tr Bloomberg/Getty Images, tl Rob Verhoeven & Alessandra Magni/Getty Images, c SPL/Getty Images, bl Chris Knapton/SPL Creative/Getty Images, br VoTrung/Grazia/Corbis; 134 Petr Gross/Corbis; 134–135 Shutterstock; 135 Mary Evans/Retrograph Collection/AAP; 136–137 Shutterstock; 137 Shutterstock; 138 t Shutterstock, b Imaginechina/Corbis; 139 Shutterstock; 140 t iStockphoto, b Getty Images; 141 Lonely Planet Images/Getty Images; 142 Getty Images; 143 tl Shutterstock, br SPL/Getty Images; 144 t SPL/Getty Images, b Erlend Haarberg/Nature Picture Library; 145 SPL/Getty Images; 146–147 Main Panoramic Images/Getty Images; 147 clockwise from top left Shutterstock, Shutterstock, Edward Duarte/Corbis, Shutterstock, Shutterstock, Shutterstock, Shutterstock, Shutterstock; 148–149 Shutterstock; 149 Rick Friedman/Corbis; 150 Shutterstock; 151 t SPL/Getty Images, b Shutterstock; 152–153 Chris Newbert/Minden Pictures; 154 Heidi & Hans-Jurgen Koch/Minden Pictures; 154–155 Shutterstock; 155 Ernie Janes/Nature Picture Library; 156 Heidi & Hans-Jurgen Koch/Minden Pictures; 157 Shutterstock; 159 Medical Detection Dogs; 162 tr SPL/Getty Images, bl Shutterstock; 163 tr Shutterstock, bl Shutterstock; 164 De Agostini-UIG/Auscape; 165 Maggie Steber/National Geographic Society/Corbis; 166 SPL/Getty Images; 166–167 Shutterstock; 167 SPL/Getty Images; 168 Moodboard/Corbis; 168–169 Ernie Janes/Nature Picture Library; 170 National Geographic/Getty Images; 171 Corbis; 172 Yasuyoshi Chiba/AFP/Getty Images; 173 tl APOPO; r Yasuyoshi Chiba/AFP/Getty Images; 174 Bruce Dale/National Geographic/Getty Images; 175 National Geographic/Getty Images; 176 Suzi Eszterhas/Minden Pictures/Corbis; 177 br Konrad Wothe/Minden Pictures/Corbis, l Image Brief, c Philip Dalton/Nature Picture Library, tl Shutterstock, tr Shutterstock; 178 Georgette Douwma/Nature Picture Library; 179 Hermann J. Knippertz/AP/AAP; 180 David Nunuk/All Canada Photos/Corbis; 181 All Canada Photos/Getty Images; 182 James Gathany/CDC; 183 Don Johnston/Getty Images; 184 Professor Mark Merchant; 185 National Geographic Stock; 186 Professor Miodrag Stojkovic/SPL/Getty Images; 187 Dario Lins; 188 Mark Moffett/Minden Pictures; 191 br Jeffrey L. Rotman/Corbis, tl Getty Images, cr Oxford Scientific/Getty Images, tr Mark Moffett/Minden Pictures, tc Daniel Heuclin/Nature Picture Library; 192 Rod Williams/Nature Picture Library; 193 Jeffrey L. Rotman/Corbis; 194 Getty Images; 195 Marko Koenig/Imagebroker/Biosphoto; 196 tr Mark Moffett/Minden Pictures, br Mark Moffett/Minden Pictures; 197 tr Bill Gozansky/Alamy, c Chris Mattison/Alamy, bl Alamy, tl Sandy Watt/Alamy, br Larry West/Minden Pictures; 198 Visuals Unlimited/Getty Images; 201 Daniel Heuclin/Nature Picture Library; 203 David Scharf/Science Faction/Getty Images; 205 Shutterstock; 206 Reavell Creative Ltd./the food passionates/Corbis; 207 Stephen Dalton/Minden Pictures/Getty Images; 208 t Katsumi Kasahara/AP/AAP, b Shutterstock; 208–209 SPL/Getty Images; 209 t SPL Creative/Getty Images, bl SPL/Getty Images, br Piotr Naskrecki/Minden Pictures; 210 t Dreamstime, b Photo Researchers/Getty Images; 211 t SPL/Getty Images, b SPL/Getty Images; 212–213 John Abbott/Nature Picture Library; 213 Christina Kennedy/Alamy; 214 Martin Dohrn/SPL/Getty Images; 215 t iStockphoto, c SPL/Getty Images, b SPL/Getty Images; 216 Shutterstock; 217 Clockwise SPL/Getty Images, Matthias Schrader/Corbis, Science PR/Getty Images, Studio Wilke/Getty Images, Splash News/Corbis; 218 t Photo Researchers/Getty Images, b Jurgen Freund/Nature Picture Library; 219 Daniel Heuclin/Nature Picture Library; 220 t SPL/Getty Images; b Daniel Heuclin/Nature Picture Library; 221 Shutterstock; 222 James King-Holmes/SPL/Getty Images; 223 Barry Turner/Alamy; 224 t SPL/Getty Images, b Shutterstock; 225 t Yoji Miyazaki, b SPL/Getty Images; 226–227 Shutterstock; 226 t Shutterstock, b Shutterstock; 227 Shutterstock; 228 David Maitland/Getty Images; 229 t Giel, O./Juniors Bildarchiv, b Dr.Tony Brain/SPL RM/Getty Images; 230 James Forte/National Geographic Society/Corbis; 231 Karen Gowlett-Holmes/Auscape; 232 Steve Wilson/Howard Hughes Medical Institute; 233 Norbert Wu/Minden Pictures; 234 Jeff Rotman/Alamy; 235 Nashworld/Flickr; 236 The Image Bank/Getty Images; 237 Joseph Doherty; 238–239 Background Shutterstock; 238 Jeff Rotman/Nature Picture Library; 239 l Chris Newbert/Minden Pictures, tr Jurgen Freund/Nature Picture Library, br David Shale/Nature Picture Library; 240 Jurgen Freund/Nature Picture Library; 241 Frans Lanting Studio/Alamy; 242 Adrian Davies/Nature Picture Library; 243 WaterFrame/Getty Images; 244 Piotr Naskrecki/Minden Pictures; 245 Mark Thiessen/National Geographic Stock; 246 Hans Leijnse/Foto Natura/Minden Pictures; 247 Sue Daly Nature Picture Library; 248–249 Alaska Stock/Alamy; 249 Kallista Images/Getty Images; 250 Getty Images; 250–251 David Shale/Nature Picture Library; 251 SPL/Getty Images; 253 Getty Images; 254 Roberto Rinaldi/Bluegreen Pictures/Nature Picture Library; 255 Shutterstock; 256 Robert Fenner; 257 t Lonely Planet Images/Getty Images, b Shutterstock; 258–259 Wild Wonders of Europe/Lundgren/Nature Picture Library; 259 Alaska Stock Images/National Geographic Stock; 260–261 Flickr RF/Getty Images; 261 Shutterstock; 262–263 Photo Researchers/Getty Images; 264 Lonely Planet Images/Getty Images; 264–265 Photo Researchers/Getty Images; 265 FLPA/Alamy; 267 SPL/Getty Images; 268 SPL/Getty Images; 269 SPL/Getty Images; 270 SPL/Getty Images; 271 Hulton Archive/Getty Images; 272 Michael Rosenfeld/Getty Images; 273 SPL/Getty Images; 275 Flickr RF/Getty Images; 276 br Alamy, tl Getty Images, bl Getty Images; 277 bl MIXA/Getty Images, tl Shutterstock, tr Shutterstock, br Shutterstock; 279 tl Bio Agens Research and Development (BARD), Prague, Czech Republic, bl Bio Agens Research and Development (BARD), Prague, Czech Republic, br Image Brief; 281 tr Patrick Fort/AFP/Getty Images, b Paul & Paveena Mckenzie/Getty Images; 282 Corbis; 283 Alamy; 284–285 t Getty Images/National Geographic; 285 Thierry Rousseau/Corbis; 286–287 Alamy; 287 Getty Images; 288 SPL/Getty Images; 289 Photo Researchers/Getty Images; 290 TopFoto/Austral Press; 291 t SPL/Getty Images, b Shutterstock; 292 Bettmann/Corbis; 293 Shutterstock; 294 SPL/Getty Images; 295 George Steinmetz/Corbis; 296 Hemera/Getty Images; 297 tl Visuals Unlimited/Getty Images, tr Richard Cisar-Wright/Newspix; 298–299 SPL/Getty Images; 299 SPL/Getty Images; 300 bl SPL/Getty Images, br SPL/Getty Images; 301 tr Dreamstime, tl SPL/Getty Images, bl SPL/Getty Images, c iStockphoto, br SPL/Getty Images; 302 Natalie Zizic; 303 Dennis Kunkel Microscopy, Inc./Visuals Unlimited/Corbis; 304–305 Frans Lanting Studio/Alamy; 306 Charlie Brown/FLPA/Minden Pictures; 307 bl Gideon Pisanty/Wikipedia Commons, tr Visions Pictures/Minden Pictures; 309 Shutterstock

THE AMAZING HEALING POWERS OF NATURE

Consultant Karen McGhee
Authors Jack Challoner, Celia Coyne, Sari Harrar, Becky McCall, Karen McGhee, Abbie Thomas

Project Editor Scott Forbes
Project Designer Jacqueline Richards
Picture Research Natalie Zizic
Proofreader Kevin Diletti
Indexer Glenda Browne
Senior Production Controller Monique Tesoriero

READER'S DIGEST GENERAL BOOKS
Editorial Director Lynn Lewis
Managing Editor Rosemary McDonald
Art Director Carole Orbell

The Amazing Healing Powers of Nature is published by
Reader's Digest (Australia) Pty Limited
80 Bay Street, Ultimo, NSW, 2007
www.readersdigest.com.au; www.readersdigest.co.nz;
www.rdasia.com; www.readersdigest.co.in

First published 2013. Reprinted 2014.

National Library of Australia Cataloguing-in-publication data:

Title: Amazing healing powers of nature: discovering new treatments and cures from the natural world.

ISBN: 9781921569845 (hardback)
9781922083357 (paperback)

Notes: Includes index.

Subjects: Nature, Healing power of. Naturopathy.

Other Authors/Contributors: Reader's Digest (Australia)

Dewey Number: 615.53

Prepress by Colourpedia, Sydney
Printed and bound by Leo Paper, China

We are interested in receiving your comments on the content of this book. Write to: The Editor, General Books Editorial, Reader's Digest (Australia) Pty Limited, GPO Box 4353, Sydney, NSW 2001, or email us at: bookeditors.au@readersdigest.com

To order additional copies of *The Amazing Healing Powers of Nature* please contact us at:
www.readersdigest.com.au or phone 1300 300 030 (Australia)
www.readersdigest.co.nz or phone 0800 400 060 (New Zealand)
or email us at customerservice@readersdigest.com.au

Note to readers While the creators of this book have made every effort to be as accurate and up to date as possible, medical and pharmacological knowledge is constantly changing. The information in this book should not be substituted for, or used to alter, medical therapy without your doctor's advice. For a specific health problem, consult your doctor for guidance. The writers, researchers, editors and publishers of this work cannot be held liable for any errors and omissions, or actions that may be taken as a consequence of information contained within this book.

Concept code AU 0744/G
Product number 041 4052 (hb)
041 4904 (pb)

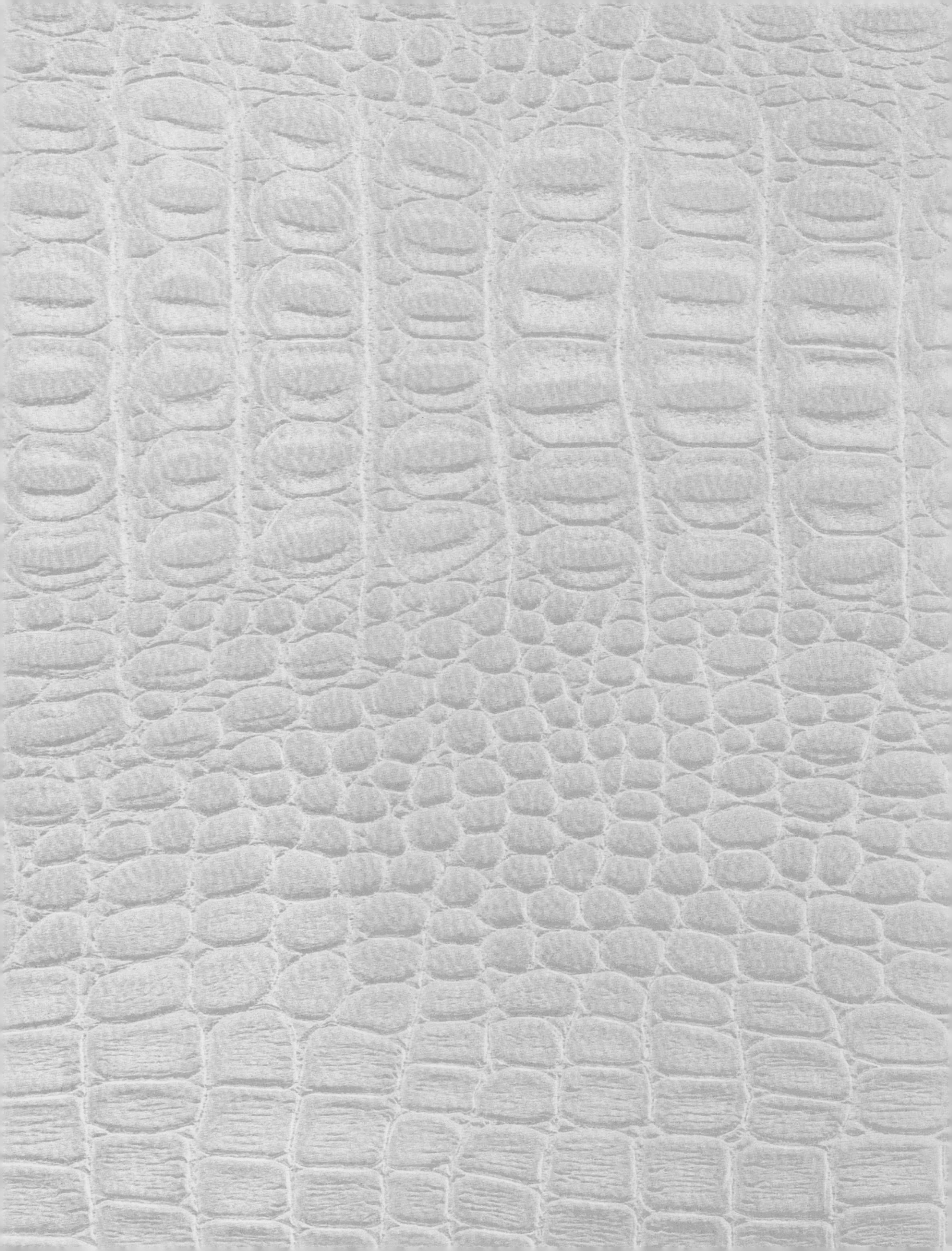